Folens

Applied AS

Health and Social Care

Contents

About the Course

In this broad-based AS course you will have the opportunity to achieve a qualification in Health and Social Care. The AS Level can be followed as a single course or as part of an A2 qualification.

The units within the AS Level are:

Unit No.	Unit Title	Mode of Assessment	Mandatory/Optional
1	Promoting Quality Care	External	Mandatory
2	Communicating in Care Settings	Portfolio	Mandatory
3	Promoting Good Health	Portfolio	Mandatory
4	Health and Safety in Care Settings	External	Optional
5	Caring for People with Additional Needs	Portfolio	Optional
6	Working in Early Years Care and Education	Portfolio	Optional
7	Health as a Lifestyle Choice	Portfolio	Optional
8	Complementary Therapies	Portfolio	Optional
9	Caring for Older People	External	Optional

Candidates must complete the Mandatory units. The Optional units chosen will depend on the award you are following. You will need to consult with the specifications and with your tutor to make sure that you have chosen the correct units for the award that you have decided to follow.

The AS Level can be taken as a course in its own right or the units can form part of the GCE Double Award which will include units from the A2 Level. The units can, therefore, be part of a two-tier qualification which contains both AS and A2 level units.

The course will provide you with a choice of assessment methods which will suit your interests and your strengths. You will have the opportunity to interact with the health, social care and early years sectors, and, where time is available on your timetable, to experience working with these sectors, using the knowledge, understanding and skills gained to contribute to your written responses within the units.

How to use this book

Throughout the book there are a number of features that are common to all units. For example:

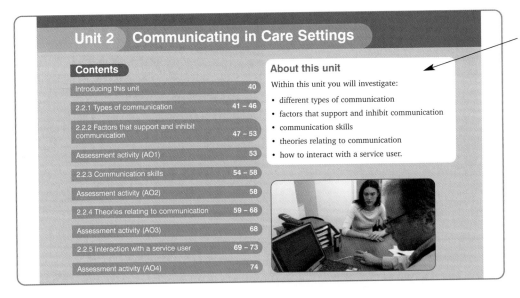

About this unit

Within this unit you will investigate:

- different types of communication
- factors that support and inhibit communication
- communication skills
- theories relating to communication
- how to interact with a service user.

About this unit
This will list the knowledge and skills that will be covered within the unit.

Introducing this unit – A broad outline which gives some focus to the content of the unit. This is intended to help you think about the scope of the unit and what the study may involve.

Communicating in Care Settings
Introducing this unit

Introducing this unit

Think about the number of times that you have communicated already today. You have probably used oral skills more than any other type of communication. You may have spoken to parents, teachers, friends or acquaintances. You may have done this face to face or on the telephone. Some of you will have used the computer today to send an email or to do research using the Internet. Others will have used writing as a form of communication or may have communicated with someone using special methods such as sign language or Braille.

In care settings all forms of communication are used whether it is a health, social care or early years setting. It is very important for care settings that communication is effective whether communicating orally or to a group or to other professional care workers. The skills involved when communicating maximise personal effectiveness because they underpin all other skills when working with people. Knowing ourselves, our attitudes and values will help us to know more about our effect on others.

Some factors that are used when communicating will encourage, for example valuing service users and promoting equality and diversity. Other factors can inhibit communication, for example noise, inappropriate positioning and verbal abuse. Application of factors such as applying the care values can encourage service users to share their problems with care workers.

socialised. Socialisation is almost like having a series of lessons which prepares a child for its adult role. Whether the family is a **nuclear** unit with mother, father, brothers and sisters or an extended family, or whether it is a single parent family or commune, it is the family who are the main people who contribute to learned attitudes and beliefs. It is in this context that a child will learn the way of behaving according to the particular culture of the family in which he/she lives. The **values** and **norms** of the society in which the child is being brought up become the accepted way for the child.

The family is responsible for **primary socialisation**. The family develops the 'conscience' of new

Discussion point

How has primary socialisation affected the group you are working with?

A family may have either conscious or subconscious prejudice which children will learn.

Prejudice is making a decision about a person without knowing anything about them. It is judging them by a particular characteristic, e.g. their looks, clothing or accent. It usually involves making an unfair decision about a person.

Discussion point – As you work through each section of the book there are questions to help you check that you have understood the knowledge that has been given.

3

Theory into practice

– This section deals with the application of knowledge and skills to practical situations in settings.

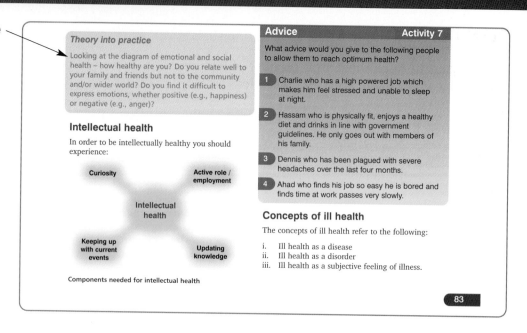

Theory into practice

Looking at the diagram of emotional and social health – how healthy are you? Do you relate well to your family and friends but not to the community and/or wider world? Do you find it difficult to express emotions, whether positive (e.g., happiness) or negative (e.g., anger)?

Intellectual health

In order to be intellectually healthy you should experience:

Curiosity

Active role / employment

Intellectual health

Keeping up with current events

Updating knowledge

Components needed for intellectual health

Advice   **Activity 7**

What advice would you give to the following people to allow them to reach optimum health?

1. Charlie who has a high powered job which makes him feel stressed and unable to sleep at night.

2. Hassam who is physically fit, enjoys a healthy diet and drinks in line with government guidelines. He only goes out with members of his family.

3. Dennis who has been plagued with severe headaches over the last four months.

4. Ahad who finds his job so easy he is bored and finds time at work passes very slowly.

Concepts of ill health

The concepts of ill health refer to the following:

i.   Ill health as a disease
ii. Ill health as a disorder
iii. Ill health as a subjective feeling of illness.

83

Ofsted has four main functions:

1. **Registration** of childminders and day care providers who care for children under eight. Registration includes checking the suitability of the person providing the care and, where relevant, others living in the premises. It also checks the safety and suitability of the premises.

2. **Inspection** – within seven months of registration Ofsted inspects childcare providers and then at least once every three years to ascertain that the quality and standards of provision meet the requirements.

Did you know?

It is planned that SureStart centres will provide services for about a third of children (400,000) under four years old who are living in poverty in England.

197

Did you know? –

Small pieces of information that add interest to the topic.

Key words – Throughout each unit there are 'key words'. These key words are in bold within the text. The meanings of such words are given in the glossary at the end of the book.

low income has an impact on the development of children and their health. Often parents are stressed because they are struggling to pay bills, to buy food and to maintain their poor standard of living.

Physical factors – additional needs could be a physical or learning disability which affects the way the person with disability is treated. Some people would view a person with a disability as unhealthy because they would believe that there is no cure for most disabilities. People with disabilities are often categorised by their disability. Although a person with a disability may feel fine, they may need assistance in getting out of bed and getting dressed. This could impact on their mental health as they may feel disempowered by their inability to be independent. Similarly, if it is a lot of effort for them to go to the cinema or go onto a train, they could feel that it is not worth the effort involved. People sometimes stereotype and treat all people with a disability as if they were children. People who have disabilities have often had their disability since birth, so they do not feel unhealthy because of it. However, they may feel unhealthy because they cannot exercise because of their disability. People with learning difficulties may not be able to make choices about their health or lifestyle. Sometimes they have to rely on carers to make choices for them.

information given to them. There are some specific resources available for people with learning disabilities. Carers should ensure these resources are available to their service users and be prepared to discuss them and ensure they understand the information.

Health promotion   **Activity 18**

1. Go to your Health Promotion Unit or Health Centre and pick up some health care leaflets. How accessible do you think these are for someone with a learning disability?

2. Ask if there are any leaflets available for someone with a learning disability.

3. If available, is this leaflet easier to understand?

Try this out

How physically accessible is your local Health Centre or chemist?

Borrow a wheelchair from a local residential home and see if you can manoeuvre your way around. Whilst you have the wheelchair, see if a person with a physical disability who wants to keep fit could have access to your local gym.

103

Try this out – Actually trying out or practising a task.

Activities – have been included in each unit. These will help you to check your understanding of the text that you have read and could help you to build up evidence for your portfolio. Sometimes these are preceded by a short scenario.

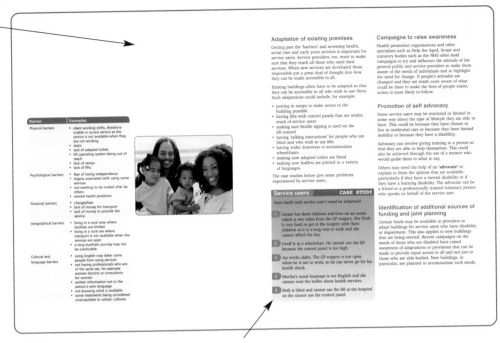

Case studies – these are used periodically throughout units. Sometimes they have questions attached and at other times they will be used to try and explain a point that is being made.

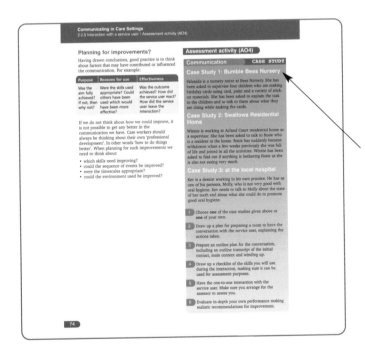

Assessment activities – these will occur at the end of each piece of underpinning knowledge for the unit. The purpose of the Assessment activities is to help you focus on what is required as portfolio evidence from a particular strand in the Assessment Evidence grid. This will form part of the evidence collected by you for the portfolio and should be completed individually. Sometimes the Assessment activity will begin with a short scenario and will be followed by tasks that must be completed, preferably by individuals.

Assessment questions – these are provided for Units 1, 4 and 9, where portfolio evidence is not required. Questions have been prepared to help you focus on the knowledge acquired and on the style of writing needed for the external assessment. Sometimes you will be asked to answer these questions in class and on other occasions you may be asked to complete a number of questions for homework. Whichever is the case, it is important to attempt these questions, as you should then be more confident and competent when taking the actual external assessment.

Bibliography – a bibliography is provided for each unit at the end of the book. This gives a full list of references so that you can carry out further reading and research if you wish.

We hope that you will be successful in the GCE Health and Social Care course and that this book may help you to achieve your goals.

Author details

Angela Fisher is a former Senior Manager of a comprehensive school. She has worked for an awarding body for a number of years as a Senior Examiner and Moderator and has helped to develop a variety of qualifications. She has been a major contributor to a wide range of textbooks and learning resources in the field of Health and Social Care. This has included being a writer and editor for Folens GCSE and a writer and editor for Heinemann for GNVQ and OCR Nationals. She has also consulted for QCA and for business organisations.

Mary Riley teaches across the spectrum of Health and Social Care courses as Head of Department at a comprehensive school, having first introduced BTEC First and Nationals into the school in 1989. She has worked as a Senior Examiner and Moderator for many years and has trained as an OFSTED inspector.

Stephen Seamons worked for 25 years as a clinical manager in diagnostic radiography. He currently teaches post-16 Health and Social Care and Human Biology and is a Senior Examiner and Moderator in health-related subjects for several examining boards. He is a contributing author to several recent Health and Social Care publications.

Marion Tyler is an award-winning qualified health professional specialising in stress management and complementary therapies. Marion has developed an acclaimed 'train the trainers' course in stress management and has more than 20 years' private and public sector experience training groups and individuals.

Carol Blackmore is a Senior Examiner, Moderator and Trainer with a major awarding body. She has responsibility for the co-ordination of vocational programmes in Key Stages 4 and 5 in a large community college. Carol has taught Health and Social Care for many years and has a wide range of experience and accreditation working within the health, social care and early years sectors. She is a contributing author to several recent Health and Social Care publications.

Stuart McKie is an External Verifier and Moderator for a major awarding body. As well as being a qualified Probation Officer and FE lecturer in Health and Social Care, he has worked extensively in the voluntary sector, including for a London-based homeless charity, a homeless and ex-offenders residential care charity and Age Concern.

Unit 1 Promoting Quality Care

Contents

About this unit

Within this unit you will investigate:

- the effect of attitudes and prejudice
- rights and responsibilities of service users and providers
- facilitation of access to services
- application of care values
- safe working practices.

Quality care promotes well being in care settings

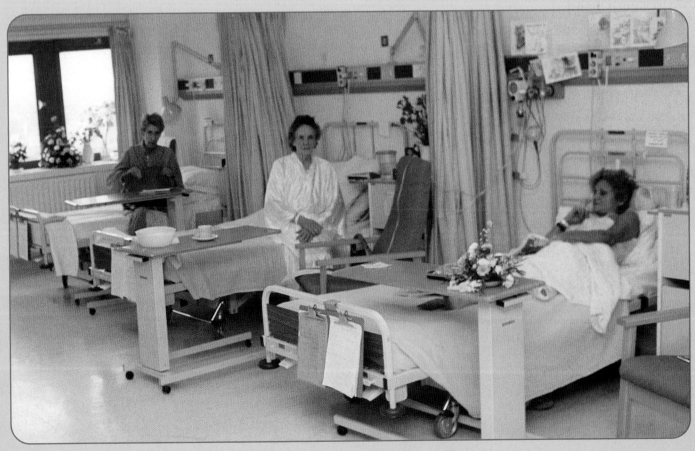

Quality care means making sure vulnerable service users are treated with equality

Introducing this unit

What is quality care? It is making sure that all people have access to the services they need and ensuring that they do not experience discrimination. This means allowing people the right to choose, for example to be called by their preferred name, allowing service users the right to complain and helping individuals to reach their full potential. Sometimes this will mean balancing tensions between the rights of individuals with the needs and resources of the organisation. This could lead to dilemmas occurring where there is no right answer but where decisions have to be made.

How is quality care achieved? Quality care is achieved through professional care workers recognising and being aware of their own opinions, attitudes and prejudices. Care workers will need to think about their primary and secondary socialisation and the possible effects these could have on those for whom they care. The rights and responsibilities of care workers are fundamental human rights which legislation safeguards. Professional care workers will need to know what rights service users have and about the laws that protect them. Quality care is achieved when care settings observe the rights of service users, follow legislation that protects both service users and care workers, and by following procedures that are in place within care settings. This ensures the health and safety of all who live and work in care settings.

Quality care therefore encompasses:

1.2.1 Attitudes and prejudice

Service users who use health, social care and early years facilities are likely to be **vulnerable**. This is because they may be in poor health, or they may be using a service for the first time and as a consequence they may feel unsure of themselves and not in control. They will be dependent on care workers and as such it will be very important that the attitude of the professionals with whom they come into contact is completely objective and without prejudice. This will only be so if the care workers have closely examined their own views and opinions to ensure that they do not consciously or subconsciously carry any prejudicial attitudes.

Primary socialisation

Different types of family each provide primary socialisation of their children

The home is the first place where an individual is socialised. Socialisation is almost like having a series of lessons which prepares a child for its adult role. Whether the family is a **nuclear** unit with mother, father, brothers and sisters or an extended family, or whether it is a single parent family or commune, it is the family who are the main people who contribute to learned attitudes and beliefs. It is in this context that a child will learn the way of behaving according to the particular culture of the family in which he/she lives. The **values** and **norms** of the society in which the child is being brought up become the accepted way for the child.

The family is responsible for **primary socialisation**. The family develops the 'conscience' of new members. Once a bond has been formed between a child and its parent or main carer any threat to that bond will cause the child anxiety. Therefore, rather than losing the close association that it has with its parent or main carer the child will adopt the norms and values taught by them. This includes the young child's learning and experiences of prejudice, gender roles and the skills of language. For example, if the family has the attitude that some people are **inferior** to their own family, then the children in the family are likely to follow their example.

The family will live in a **society**. That is, it will live with groups of other people who all have a similar pattern of life. The society will have its own rules, traditions and organisations, with perhaps its main beliefs. This is known as **culture** which is about the way we live. In today's society in this country we have a **multi-cultural society**. This is because people from a variety of different cultures have been born in this country and have grown up here. A child today would, therefore, probably be used to different patterns of living and different beliefs and so would be more accustomed to the approach.

Good cultural attitudes can be used as tools to help with shared thinking. Richard Dawkins, a biologist, calls this the **social evolution approach** as he believes that social learning is a shared process with the exchange of ideas and information between people. Every culture has its own way of doing things and in some cultures new ideas are more acceptable than in others. Societies that reflect this approach are known as **open societies** whereas those who are not so open are known as **closed societies**. Cultures can be rich in expressive arts and as a result the valuing of such traditions is well guarded.

Discussion point

How has primary socialisation affected the group you are working with?

A family may have either conscious or subconscious prejudice which children will learn.

Prejudice is making a decision about a person without knowing anything about them. It is judging them by a particular characteristic, e.g. their looks, clothing or accent. It usually involves making an unfair decision about a person.

Prejudice should not be present if providing quality care is the practice of the setting

Prejudice may occur because it is an easy way to group people together and to give them a label. This form of grouping people together could have developed from a variety of sources, for example from family, neighbours, peers and the wider community.

Not being prejudiced means not grouping people with a different appearance to ourselves as being 'less worthy than ourselves'. Prejudice can lead to discrimination. It can cause a person to treat another with less respect and to think of them as inferior.

Assumptions and prejudicial views are learnt and do not come naturally. For example, children will notice skin colour, but they will not have a concept that one skin colour is 'better' or superior to another. Views such as this are learnt. When growing up, children may hear their parents, brothers and sisters, or friends express jokes or opinions about others that are detrimental. They may then grow up to express them as their own point of view.

Care workers need to carefully examine their attitudes, views and opinions to make sure these are not being reflected within the day-to-day tasks that they perform.

Jaslima · CASE STUDY

Jaslima, aged 25 years, is working as a nursery nurse in a playgroup. She has quite a busy morning ahead of her with lots to do. As she is busy getting out the playthings for the children in the group, a mother enters the room unexpectedly with three children.

Jaslima notices the service user has an ear ring in both eyebrows, another in her nose and another in her lip. Her clothes are old and not very clean. The children look as though they have not been washed and immediately, on seeing the playthings rush to grab some of them.

Jaslima's attitude is very unsympathetic. She assumes the family are gypsys who have moved in on the outskirts of the town. She makes these judgements based on the appearance of the mother and the children. She is very surprised when the woman speaks, as she has an educated vocabulary.

Jaslima realises that she is displaying an attitude of prejudice. She has allowed her own views to be clouded by the appearance of the person in front of her. This type of attitude can lead to discrimination.

Discussion point

Where do you think Jaslima's prejudice had originated?

Discussion point

How could prejudice affect the work of a nurse in a hospital?

Gender socialisation is also associated with culture. It is the way in which we learn the roles that we are to take for the future, for example male and female roles. It is thought that gender roles are learned depending on what is taught as being acceptable to the male and female. For example, in the past girls would be given dolls to play with and would be expected to play with cooking and washing up equipment, thus beginning to learn their roles for later life. Boys, on the other hand, would have been given cars, trains and building materials, preparing them to work outside the home. In today's Western society this has changed enormously. If you were to walk into a nursery class or a playgroup, it would be possible to see boys playing with dolls and girls playing with building equipment. The roles between males and females are no longer clearly defined and are often merged.

Discussion point

Why is it important to encourage boys and girls to play with toys that interest them when at nursery school?

Carlie

Carlie is the youngest of three children in the Hooper family. She has a brother aged 11 years, a sister who is 7 years old and Carlie is 5 years old. Her father is a teacher and her mother is the manager at the local nursery school. The family have a four-bedroomed house in a village five miles from the nearest town of Porchester. Carlie loves dancing and acting and has joined clubs to help her develop the skills she needs.

1 The family will be the main influence in Carlie's primary socialisation. Explain why this is so.

2 Explain how genetic influences are likely to affect Carlie.

3 Which environmental factors are likely to affect Carlie's development?

4 Why is gender socialisation important in Carlie's life? How is this likely to occur?

5 Explain what is meant by the term 'prejudice'. Give an example, to show understanding of the term.

Secondary socialisation

Secondary socialisation refers to those things that affect us as we grow and develop. A child will learn things from the 'wider society', such as the people it meets and the organisations with which it has contact. As the child meets more people and has contact with a number of organisations, some of the views and opinions previously accepted from the family are questioned. This process may begin when the child is at playgroup or attends nursery school and continues throughout school life and through experiences in adolescence, adulthood and later adulthood.

Secondary socialisation can include:

Education

Within the education system children have the opportunity to learn new skills, gather information and to pass a number of national examinations. Such examinations are important as they allow the individual to access employment, which in turn can lead to a good and consistent income. While going through the education system children learn about their past history, about the world around them and about different cultures and attitudes. It is through exposure to such topics and through the people they meet while being educated that secondary socialisation will take place. Attitudes and opinions can change quite drastically as a result.

Education
School/college and the influence of learning

Health care
Ease of access to services and the quality of care received will influence attributes

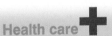 **Income**
Influences what we buy and the social class we consider ourselves to be in

 Housing
The location in which we live and the type of housing we experience

Media
TV, advertisements, newspapers – what we see and what we hear

Work
Valuing the type of job and the people we associate with each day

Religion
The beliefs we have

Secondary socialisation

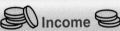 **Peers**
The influence of friends and people who are the same age as ourselves

Discrimination
If we are treated differently from others and not valued for who we are

Educational achievement can, however, be influenced by particular factors, some of which are **genetic** and others which are **environmental**. Intelligence is an inherited factor passed down from parents while environmental factors are linked to where you live. Both genetic and environmental factors can affect educational success. One of the current debates is 'what causes under-achievement?' in education.

Research has shown that gender, race and social class can affect educational success. Research has also shown that factors such as low income, housing and family size can also influence educational success. Working-class children, in particular, are disadvantaged by these factors and are less likely to do well at school. Working-class parents are likely to encourage their children to leave school and get a job at the end of compulsory education. On the other hand, middle-class parents are more likely to encourage their children to do well at school and to stay on into higher education, which is likely to result in acquiring higher paid jobs which are far more fulfilling. Currently, there is a slightly less obvious divide as more working-class parents are attempting to persuade their children to fulfil their full potential.

Discussion point

Why do you think working-class parents are encouraging their children to stay in higher education?

Secondary socialisation is also learnt from teachers and from peers. If you were to observe the same students with two different teachers, it is possible that behavioural changes would be apparent in each class. Some teachers allow the students to talk within class and to have more freedom. Others do not permit talking and demand one hundred per cent concentration. Through this tolerant/non-tolerant approach children are being socialised, albeit in different ways.

Behaviour and learning affects primary socialisation

Discussion point

How can parental attitude influence achievement in the learning environment?

The media

The media involves communicating with a large number of people without having direct personal contact. The media can include:

- books
- television
- magazines
- films/DVDs
- advertising
- radio.

Each is a source of information with ideas that will influence secondary socialisation, television being the most persuasive medium. The media, whatever the form, does tend to present a **stereotype** view of people and this itself can have an effect on how people see themselves and others in the world, but as a consequence it is an influence on secondary socialisation. For example, men, when in domestic situations, are sometimes portrayed as being incompetent!

Many people see the media as reporting items of news that are completely truthful and honest, when perhaps aspects of the actual story have been omitted. The media does have a great influence on secondary socialisation as very often people believe and absorb what they read and could spread such opinions to others who eventually absorb the ideas.

The media can act as a pressure group influencing both those in government and all others to make decisions, take sides and to form opinions.

Women's group raise money for local charity

The media can greatly influence secondary socialisation

Care workers need to be mindful of this when talking with service users, making sure that they are not showing prejudice or **bias** within any conversations they have.

Work

The work that people do will often lead to dividing people into layers or **strata**. Most societies tend to have some form of **stratification** system that distinguishes people as more, or less, important than others. In Britain the stratification system is known as the 'class system', the differences between the classes being in terms of educational success, the type of work that is being undertaken and the money earned. A person's occupation is, therefore, often used to assess the importance of people. These differences are recorded in scales. For example the Registrar-General's scale:

Class	Definition	Example
A or 1	Higher Professional & Higher Managerial	lawyer, accountant, doctor, minister, bank manager
B or 2	Lower Professional & Lower Managerial	nurse, teacher, farmer, school teacher, MP, police officer
C or 3	Skilled Manual and remainder of Non-manual Workers	plumber, shop assistant, typist, mechanic
D or 4	Semi-skilled Worker	lorry driver, assembly line worker, postman, bus conductor, agricultural worker
E or 5	Unskilled Worker	window cleaner, labourer, messenger, road sweeper, cleaner

C is often sub-divided into two, known as C1 and C2.
Classes **1**, **2** and **3**, are middle classes, **4** and **5** are working class.

The Registrar-General's scale

This scale is often considered to be 'top heavy', with more middle-class type occupations and working-class jobs. On the other hand, the 'Hall Jones scale' has seven categories rather than five and is, therefore, preferred as being fairer by many people.

Class	Definition
1	Professional and high administrative
2	Managerial and executive
3	Inspectional, supervisory and other non-manual, higher grade
4	Inspectional, supervisory and other non-manual, lower grade
5	Skilled manual and routine grades of non-manual
6	Semi-skilled manual
7	Unskilled manual

The Hall Jones scale

Discussion point

In what way is the Hall Jones scale different from the Registrar-General's scale?

It is generally believed that belonging to a social stratum in a system of stratification affects a person's chances in life. This means that it influences people's opportunities, for example education, leisure activities and work opportunities.

Providing quality service means not making judgements about a person because of their social class but providing all with the same access to services according to their needs. A person who is judged by their social class could be reluctant to ask or enquire about services that are available and as a result go without health care that is vital.

Peers

A peer group is composed of members who share a similar status in society. For example, they may be of the same age or share a similar type of situation in that they all work for the same employer, such as being a care worker in the NHS or being a teacher.

Most people want to be accepted by those with whom they work or who they are with for long periods of time and will, therefore, conform to **peer group norms**. This means they will follow the unspoken rules of the group and will not risk breaking these. In health and social care settings professional care workers will often hear a service user say, 'I must find out what my colleague thinks about that' or 'I won't make a decision before I have discussed what I should do with my friends'. People are anxious to take decisions that are approved of by those around them. In a school it is often stated by a child, 'I took drugs because all my friends do and I didn't want to be different'.

A peer group can be a very important influence upon others, as what others think can contribute to the way a service user or a child sees themselves and to the picture they build of themselves. This means that their self concept is influenced as the individual will measure their success against the opinions and views of others and act accordingly.

Ian | Activity 2

Ian is eight years old. He is attending the local Middle school and until recently was doing quite well. He has, however, become very poorly behaved recently and is being put on detention at least twice every week. Ian has started to go around with a group of boys and girls from the school who roam the streets at night and who are noisy and rude to passers-by. At the weekend some of the older boys in the group supply the members of the group with alcohol.

Ian's parents, his mother is a manager at a nursery school, and his father is a consultant at the local hospital, are very worried about the situation and have tried to stop Ian from going out with the group. Recently, Ian has been creeping out of the house while his parents are watching TV. Ian has returned home quite late and refuses to take any notice of his parents' discussions with him.

1 Discuss how social class has influenced the behaviour of the family?

2 How is the peer group affecting Ian?

3 How is education going to affect Ian both positively and negatively?

Health and well being

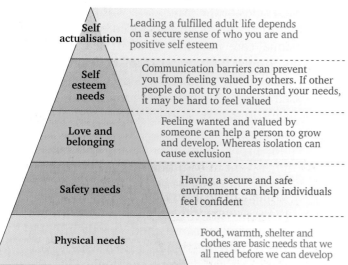

Maslow's hierarchy showing basic needs

Self actualisation	Leading a fulfilled adult life depends on a secure sense of who you are and positive self esteem
Self esteem needs	Communication barriers can prevent you from feeling valued by others. If other people do not try to understand your needs, it may be hard to feel valued
Love and belonging	Feeling wanted and valued by someone can help a person to grow and develop. Whereas isolation can cause exclusion
Safety needs	Having a secure and safe environment can help individuals feel confident
Physical needs	Food, warmth, shelter and clothes are basic needs that we all need before we can develop

Discussion point

What would you fit into each section of Maslow's hierarchy of needs?

The effects of prejudice and poor attitudes on individuals, for example experiencing discrimination, can have major repercussions on health.

Discrimination will be discussed a little later in this unit, but repeated episodes of discrimination are likely to have an impact on an individual's physical, intellectual, emotional and social development as one can affect the other. For example, if a person becomes depressed they may fail to socialise. This could negatively affect them because they will not be receiving any intellectual stimulation through conversation. Increased isolation could cause them to 'vegetate', which means they could be sitting around a lot and could therefore put on weight. The combined effect could result in:

- proneness to illness
- mental ill health
- insecurity
- an inability to build relationships
- poor performance.

Self esteem

Self esteem is understanding ourselves, having **self awareness** which leads to us forming an opinion about ourselves. Our self esteem involves:

- having knowledge about ourselves
- receiving feedback from other people.

From these two perspectives we will form an opinion of ourselves, so that we either have a high self esteem or a low self esteem. This is part of emotional and social development and can be influenced by the experiences we have, the life events we experience and the age or life stage we are in.

A high self esteem helps individuals to relate more easily to the people we meet, such as family, friends and colleagues. A person who has a high self esteem will often view life very positively and value themselves as a person. If a person thinks they are valuable, they will expect others to value them.

An individual with low self esteem will not feel good about themselves. They will not like the image they have of themselves and as a consequence may not be able to relate well to others. They may feel that others do not value them and that they are unable to make a worthwhile contribution to society. The overall result will be that such people have a very low opinion of themselves and a poor self portrait.

Self esteem can be influenced by a number of factors, for example:

Factors that influence self esteem	Effect on self esteem
Age	If a person is treated harshly or abused as a child then they are more likely to grow up with a low self concept. On the other hand, if a person is really successful at work and has a good family relationship, they will feel they are making a positive contribution to society and are likely to have a high self concept.
Body shape	Both males and females become concerned about their body shape. If they are overweight, strategies for slimming are likely to be implemented. Some will go to extremes and eating disorders such as anorexia nervosa may develop. The result is likely to be a low self esteem.
Gender	Gender is not the same as sex. Gender is about the way society expects individuals of both sexes to behave. Gender affects self esteem because individuals have to learn how someone of their sex behaves. This is known as gender role. A person who does not conform to the role expected often suffers extreme emotional torment.
Appearance	Sometimes a person will not like the way they look, for example an adolescent who has acne. This can cause them to have a low self esteem and to become withdrawn. Facial expressions play a major role when interacting with others as our facial appearance often reflects our innermost feelings.

Discussion point

Have you a high or low self esteem? What has contributed to this image?

Empowerment

What is **empowerment?** It is allowing the service user to take control of their own lives. This means presenting them with all the **relevant** information and allowing them to make choices and decisions. A service user who feels that their views and decisions are valued is more likely to respond positively. Service users will need to feel that they are equal to others and not someone for whom 'things are done or arranged'. The target is to form a good working relationship or partnership where each **contributor** is valued. This will mean:

- respecting the service user's rights
- maintaining confidentiality
- respecting the person's beliefs, cultural views and opinions
- allowing service users to express their views and opinions
- tolerating **diversity** when service users do not act as we do or have the same opinions as our own.

Empowerment enables the service user to retain their own identity and does not involve the care worker imposing their identity on the service user.

Discussion point

How can care workers empower service users when carrying out their day-to-day tasks?

Unfair treatment – direct and indirect discrimination

Discrimination is considering a race or culture or type of person to be of less value than one's own or to deliberately act against a group of people or to favour one group above another.

Society is made up of different types of people, each having their own traditions, beliefs and culture. Some people consider their own race or culture to be superior or better than others. They have a narrow view and think the beliefs and values they hold are the only correct ones to have.

They are not prepared to be open to the values and beliefs of people from other cultures.

There are two main forms of discrimination. These are:

- **indirect** discrimination, e.g. only printing information in one language which could exclude a number of people from accessing it
- **direct** discrimination, e.g. talking to someone disrespectfully.

Indirect discrimination is less obvious and more subtle. Sometimes it is unintentional, arising because a person has not given a situation sufficient thought. Service users are undermined by indirect discrimination, experiencing inequality even when other individuals are apparently being treated the same. Indirect discrimination occurs when a condition is made that is harder for one group to meet than another. For example, a school makes a rule that no headwear is to be worn inside the building. For Western Europeans this would not be a problem, but for a child who is a Muslim and whose family follow the traditions of their faith, this could be difficult to accept.

Direct discrimination is where individuals are treated differently in an open manner because of their race, colour, gender, sexual orientation, age, class or disability. Obvious unfair treatment shows prejudice and is intentional. An example of direct discrimination is excluding someone who has a different colour than oneself from joining a group. Or it could take the form of parents lobbying a nursery school trying to prevent a child who is know to have extreme learning difficulties from being admitted.

Discussion point

How are indirect and direct discrimination likely to be shown in a day care centre?

Whether discrimination is direct or indirect it can have serious physical, emotional, intellectual and social effects on an individual, particularly if the discrimination is regular and systematic. It can lead to depression, low self esteem and can completely destroy a person's belief in themselves.

Assessment activity 1.2.1

Rupesh CASE STUDY

Rupesh is the youngest of three children. His father is manager of a bank and his mother is a teacher. The family live in a small village which is five miles from the town where his parents work. The family live in a detached five-bedroomed house which has a large garden.

Rupesh has just started at the local primary school. He has frequent epileptic fits. Some of the children in his class are calling him names and refusing to sit next to him.

1. Explain how a caring home life can affect Rupesh's primary socialisation.

2. Identify **three** secondary socialisation factors that could influence Rupesh's' development. Explain how each is likely to influence him.

3. Identify **one** form of discrimination experienced by Rupesh. Give two examples to illustrate how this occurs.

4. Identify **four** likely effects of discrimination on Rupesh. Explain how each is likely to affect him.

5. Explain the difference between 'direct' and 'indirect' discrimination. Give **two** examples to illustrate how each could occur.

6. Explain what is meant by the term 'self esteem'. Explain **two** ways Rupesh's self esteem is likely to be affected positively and **two** ways it is likely to be affected negatively.

7. Explain how service users in care settings could be empowered.

8. Explain why care workers need to be aware of their prejudices and poor attitudes when caring for service users? Give examples to illustrate the points made.

1.2.2 Rights and responsibilities of service users and providers

Being aware of the principles of legislation is an important part of a care worker's job

When a person decides to live in a residential home or goes into hospital for treatment it does not mean that they have fewer rights than anyone else. Rights are broadly divided into:

- human rights
- rights that are provided by legislation.

The Children Act 1989

Local authority Social Services departments are required by the Children Act 1989 to act together to provide services and support for children, young people and their families, including disabled children. The Act covers children and young people under 18. Key features of this piece of legislation are:

- to protect children who are at risk – the **paramouncy principle**
- children have the right to be heard
- children's wishes have to be taken into consideration
- support to be provided to keep families together where this is at all possible.

The physical, emotional and educational needs of the child must be considered when a child protection case is being discussed. Decisions have to be reached as to whether the parents have the ability to meet these needs when caring for the

child. The panel of professionals, who have responsibility for the child or children, have to take into account any harm that the child is caused and the risks that are associated with this. They also consider whether any circumstances have changed for the child and whether such changes could have a positive or negative effect on the child.

The services provided under the Children Act 1989 can include:

- social work
- help with housing and support
- equipment and adaptations
- occupational therapists or other specialists
- short-term breaks
- counselling
- interpreters
- an advocate or representative for individuals or families.

The main purposes of child protection are to keep a child safe and secure, protecting the child from harm. Children now have to be kept informed about what is likely to happen to them and their opinions should be sought, particularly if decisions are to be made that will affect their future.

The local authorities have a statutory duty to investigate any reported cases of child abuse in order to protect the child from harm. Abuse could be in the form of verbal, sexual or physical punishment or emotional torture. When the child protection conference is convened a decision may be made to place the child being discussed on the **child protection register**. Both the child and their parents are then supported by Social Services to try and avoid any future difficulties. An approved social worker is often provided to help with such responsibilities.

There are several ways in which help can be provided in emergency situations. These can include:

How help can be provided	What is involved?
Emergency Protection Orders	This is a crisis situation where a child needs immediate help. Social services will make an application to the court for an order which will allow them to act.

How help can be provided	What is involved?
Care Orders	Under this type of order the child is usually removed from the parents and placed in a foster home as a temporary measure. Often this action is taken when an Emergency Order has been served. A Care Order can only be made when it is considered that a child is likely to be harmed either physically or emotionally. Children who are taken into care are known as 'looked after' children.
Education Supervision Orders	The aim is to make parents more responsible when their child is failing to attend school. The order places the child under the supervision of the local education authority.

As a result of the Children Act 1989 the county court has the ability to protect a child by making it a ward of court and placing it under the protection of the court and the Official Solicitor. They also have the ability to make orders that can remove a child to safety or take other protective action.

The Children (Scotland) Act, 1995 and the Children (Northern Ireland) Order, 1995 have similar provisions for children's services in Scotland and Northern Ireland.

Theory into practice

Invite a child protection officer to the Centre to find out about:

- How a child protection register is set up and organised

- How a family can benefit from being on a child protection register

- How a child can benefit from being on a child protection register

- The disadvantages to both the family and the child of having problems but not being placed on the child protection register.

Strengths of the Children Act 1989

- As a result of the Act children are protected from harm through the 'paramouncy' principle.

Abuse can make a child withdrawn and can prevent learning

- Children are able to express their preferences and views and these have to be 'listened to', in other words taken into consideration.
- Parents have 'responsibilities' which they must accept.
- The local authority must work in partnership with parents.
- Children have 'rights'. People who are dealing with children cannot just 'do things to them' or 'make arrangements for them', without their consent or without listening to their opinions.
- Details are provided about the circumstances under which children can be 'taken into care', but it is clear that such action should only be taken as a last resort.

Weaknesses of the Children Act 1989

- There is little accountability of social care workers involved in cases. In other words social workers are not held to account by others outside their department.
- Court cases that involve child protection are heard privately so there can be no public scrutiny of procedures.
- Children under the age of ten years are not considered to be old enough to be held accountable, for example for committing a criminal offence.

Discussion point

How does the Children Act 1989 help a child who is being physically abused?

Sophie — Activity 3

A teacher is concerned that Sophie, a child in her reception class, could be being sexually abused at home by her father. When talking to the teacher in private, Sophie tells her that she does not like it when her mother goes out to her cleaning job in the evening as her father does things to her when she is getting into bed. The teacher is quite worried about Sophie as she has become very withdrawn and cries a lot. She tells the named person responsible for child abuse at the school who decides to pass on the information to Social Services.

1. How can the Children Act 1989 protect children who are abused?

2. Invite a social worker to the Centre to find out how a child in Sophie's position would be helped by Social Services.

3. Write up the notes you have taken from the social worker to explain how Sophie would be helped.

4. What are the parents' rights in this case?

Children Act 2004

This Act was prompted by the failure of social services and other organisations who were involved in the care of Victoria Climbie to protect her. They had not shared information across the different services, for example health, education and social services. A report, the *Victoria Climbie Report (2003)* and the green paper, *Every Child Matters (2003)* proposed changes to legislation and policies in England, in order to minimise risks to all children. The Act is intended to force different services, who are involved in the care of children, to work much more closely together in an attempt to prevent other deaths.

The Act requires local authorities in England to have in place a 'Director of Children's Services' who will be accountable for children's services. These services will be inspected and departments will have their performance levels 'rated' so that the accountability set out as a requirement under the Act can be clearly seen. Also an 'information database' will be established. This will make it easier for professional care workers to network and share information about children for whom they are concerned.

Local authorities will be required to produce plans for children that take into consideration their specific needs and which make children aware of the forward planning that is intended. This will be linked to the appointment of a *'Children's Commissioner'* whose task will be to:

- initiate enquiries on behalf of children
- find out about the needs of children and young people
- investigate specifically the needs and interests of children and young people.

Discussion point

How could the Children Act 2004 have affected the life of Victoria Climbie if it had been in place before her death?

The Sex Discrimination Act 1975

The Sex Discrimination Act 1975 (SDA) covers direct and indirect discrimination.

- Direct sex discrimination is when a person is treated less favourably than a person of the opposite sex when both are in exactly the same situation.
- Indirect sexual discrimination occurs when far fewer members of one sex can take advantage of a situation than the other sex. For example, if a childminder excluded single parents from using the service this might be seen as discrimination against women as more single parents are women.

The Act makes it illegal for marital discrimination to occur to both men and women.

- Discrimination of both sexes if both are doing exactly the same job but one is being treated less favourably, e.g. a female care assistant is paid less than her male counterpart when she is doing exactly the same work and exactly the same hours.
- Discrimination by applying conditions on a woman that would not be applied to a man, e.g. all women must tie back their hair and remove rings.
- Discrimination against a man by treating him differently according to his marital status, e.g. 'We are not paying you as much because we know your wife is working so you already have two pay packets coming in.'

The second part of the Act deals with discrimination in the field of employment. An employer is acting unlawfully if it is stipulated that the person who is to be employed must be a man and also if an employer deliberately refuses a woman employment on the grounds of her sex, for example by saying 'we know you will want to start a family soon, so we have offered the job to Stan'. Also an employer is discriminating if a woman is prevented from accessing promotion, transfer or training by deliberately preventing her from accessing such benefits. Women must be given equal treatment with men.

Strengths of the Act

This Act has many strengths as **'an equality clause'** is implemented. This means that:

- where a woman is employed on like work with a man in the same employment, the terms of her contract must not become less favourable
- a woman doing like work to a man must be paid the same wage if in the same employment
- it is illegal to discriminate according to gender in areas of recruitment, selection, promotion and training
- it is illegal to discriminate because a person is married
- it tries to prevent direct discrimination, for example where one person is treated differently because of their sex
- it tries to prevent indirect discrimination, for example where conditions are applied to a situation which favours one sex more than another
- the Act tries to prevent **victimisation** where a person is treated less favourably because they have complained about sex discrimination in the past.

The Sex Discrimination Act 1975 set up the Equal Opportunities Commission to help promote equal opportunities for men and women.

Discussion point

You are a female nurse in a large Health Centre. Your supervisor, who is a married man, has started to sexually harass you. You have politely asked him to stop, but he says it's only joking and continues to tell embarrassing jokes. The harassment continues. What would you do and why?

Weaknesses of the Act

- the law is complex and difficult to unravel. As a result it is possible that many women and men may not make a complaint or seek redress because it is still very difficult to do

- it may be difficult, if seeking redress, to prove that certain actions have been taken and that there is direct and/or indirect discrimination
- the fear of losing employment if a complaint is made may be sufficient to stop a complaint being made.

Why should you have more pay than me when we are both doing the same job?

Andre and Gracia   Activity 4

Andre and Gracia both work as care assistants at Mobrey Nursing Home. Both work the same shift and do exactly the same jobs. The tasks they cover each day are the same as they have the same job description as care assistants.

When talking to Andre in their morning break time, Gracia learns that he is receiving 75p more an hour than she is getting. Also Andre tells her that he has been offered promotion as a supervisor at the nursing home.

Gracia seeks an appointment with the manager of the home to find out why she is not being paid the same as Andre and why she wasn't given the opportunity to become a supervisor.

The Manager tells Gracia that Andre is receiving more money because he has a family to support and that Gracia has her husband's income to help with their expenses. As far as the supervisor's job is concerned, it was not offered to Gracia as she might have another child and the home wanted continuity for the sake of the residents.

Andre and Gracia — Activity 4

1. What type of discrimination has Gracia experienced?

2. Explain how Gracia been discriminated against?

3. How could the Sex Discrimination Act 1975 help prevent Gracia from being discriminated against?

Disability Discrimination Act (1976, 1995, 1998)

The Act is concerned with preventing discrimination against people with disabilities. It covers housing, transport, employment, access to education and obtaining goods and services. This act is constantly in the process of being reviewed. Many of the provisions relating to employment of disabled persons came into force on 1 December 1998.

- The Act does not apply to prison officers, fire-fighters, police officers, members of the armed forces, people working aboard ships, aircraft and hovercraft. It also does not apply to employees working wholly or mainly abroad or to employers who employ fewer than 15 people.

- The Act does include permanent, temporary and contract workers, as well as full-time employees. It covers any employees or potential employees with a 'physical or mental impairment', which has long-term effects on their ability to carry out day-to-day tasks. It also covers people who have had a disability in the past. ('Long-term effect' is taken to be at least 12 months.)

- Employers must not discriminate against an employee (whether they are actually employed or could be employed in the future) with a disability or who has had a disability in the past. This includes ensuring that the interview and selection process, the practices and rules and the premises of the employer do not put a disabled person at a disadvantage as compared to a person without a disability. This also includes promotion opportunities, training, pensions and other benefits.

- Other responsibilities an employer will have to a disabled employee include providing supervision, modifying instructions or reference manuals so that they are, for example, in large print or Braille, allowing absences from work or rehabilitation related to an employee's disability, modifying or purchasing new equipment to meet a disabled employee's needs.

- Any such adjustments must be reasonable bearing in mind, amongst other things, the cost to the employer, the disruption it will cause and the effectiveness it will have in removing or preventing any disadvantage to the disabled employee.

- Any employees who believe that they have been the subject of discrimination can apply to an Employment Tribunal within three months of the date of the discrimination.

The Employment Tribunal can:

- make a declaration about the rights of the disabled employee
- order the employer to pay compensation to the disabled employee
- recommend that the employer take reasonable action within a certain period of time to prevent or reduce any disadvantage to the disabled person or to make reasonable adjustment.

As from 1 October 1999 Part 3 of the Disability Discrimination Act 1998 came into force.

Amongst other things this part of the Act relates to adjustments service providers have to make to ensure access by disabled people to their services. This includes, for example, providing poor-sighted people with information in large print, Braille or tape, or hard of hearing people with written information, or providing wheelchair access and allowing guide dogs onto premises.

This also means that government and public service websites must provide content in a format that can be read by those with poor sight. A good example of this is the BBC which has spent a considerable amount of time ensuring that their websites can be reformatted and displayed in larger fonts.

A discriminatory act will not be unlawful if it is done in pursuance of an Act of Parliament or to safeguard national security. Charities are also allowed to discriminate in pursuance of their charitable activities, if those are connected with disability, for example, treating a particular group of disabled workers more favourably than others.

Farxiya — Activity 5

Farxiya is seeking a room in hospital accommodation for staff, as she is a receptionist at the hospital. She is physically disabled and needs a ground-floor bedsit that has been adapted for a person in a wheelchair. She is told by the accommodation officer that they cannot offer her any accommodation as all the ground-floor bedsits are going to be let to able-bodied staff who work at the hospital.

1. How is the accommodation officer not meeting the requirements of the Disability Discrimination Act?

2. Who is not included in the Disability Discrimination Act?

3. Investigate to whom Farxiya could appeal to help her with her case. Explain the system of redress that would help Farxiya.

The Race Relations Act 1976 (Amendment) 2003

This Act makes racial discrimination illegal in public life. It states that people can take action if they feel they have been discriminated against because of their race in situations involving employment, housing, education, and provision of goods and services.

The Act describes discrimination as treating a person less favourably because of their race, colour, ethnicity and national origins. Direct and indirect discrimination on racial grounds in employment, education, housing and in the provision of goods and services is outlawed. Discrimination is seen as applying criteria that works to the disadvantage of one group of people over another.

Victimisation is also illegal under this act as it is illegal to treat somebody differently because they have made a complaint about discrimination.

The Race Relations Amendment Act (2000) requires public authorities to promote racial equality and to provide fair and accessible services to all and to improve opportunities in employment. The NHS, for example, which is a public body, is now required as a general statutory duty to eliminate unlawful racial discrimination and to promote good relations between different racial groups.

Strengths of the Act

- There is emphasis on promoting good relationships between different racial groups rather than merely preventing racial discrimination. This is a more positive and proactive requirement.

- It is recognised that all public bodies, like the NHS and others, must make all services offered accessible to people with different types of racial issues, for example, cultural differences.

- Both direct and indirect discrimination relating to race must be eliminated. For example, indirect discrimination: insisting that all who are working in an establishment must not wear any form of headgear is indirectly discriminating against those whose faith requires them to wear it.

Weaknesses of the Act

- It is quite difficult to know what happens on a daily basis in care settings unless poor practice is monitored. For example, if a service user in a nursing home is told by a care worker 'to stop talking to his visitors in his own language because it is upsetting other visitors', the authorities are unlikely to hear about it unless it is mentioned by the service user when the setting is being inspected or if another care worker reports such treatment to a supervisor at the nursing home.

- Laws can be passed but it is difficult to 'police' attitudes, views and opinions of individuals when they occur in private homes. Some attitudes have been passed down by family members to others within the family group. Unless an individual's awareness is raised about such attitudes, they are likely to be carried into the workplace.

- Forms of redress require individuals to know their rights and also to know how to ensure their rights are maintained. This means that if a person wishes to make a complaint, they could find that their situation is made worse by those who care for them. Also those concerned need to know to whom they can turn for help.

Suresh	Activity 6

Suresh is 81 years of age. He has recently moved to Hartshead Residential Home. He is very unhappy as he is the only resident from his own culture and he feels left out of conversations and activities because English is not his first or preferred language.

Care workers do not ask Suresh what he would like to choose from the menu. They just serve what they think he should have. The menu is only written in English. They also call Suresh, 'Sam' as they say it is easier for the other residents to say. When Suresh tries to protest about this the care workers tell him, 'don't be silly. You still know who you are, just think of the others, it will make it easier for them.'

1 Give an example of direct and indirect discrimination giving an explanation of how each is likely to affect Suresh.

2 Explain how the Race Relations Act tries to prevent the types of discrimination experienced by Suresh.

3 Research information about the Commission for Racial Equality. Produce a handout to show what their role involves.

The Mental Health Act 1983

Mental health problems can affect people at different times in their lives and can do so in a variety of different ways. A person who has mental ill health can experience anxiety, depression, schizophrenia and dementia. They may also self harm.

The Mental Health Act 1983 clearly sets out the circumstances in which a person who has a mental disorder can be treated without their consent. It also sets out the safeguards to which the person with the disorder is entitled.

The Mental Health Act 1983 gives relatives and approved social workers and doctors the right to have a person detained under the Act for their own safety or to ensure the safety of others.

The Mental Health Act 1983 involves checks that are made through:

• The Mental Act Managers' Hearings
• The Mental Health Review Tribunals
• The Mental Health Act Commission.

The Mental Act Managers' Hearings is composed of a group from the local community who oversee the administration of the Mental Health Act 1983 to ensure that it is used in a reasonable way.

The group can hold hearings and release individuals who have been detained under the Act under sections 2 and 3.

The Mental Health Review Tribunal consists of a doctor, a solicitor or a barrister and a lay person who has been appointed by the Lord Chancellor. A person who applies to the Mental Health Tribunal has the right to be represented by a lawyer and to receive legal aid.

The Mental Health Act Commission is mainly concerned with giving consent for treatment and tries to ensure that hospitals use the Mental Health Act 1983 correctly. They also make sure that a second doctor is present to give a second opinion, when a person is held under compulsory section and refuses treatment.

Various people can, under the Mental Health Act 1983, ask for a person to be compulsorily admitted. These are:

• approved social workers
• the service user's relatives in the following order of preference:
  – husband or wife
  – son or daughter
  – father or mother
  – brother or sister
  – grandparent
  – grandchild
  – uncle or aunt
  – nephew or niece
• an approved doctor
• a qualified mental health or disabilities nurse
• police officers.

A person who is compulsorily admitted under the Mental Health Act 1983 can be detained for 28 days. This arrangement cannot be renewed. Such detention must be applied for, usually by the service user's nearest relative or an approved social worker, but the application must be approved by two doctors.

When a person is discharged, aftercare arrangements are made. This can include, for example:

• counselling
• visits by community psychiatric nurses
• visit to or by clinical psychologists
• visits by occupational therapists.

The government are preparing a **Draft Mental Health Bill** which is likely to replace the current Mental Health Act. This is likely to be implemented in 2007 and takes into account human rights laws and new patterns of care and treatment.

Theory into practice

Visit a care setting or invite a specialist into the Centre to find out how the Mental Health Act 1983 has affected their practice.

Strengths and weaknesses of the Mental Health Act 1983

Strengths	Weaknesses
The Act protects people who lose the ability to make decisions for themselves.	The law states that 'everyone should make their own decisions for as long as they are able to do so'. This means that on some occasions long periods of time elapse before any action is taken.
The Act prevents an individual from harming themselves or others by allowing a compulsory section order.	A compulsory detention or section order can cause a person to feel that they have a stigma after they have had a compulsory detention order.
Very careful procedures are followed when admitting an individual against their will to make sure their rights are safeguarded.	The Act does not take into account an individual's human rights. This means that values that are held by the individual are not considered and that human rights under European law are not applied.
Systems are in place to ensure accountability of those who are making decisions as checks are made by independent bodies.	Consideration is not given to new forms of community care that are available.
Treatment cannot be forced on an individual unless their mental illness is so severe that the opinions of other specialists support such a decision.	

Molly — Activity 7

Molly lives alone as her husband died three years previously. Molly has found it very hard to cope without him. She worries about not having enough money and forgets to pay many of her bills. She is not eating properly, has lost a lot of weight and has been found wandering around the streets at night.

Molly has no children, her nearest relative being a niece who visits her twice a week, but who now feels that Molly needs more help as she has become aggressive and has started to throw things at the neighbours when they are in their garden.

1. How can Molly's niece obtain a compulsory admissions order under the Mental Health Act 1983?

2. What is the approved order for relatives who are seeking a compulsory section order?

3. What is the main purpose of the Mental Health Commission?

Human Rights Act 1998

Human rights are a set of values. They reflect the way that individuals should act towards one another. Examples of human rights include:

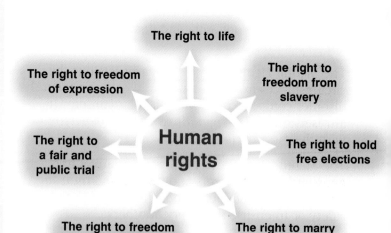

Human rights are an entitlement that everyone has irrespective of ethnic origin, gender, age or class. They promote and encourage acceptance of others. The Human Rights Act of 1998 allows people in the United Kingdom to seek **redress** if they believe their human rights have been infringed by any public organisation.

Health, social care and early years organisations that are affected by the Human Rights Act 1998 are:

- residential and nursing homes
- voluntary organisations
- public services
- education and childcare.

Professional care workers in all health, social care or early years settings are affected by the Human Rights Act 1998. Organisations that carry out a public function or that carry out work in a public area will have to take human rights into consideration when planning and implementing their work. For example, a private nursing home has to make sure that services are provided within the Human Rights Act 1998, as it is registered with the local authority and inspected, as it is part of the public domain. Similarly, childcare and education services have to make sure they are, in their day-to-day tasks, operating within the requirements of the Act. In other words they must ensure they do not prevent anyone from receiving what is rightfully their legal entitlement.

The Human Rights Act 1998 originates from the 'European Convention on Human Rights' which was set up during World War II. It is set out in 'articles', many of which have been incorporated into the new Act.

Some Principles of the European Convention on Human Rights

Section of the Human Rights Act 1998	How it affects individuals
Article 2: The right to life	There are very few reasons why someone should take the life of another. An example could be if it is an act of self defence by a person who is maintaining the law. **Q: Should a life support machine be switched off if a person is considered to be 'brain dead' and has been in that condition for a long time?**
Article 4: The prohibition of slavery and forced labour	Individuals cannot be forced to work or be treated like a slave. **Q: How does the idea of a 'minimum wage' link with this article?**
Article 5: The right to liberty and security	An individual cannot be detained or deprived of their freedom except if they have been involved in a crime or are considered to be mentally unstable and a danger to themselves and others. **Q: Is it right to make compulsory admissions for individuals who need to be detained under the Mental Health Act 1983?**
Article 8: The right to respect privacy and family life	Only in the interest of public security can this article be overturned. Everyone has the right to privacy. In other words, people can 'shut their doors' and be away from others. **Q: How can privacy be maintained in a residential home or if a person is in hospital?**
Article 9: Freedom of thought, conscience and religion	Each individual has the right to their own faith. They can also hold views and opinions. However, they may not express in public, views and opinions that are discriminatory. **Q: Why do you think discriminatory views and opinions cannot be expressed in public?**
Article 10: Freedom of expression	Individuals can have their own opinions and can express these. **Q: Why, as a result of recent terrorist attacks in Britain, have some faith leaders been detained for expression of their views?**
Article 12: The right to marry	The age at which a person can marry is decided by the law of a particular country but everyone has the right to marry. **Q: Should two people, both of whom have severe learning difficulties, be allowed to marry?**
Article 14: Prohibition of discrimination	This article is not included in the Human Rights Act as the government considers it is already covered by legislation. This article makes it illegal to treat individuals differently because of their race, religion, or for any other reason. **Q: Why should people who are from a different race to our own not experience discrimination?**

Redress in this country instead of having to go to the European Court of Human Rights

Individuals must have the right to the provision of education

Individuals must have their rights considered when organisations are making decisions

Social security law can be overridden if it is incompatible with the Convention

Strengths of the Human Rights Act

The state must provide laws that protect life

Service users who are ill have the right to drugs that are available even if the government has decided they are not going to provide them

Since the European Convention of Human Rights has published the 'articles' some additions have been made. These additions are known as 'protocols' and include:

- the protection of property
- the right to education
- the right to free elections
- the abolition of the death penalty.

Human rights help to prevent **social exclusion**. If a person experiences social exclusion through unemployment, poor housing, lack of education or low income, it is likely that the effect will be:

- low self esteem
- anger and frustration
- less likely to gain employment
- less likely to have a good relationship with others
- lack of trust
- unable to access health and social care services.

All individuals have moral rights. Sometimes maintaining human rights means imposing obligations on others. In order to live alongside one another in peaceful co-existence this has to be accepted. If rights are not accepted, individuals can seek to enforce their rights by taking action in the courts.

Discussion point

How can a child who has been abused be protected by the Human Rights Act 1998?

Strengths of the Human Rights Act 1998

The Human Rights Act is now well established in Britain; consequently individuals who feel that their human rights have been violated can get redress. The strengths of the Human Rights Act 1998 are shown above:

The Human Rights Act 1998 does support the individual in that it prevents discrimination and encourages quality practice in health, social care and early years services. Much more thought has to be given by managers when making decisions that are going to affect the lives of others.

Weaknesses of the Human Rights Act 1998

There are three aspects of the Human Rights Act 1998 that are still unclear and have not yet been proved through the courts. These include:

- who are the 'public authorities'? – these are not fully defined
- some legislation is not compatible with Convention rights
- some 'restrictions' placed on individuals may not be compatible with Convention rights.

The weaknesses of the Act are overwhelmed by its strengths. It helps to prevent discrimination, promotes freedom of speech and gives individuals the right to security, education and life.

Petroc — Activity 8

Petroc is an asylum seeker who has legally sought to enter this country. He is trying to build a new life for himself and to enable this to happen he is seeking employment. He tries to find work on several building sites but he is unsuccessful. Eventually he is told that if he turns up at a certain place at 6.00 am he is likely to be employed but will receive a very low wage.

Petroc decides that he must turn up as he needs the money to pay for his accommodation and food. He would have liked to attend an evening class to improve his education but he is told by someone who has done this type of work previously that he will not finish working until very late.

1. Explain **three** rights Petroc has under the Human Rights Act 1998.

2. How is Petroc likely to be affected by lack of education?

3. How is Petroc likely to be affected if his human rights are not upheld?

4. Explain the origins of the Human Rights Act 1998.

5. Work in pairs to carry out research. Investigate one of the 'articles' listed below and give a short presentation to others about its content:
   - Article 4
   - Article 6
   - Article 7
   - Article 11.

Legislation that applies to other parts of the UK

Legislation that is applied in the UK is not always the same as in other parts of the country, for example Northern Ireland. The Acts which do apply are given in the table below:

Legislation	Overview of the legislation
Sex Discrimination (Northern Ireland) 1970 (amended 1984) Order	This Order makes exceptions relating to the special treatment of women relating to pregnancy and childbirth, to ministers of religion and to goods and services that could cause an offence to others.
Race Relations (Northern Ireland) Order 1976 (amended 1988)	This Act specifically outlaws discrimination against the Travellers Community in Ireland. The Order very closely follows the Race Relations Act 1976 in England.
Equality (Northern Ireland) Order 2000	The Equality Commission Northern Ireland is required to work towards the elimination of discrimination towards disabled people and to promote equal opportunities for disabled people. Other responsibilities involve the preparation of statutory codes of practice, so that practical guidance to employers is also to be part of the work undertaken. From the perspective of health and social care, the Equality Commission Northern Ireland are required to provide conciliation, similar to that provided by ACAS in England, between service providers and disabled people.
Northern Ireland Act 1998	Requires the public authorities in Northern Ireland to promote equality of opportunity between people of different religious beliefs, between men and women and between people with disability and able-bodied individuals and groups. The public authorities are also required to promote equality between people who have differences of political opinion, those who have different sexual orientation and between people of different age groups.

Routes of redress

In any health, social care or early years setting a complaints procedure is a route of redress for all service users. If a service user feels they have not received the care they should have, or their rights have not been met, they have the right to complain.

The NHS has a national complaints procedure which states:

> NHS staff will do whatever they can to make sure you are treated properly. But sometimes things go wrong.
>
> You have every right to complain if the services you receive fall short of what you expect.
>
> Here is what you do if you are not happy with any aspect of the NHS.
>
> The first step is to contact the local organisation with which you are unhappy to seek local resolution of your complaint.
>
> If you are still unhappy, you can ask for an independent review to take place.
>
> Finally, if your complaint is still not resolved to your satisfaction, you should contact the health service commissioner.
>
> Source: www.nhs.uk

I am not happy with the treatment I have received

All care workers have a responsibility to the service users they are caring for to make sure that they have no cause for complaint. Any complaint which arises must be dealt with promptly to prevent the situation becoming worse. Details of the complaints procedure are usually provided to the service user on or before their arrival at a setting. When a service user makes a complaint, the care worker must inform their supervisor/manager to ensure that the complaint is dealt with effectively.

If a service user has a complaint they should complain to the manager or person in charge of the care setting. If the service user feels the complaint has not been dealt with in a suitable manner then they should complain to the registration authority. In the event that the complaint is still an issue that is unresolved, the service user should seek support from organisations that have experience in dealing with such issues. Addresses of such organisations are usually included in the package of information provided for the service user on admission. Alternatively the CAB (Citizens Advice Bureau) will provide the information required.

If a complaint becomes a major issue there are organisations that can give advice and guidance to those seeking redress. The diagram below indicates some examples of such organisations:

Organisations that assist with redress

Discussion point

How could having an issue that is in need of redress cause physical and emotional upset to a service user?

Commission for Racial Equality

The Commission for Racial Equality (CRE) was set up by the Race Relations Act 1976. The CRE is responsible to the Home Office and has the following responsibilities:

- working towards the elimination of all discrimination
- promoting equality of opportunity and good relations between persons of different racial groups
- reviewing the workings of the Act and drawing up proposals for improving and amending it
- giving advice to people with complaints of discrimination and in some cases representing people in court.

The CRE provides information and advice to people who feel they have suffered racial harassment or discrimination. Its aim is to make sure that policies and procedures are implemented to provide equal treatment for all.

The Equal Opportunities Commission

The Equal Opportunities Commission (EOC) was set up by the 1975 Sex Discrimination Act. This has a legal duty to enforce the Sex Discrimination Act 1975 and the Equal Pay Act 1970.

The EOC publishes leaflets and gives guidance on all issues linked to equal opportunities and offers support to service users and organisations who feel they have been discriminated against.

The Disability Rights Commission

The Disability Rights Commission (DRC) was established by the Disability Discrimination Act 1995 and started work in April 2000. The main duties of the Commission are:

- to work towards removing all discrimination towards disabled people
- to promote equal opportunities for disabled people
- to encourage good practice in the treatment of disabled people
- to advise the government on the operation of the Disability Discrimination Act 1995.

The DRC provides help for disabled people by providing information and advice, preparing and reviewing statutory codes of practice and making sure there are arrangements for access to goods, facilities, services and premises.

Promoting the rights of service users

All service users have rights. These rights are protected by laws and the application of values. The Acts already given within this unit protect the rights listed in the diagram given below:

The right to effective communication

The right to have a GP of their choice

The right to be given up-to-date information

The right to make choices and have consultations

Rights of service users

The right to confidentiality

The right to equal and fair treatment

The right to have different sexual orientation

The right to their own opinions, views and beliefs

Fostering equality and diversity means promoting anti-discrimination. This means treating service users in a way that they are given equal access to all services and ensuring that they get equal benefit from the services.

The aim of anti-discrimination is to make sure that all the population feel that they are valued regardless of their colour, belief, sexual orientation or disability. Quality practice requires not denying one service user or a service user group the same quality of opportunity or service that a different group receives. One person in a group must not be favoured over another.

Confidentiality

Confidentiality means keeping the information given to oneself. That is, not sharing it with anyone who does not 'need to know'. It means making sure personal and private information cannot be accessed by others. Any information given by the service user should not be **disclosed** without the service user's permission. Providing 'quality care' involves keeping personal information safe. Personal information can include:

- information being discussed orally, e.g. care workers discussing proposed treatment with the service user
- written information, e.g. a care plan being stored safely
- electronic records, e.g. a person's medical history being stored securely, with only authorised personnel having access.

Disclosure is passing on personal information, which is considered to be a secret between the service user and the care worker, to others.

Care workers should never make a promise not to pass on personal information. They should explain to the service user that they will not pass on personal information unless there is a very good reason to do so. Disclosure of information can be necessary in special circumstances, for example:

- if a service user intends to harm themselves
- if a service user intends to harm others
- if a service user is involved in a criminal activity
- when others may be at risk of harm.

There may be times when care workers may face **'dilemmas'** about respecting confidentiality. For example, if a care worker is told the service user is thinking of harming themselves, this must be shared with the appropriate named person in case the service user does inflict harm on themselves. Any information held about the service user is, however, protected by law.

Discussion point

A neighbour who has reported possible child abuse approaches a social worker to find out what is happening with the family and the child. What should be the response? Why?

How far have you got with Natasha's case then?

Sometimes tensions can arise between:

- service users and other service users
- service users and staff
- service users and the organisation
- service users and the resources available.

Sometimes a **compromise** has to be made. It is not always possible to satisfy the rights of a service user. Listening and using effective communication skills are essential, if solutions are to be found. Through discussion it may be possible to meet half way in order to resolve the issues that arise.

Balancing services users' rights against their responsibilities can cause **tensions** and disagreements. Service users have a responsibility towards those who are offering the service. They also have rights. Balancing these two perspectives could at times be very difficult. For example, if a service user, who requires support when bathing, wants a bath when few staff are available to help, tensions could arise. The service user has the right to have a bath when they wish but the care workers have a responsibility to ensure the service user is safe.

Discussion point

Leslie is watching a documentary on TV. Three other residents want to watch a soap. How can care workers balance service users' rights against their responsibilities?

Service users have a right to have their needs met. Each service user will have specific needs. Although these may appear to be the same, they may require different application. Settings, for example a hospital, often have to make very serious decisions. An adolescent may need major heart surgery that involves a great many specialists and support staff, the cost of which could be half a million pounds. For the same money they could do 250 knee replacement operations. Which should they do? Needs and resources have to be balanced.

On a smaller scale, a child in a reception class may have very challenging behaviour. If the teacher spends nearly all of his/her time with the child, the behaviour of this child becomes acceptable. But the other members of the class are not having the attention they need to help them with their work. The teacher concerned has to balance needs against the resources he/she has: the resource being human resources, i.e. himself/herself.

Sometimes the unavailability of resources can create tensions in care settings. For example, in a residential home only one or two wheelchairs are available but five or six are needed if a number of older people were to be taken on an outing. The residential home may not be able to afford to hire additional wheelchairs, so some residents may have to be left behind. Such difficulties related to resources have to be balanced, one against the other.

Assessment activitiy 1.2.2

Rights and legislation   CASE STUDY

Andre is living with ten other residents in a residential home for adults with learning difficulties. Several examples of poor practice are observed by a new member of staff. These are:

- Andre is disabled but access is poor at the residential home and Andre has to stay in his room most of the time.
- Anita has severe depression and is being locked in her room for long periods to prevent her harming others.
- Usha is from a different culture and is not being given anywhere to pray during the day and she is not allowed to return to her own room.
- Bryony is told that she will have to wear someone else's clothes as it does not really matter that her own cannot be found.
- Petra wants to make a complaint and is told that 'we don't allow that to happen here'.
- Jordon is called names and is discriminated against when food is served and when activities are organised, as his English is poor and the care workers cannot understand him.

1   How are the rights of Anita not being met? Show how legislation could help to protect Anita.

2   Explain the main principles of the Mental Health Act 1983 and how it can affect service users who have mental ill health.

3   Describe how the Race Relations Act 1976 promotes the rights of service users such as Usha and Jordon. Evaluate the effectiveness of the legislation.

4   Outline how the Sex Discrimination Act 1975 protects both the residents' rights and care workers' rights in the workplace. Assess the effectiveness of the legislation.

5   Explain the main principles of The Human Rights Act 1998, showing how it could help to protect individuals who are service users in health and social care.

6   Identify legislation that helps to promote the rights of service users who are disabled. Assess how effective legislation is in protecting people, like Andre, who are disabled.

7   How could 'tensions' arise in the residential home? Explain how **three** different tensions could be managed.

8   Explain what is meant by the term 'dilemma' when applied to health, social care and early years situations. Give examples to illustrate the points made.

1.2.3 Facilitation of access to services

Methods of referral

How will you **access** your GP? You will probably telephone the GP surgery and ask to make an appointment to see the GP. This is known as a '**self referral**', because you have gone straight to the GP and not approached him through another professional care worker. Most service users will gain access to the GP by taking themselves directly to the surgery.

The GP, however, may on some occasions want us to make an appointment with a person who has specialised in specific types of conditions or illnesses or a person who deals with specific injuries. He/she will then either telephone or write to the specialist, who is usually known as a 'consultant', to make an appointment on our behalf.

This method of making an arrangement to see someone else is called a '**professional referral**'. Perhaps such an appointment has been made for you if it is thought that an arm or leg has been fractured and the GP thinks an x-ray is necessary. Or maybe you have had an illness that the GP needs a second opinion about and has consequently made an arrangement for you to see the specialist at the local hospital.

The third way in which service users can be referred to health, social care or early years services is called '**third party referral**'. This is when another person refers a person to a professional because they are trying to be helpful or because we may not be in a position to get the help that is required.

Leigh-Anne enjoys going to playgroup each week

Leigh-Anne   CASE STUDY

Leigh-Anne attends playgroup three times each week. The nursery nurse at the playgroup becomes very worried as Leigh-Anne has bruises on her legs and on her tummy. She notices these when she takes Leigh-Anne to the toilet. The nursery nurse reports the bruising to the 'named' person at the playgroup who is responsible.

Two weeks later Leigh-Anne is found to have more bruises and she seems to be very sad and cries a lot. The named person at the playgroup telephones Social Services to report her concerns.

This is a 'third party' referral because the playgroup named person has telephoned the social worker. It is not a self referral because the child or her parent has not done the referring. It is not a professional referral because a professional care worker has not referred the child. Instead another adult has done the referring and so this is a 'third party referral'.

Discussion point

What other examples of third party referral are there?

Examples of other third party referrals could include:

- a teacher telephoning a social worker because they have concerns about a child

- a neighbour telephoning a social worker or GP because they have concerns about a child that lives next door

- a neighbour telephoning Social Services because an old person is wandering about in the garden at night or leaving the gas on

- an employer telephoning a GP about a young employee who seems to be very depressed and he is afraid the employee may harm himself

- a person telephoning the emergency services for an ambulance to take an injured person to hospital.

Barriers to access

Impossible to access

Sometimes people do not use the health, social care and early years services that they need. This could be for a variety of reasons but mainly because **barriers** prevent them from doing so. Barriers can include:

Physical barriers

Cultural and language barriers

Psychological barriers

Barriers to accessing health, social care and early years services

Geographical location

Financial barriers

Physical barriers

Imagine a person in their seventies suffering from rheumatism and needing to walk with a Zimmer frame to the GP surgery. The only way to get to the surgery is by going up some very steep steps.

Impossible!

The service user would know that they can't cope with the steps so they would probably not go for treatment in the first place! They would go without the treatment they needed because of the physical barrier of the stairs.

Quite a lot of people are prevented from using health, social care and early years services because they are unable to enter or leave a building. Or they may not be able to use the toilet because it is upstairs or the door is not wide enough for a wheelchair to enter.

Psychological barriers

Afraid to have treatment

Psychological barriers affect the way people think. Some people are afraid of going to the dentist. They have a 'fear' of dentists. This is an example of a psychological barrier. Some older people will not agree to going into a residential home because they

think they will become dependent on others or because they think people will not have any respect for them because they cannot cope. They think this is a **'stigma'** and will not accept the care offered even though they may know it is best for them.

Financial barriers

How often are people prevented from doing something because it costs too much? Most will have experienced this at one time or another in their lives. When people are unable to use a health, social care or early years service because of a lack of money, their health may suffer as a result. If someone lives some distance from health services, for example, the cost of travelling may be too much. If it is a private service, such as a playgroup, a family with several children may not be able to afford to send them to the playgroup. Cost can stop people from getting their prescription, if they have to pay for it, and so they do not get the medication they may need.

Geographical barriers

How near to your home are the health and social care services you may need? Some people live in rural areas and may find that getting to the services they need is difficult because they do not have a car and buses may run at times which are not suitable.

Older people may have difficulty getting on and off public transport and they may not be able to walk the distance to the service they require. They may put off going to see their GP because of this and as a result their condition could get worse.

Cultural and language barriers

This just does not make sense!

27

In order to find out about services it is most likely that a service user will need to read signs, leaflets or posters. If these are written in English and if this is not the language which they usually use, it may be difficult to fully understand the information that is given and so they may not know what services are available. Also, if a leaflet is provided by the GP or specialist to explain the treatment that is being proposed, the person may not be able to read or understand what is being said in the leaflet. This could cause them to become worried or frightened, so psychological barriers and cultural barriers exist.

The table below gives a summary of the barriers that can prevent people from getting the care they need.

Barrier	Examples
Physical barriers	• client working shifts, therefore unable to access service as the service is not available when they are not working • stairs • lack of adapted toilets • lift operating system being out of reach • lack of ramps • lack of lifts.
Psychological barriers	• fear of losing independence • stigma associated with using some services • not wanting to be looked after by others • mental health problems.
Financial barriers	• charges/fees • lack of money for transport • lack of money to provide the service.
Geographical barriers	• living in a rural area where facilities are limited • living in a rural are where transport is not available when the services are open • a long bus/train journey may not be practicable.
Cultural and language barriers	• using English may deter some people from using services • not having professionals who are of the same sex, for example women doctors or consultants for women • written information not in the person's own language • not knowing what is available • some treatments being considered unacceptable to certain cultures.

Katie and Max   Activity 9

Max has been living in this country for only a few months. He and his partner, Katie, are trying to learn English but they are finding it very hard. Max is unemployed and is finding it difficult to get work, but his partner has a part-time job in the local hotel. Max and his partner have two children, Bryoni, who is four and Marti, who is two years old. It is difficult for the family to get transport into town, where the health, social care and early years services are. A bus leaves twice each day but the costs are high. Both Katie and Max would like Bryoni to go to playgroup, but there isn't one in the village. Marti has to go to the hospital once a week as he has cystic fibrosis and needs treatment to clear his lungs. He is waiting to have an operation to help clear his airways but the hospital has a long waiting list and staff shortages.

New to this country

1 Explain the barriers experienced by Max and Bryoni and the effects such barriers could have upon them.

2 Explain how service providers could facilitate access to services.

Adaptation of existing premises

Getting past the 'barriers' and accessing health, social care and early years services is important for service users. Service providers, too, want to make sure that they reach all those who need their services. When new services are developed those responsible put a great deal of thought into how they can be made accessible to all.

Existing buildings often have to be adapted so that they can be accessible to all who wish to use them. Such adaptations could include, for example:

- putting in ramps to make access to the building possible
- having lifts with control panels that are within reach of service users
- making sure Braille signing is used on the lift control
- having 'talking instructions' for people who are blind and who wish to use lifts
- having wider doorways to accommodate wheelchairs
- making sure adapted toilets are fitted
- making sure leaflets are printed in a variety of languages.

The case studies below give some problems experienced by service users.

Service users   CASE STUDY

How could each service user's need be achieved?

1. Janine has three children and lives on an estate which is two miles from the GP surgery. She finds it very hard to get to the surgery with three children as it is a long way to walk and she cannot afford the bus.

2. Geoff is in a wheelchair. He cannot use the lift because the control panel is too high.

3. Jay works shifts. The GP surgery is not open when he is not at work, so he can never go for his health check.

4. Martha's usual language is not English and she cannot read the leaflet about health services.

5. Beth is blind and cannot use the lift at the hospital as she cannot use the control panel.

Campaigns to raise awareness

Health promotion organisations and other specialists such as Help the Aged, Scope and statutory bodies such as the NHS often hold campaigns to try and influence the attitude of the general public and service providers to make them aware of the needs of individuals and to highlight the need for change. If people's attitudes are changed and they are made more aware of what could be done to make the lives of people easier, action is more likely to follow.

Promotion of self advocacy

Some service users may be restricted or limited in some way about the type of lifestyle they are able to have. This could be because they have chosen to live in residential care or because they have limited mobility or because they have a disability.

Advocacy can involve giving training to a person so that they are able to help themselves. This could also be achieved through the use of a mentor who would guide them in what to say.

Others may need the help of an 'advocate' to explain to them the options that are available; particularly if they have a mental disability or if they have a learning disability. The advocate can be a friend or a professionally trained voluntary person who speaks on behalf of the service user.

Identification of additional sources of funding and joint planning

Certain funds may be available to providers to adapt buildings for service users who have disability or impairment. This also applies to new buildings that are being erected. Recent campaigns on the needs of those who are disabled have raised awareness of adaptations or provisions that can be made to provide equal access to all and not just to those who are able-bodied. New buildings, in particular, are planned to accommodate such needs.

Assessment activity 1.2.3

Marcus and Sue CASE STUDY

Marcus and Sue both use health and social care services. Marcus is 68 and has difficulty with mobility. He can walk a little but prefers to use a wheelchair outside the house as his balance is very poor.

Sue has a severe sight impairment. Although she has had two operations she can see little and has been classified as blind.

Both Marcus and Sue have to visit the GP once each month. Marcus attends the hospital for physiotherapy once a fortnight and Sue attends the hospital day care centre once a week.

1   Identify the possible barriers to accessing the services Marcus and Sue need, explaining the effects such barriers could have on each of them.

2   Explain how each service provider could overcome the barriers to their services.

3   Explain what is meant by the term 'advocacy', giving examples of how this could help a person with learning difficulties.

4   How could joint planning and funding of services make access more acceptable for service users who are impaired or disabled?

5   How can campaigns raise the awareness of service users and providers and change attitudes towards accessing health, social care and early years services?

1.2.4 Care values

The care values are based on ideas about human rights. These are the rights to which all people are entitled. A care worker will want to 'act in the best interest of the service user'. This means valuing them as an individual and treating them in a way that we would want to be treated ourselves. A care worker will, therefore, show that they 'value' each individual by applying the care values in the day-to-day tasks that they do. Providing quality care means applying the care values when working with service users.

How are you feeling about the news you have just received?

In health and social care organisations there are three main components of the care values. These are:

- promoting service users' rights and beliefs
- promoting equality and diversity
- maintaining confidentiality.

Promoting service users' rights includes

- the right to be different, e.g. sexual orientation, beliefs
- freedom from discrimination, e.g. not to be singled out and treated differently
- confidentiality, e.g. to have all personal information kept private
- choice, e.g. to be able to make own decisions and to be consulted
- dignity, e.g. to be treated with respect
- effective communication, e.g. to have things explained and to be listened to
- safety and security, e.g. to be protected from harm
- privacy, e.g. having own space which is not invaded by others without consent.

Fostering equality and diversity includes

- understanding and not showing prejudice, stereotyping and labelling
- understanding and valuing the benefits of diversity
- understanding the bases of discrimination, such as gender, race, age, sexuality, disability or social class
- understanding of own beliefs, assumptions, not being prejudiced.

Maintaining confidentiality

Confidentiality means not passing on to others either oral or written information that has been given to a person. However, care workers should not promise to maintain confidentiality as some information may have to be passed on to others on a 'need to know' basis. The term 'others' means other professionals in the same setting, or in different settings, who are responsible for the service user's care.

It is important that when talking to other professionals, the door of the room is shut so that the care workers cannot be overheard. If speaking to the professional's own family about 'what sort of a day' the care worker has experienced, it is important not to name the service users for whom care has been provided and to make sure that they cannot be identified.

Confidentiality covers areas such as:

- oral conversations
- written correspondence
- computer information.

The setting will have its own policy relating to 'confidentiality' and this must be followed by all care workers at the setting. More information is given on pages within this unit.

Remember that 'care values' are a statement of the values which underpin practical caring.

Care workers who work in early years care and education settings will need to be aware that there are other 'values' or 'principles' that will need to be applied in their day-to-day tasks.

Early years care values or principles

Working in an early years setting

The welfare of the child
The welfare of the child is paramount. Children should be listened to and their views considered.

Safety of children
Children should be kept safe. They should not be put at risk.

Providing a safe and healthy working environment
Safe working practices must exist.

Working in partnership with parents and families
Openly sharing information about children's development and progress. Respect for family traditions.

Learning and development
Children should be offered a range of experiences and activities that support all aspects of development, i.e. physical, intellectual, emotional and social development (P.I.E.S.).

Valuing diversity
Information relating to traditions should be presented in a positive way.

Equal opportunity

Each child should be offered equality of access to opportunities to learn.

Anti-discrimination

Expressions of prejudice by children or adults should be challenged.

The reflective practitioner

Early years workers need to reflect on practice and plan for development.

Confidentiality

Information about children and adults should never be shared with others without consent. Secure storage of records is legally required.

Working with other professionals

Liaison with other professionals is essential to the welfare of the child but should only be carried out with permission from the parents.

How can the care values be applied in care settings?

The care values underpin all care work to ensure that all service users are treated consistently and fairly and in the same way that the care worker would want to be treated themselves. Service users are valued for themselves, not what care workers think they ought to be.

The care values can be applied by:

Fostering equality and diversity

- Providing services that are equally accessible to all
- Meeting individual needs – person-centred approach
- Accepting service users who have different sexual orientation from those of the care workers
- Anti-discriminatory practice.

Fostering rights and beliefs

- Accepting cultural and religious beliefs even when they are not the same as those of the care workers
- Making provision for service users with different beliefs to celebrate their events
- Providing appropriate foods
- Providing a place for service users to practise their religious beliefs.

Maintaining confidentiality

- Not gossiping about service users
- Keeping information safe
- Storing written records securely
- Making sure access to electronic records is limited to specific care workers by having passwords
- Not talking about service users by name at home or in public.

Assessment activity 1.2.4

Shawn and Gwladys   CASE STUDY

Shawn is working as a nursery nurse in a local playgroup.

Gwladys is working as a care assistant in a day care centre.

1   Compare how Shawn and Gwladys will apply the care values in the workplace. You should consider similarities and differences.

2   Gwladys is going to take an older person to the toilet. How will she:

- maintain dignity?
- promote individual rights and beliefs?
- promote equality and diversity?

3   Shawn is responsible for making the welfare of the child paramount. How will he do this in his day-to-day work?

4   Explain how the 'care values' and 'principles of care' can contribute to quality practice.

5   In the early years care values/principles practitioners are required to 'work in partnership with parents/families'. How could this be achieved in:

- a playgroup?
- a day care centre?

1.2.5 Safe working

Safety provides security

Codes of practice

Codes of practice set out the standards of professional practice required from professional care workers. They are derived from law and from them policies are developed. Codes of practice are a method that contributes to the standard of care provided as they can be monitored, by observation, to check whether they are being implemented. Codes of practice set out procedures that are to be followed by professional care workers when carrying out their day-to-day tasks. Some apply to specific settings while others influence how individuals work across a number of settings. The table below shows the Nursing and Widwifery code of practice (previously UKCC) that is applicable to health care and its main function.

Code of practice	Main functions
Nursing and Midwifery Council	Recently formed, the code of practice states that registered nurses and midwives should: • respect all service users as individuals • obtain consent before giving treatment • protect confidential information • co-operate with others in a team • maintain professional knowledge and competence • be trustworthy • act to identify and minimise risks to service users.

Home Life: A Code of Practice for Residential Care was first published in 1984; some of the recommendations include the quality care checked by inspectors such as:

Staff qualities
Staff qualities should include responsiveness to and respect for the needs of individuals.

Staff abilities
The ability to give competent and tactful care, while enabling residents to retain dignity and self determination.

Selection of staff
When selecting staff at least two referees should be taken up, where possible from previous employers.

Applicants
Applicants' curriculum vitae should be checked and for this purpose employers should give warning that convictions should be disclosed.

Checklist
Home Life includes a checklist to help people assess the quality of care provided.

Cover
Minimum staff cover should be able to cope with residents' needs at any time.

Responsibilities
The range of responsibilities must be understood by staff and service users.

Quality practice
Monitoring and evaluation to be in place.

Role
Any changes in role or duty should be made clear.

The table below gives an example of the SEN Code of Practice that exists in health, social care and early years settings:

Code of practice	Main functions
SEN Code of Practice	Primary and Secondary schools follow the guidelines given within this policy. The code is also recommended for use in health, social service or any other service concerned with the education of children and SEN. Actual policies and procedures recommend: • early identification • mainstream provision if possible • LEAs to make multi-disciplinary approach to the care required • annual review of the child's assessment • the child's view to be considered.

An equal opportunities policy can be developed by an organisation or setting and should include:

• the statement
• the implementation plan
• the monitoring policy
• the evaluation of the policy
• targets and timescales.

The Mental Health for Social Workers Code of Practice published in March 1999 by the Department of Health, gives guidance to registered practitioners, managers and staff at hospitals and mental nursing homes, and approved social workers on how they should proceed when carrying out duties under the Act. Some of the guidance given includes service users:

• receiving recognition of their basic human rights
• being given respect for their qualities, abilities and diverse backgrounds
• assurance that account will be taken of their age, gender, sexual orientation, social, ethnic, cultural and religious background, but that general assumptions will not be made on the basis of any one of these characteristics
• being given any necessary treatment and care in the least controlled and segregated facilities compatible with ensuring their own health and safety or the safety of others.

Activity 10

1. Work in pairs to carry out secondary research about one of the following:
   • Equal Opportunities Code of Practice
   • SEN Code of Practice
   • Mental Health for Social Workers Code of Practice.

2. Arrange to visit a setting (with your tutor's permission) to find out how the Code of Practice you have investigated is applied in the care setting. Alternatively a care worker could be invited to the Centre.

3. On your own, prepare a presentation (with presenter's notes) to show others:
   • the content of the Code of Practice
   • how it is applied in the setting.

A policy statement

Policies will be present in all settings. Their purpose is:

• to provide a detailed account of the approach the setting will take towards a particular procedure or issue
• to develop policies to make sure that standards are maintained and that service users' rights are upheld.

Policies arise out of legislation and from codes of practice and are usually specific to each care setting. They provide a framework which enables care workers within a health, social care or early years organisation or setting, or across a number of settings, to all have the same approach to a task or procedure. The content of a policy will give guidelines on how a task should be done or to whom staff should report in the case of a particular occurrence. An organisation could have a number of polices, all of which are intended to maintain standards of care, to give guidance to staff and promote the best interests of the service user.

Examples of policies that exist in settings:

Many organisations give examples of the policies they have in their 'mission statement'. This is the document received by service users when they first enter a setting, for example a residential or nursing home. Reference is also made in such mission statements to the legal requirements of the setting and who is responsible for the implementation of policies.

Mission Statement

It is the objective of Ambreside day care centre to provide care for all service users that encompasses the fundamental principles of good care practice. This can be observed through the practice, conduct and control of quality care in the day care centre. We will strive to provide excellence of standard in accordance with 'The Statement of Values', reference policy 9 to ...

An implementation plan

Implementation means how the policies will be put into place. It is very important that there is a plan that clearly indicates how this is going to happen and who will take responsibility. The various aspects of the plan are:

Senior managers
It is vital that the responsibilities of each level of management are stated and who is to be responsible for the implementation.

Consultation with service users
The opinions of service users must be sought. This can be achieved by holding meetings with service users or through surveys or asking representatives to sit on committees.

Consultation with staff
If staff are consulted they will feel ownership of the policies and are more likely to co-operate with their implementation. This can be achieved through meetings and consultations.

Training of staff
Staff need to be updated regularly in both skills and knowledge. This could be achieved through training groups and through individual assessments.

Target setting
Every setting needs to be aware of the targets that have been set by senior management. If targets are not known by staff they are unlikely to be achieved.

Timescales
Timescales for achieving targets must be set so that all staff will be aware of the length of time they have to implement proposed policies.

Methods for monitoring
This involves collection of data, collection of information about complaints or the gender and ethnicity of those applying for jobs.

Communicating the policies
Policies must be communicated accurately whether in writing or orally if they are to be successfully implemented.

Evaluation
This involves assessing how well or otherwise the policies have been implemented.

After the evaluation stage has taken place it will be important to consider the improvements that will need to be implemented. Such improvements will lead to new targets being set to improve future performance.

Harassment and bullying

Harassment means to destroy, to wear out or to pester a person. This type of behaviour should not happen in the workplace. As a consequence and to prevent such behaviour from happening, policies are put in place. The Harassment Act 1997 makes it a criminal offence to harass another person. Harassment can lead to unpleasant feeling between staff and/or service users. It can also cause depression, stress and absence from work. Any form of harassment should be reported immediately to a supervisor.

Bullying is unfortunately becoming more common, particularly in schools. All who work in health, social care and early years services must be alert to the signs of bullying. Whether at work or at school those who are being bullied may:

- be frequently absent
- be depressed
- become withdrawn
- be aggressive
- cry a lot
- self harm.

A **mentoring system** can sometimes be helpful to those who are being bullied. In some workplace settings training is given in assertiveness to help individuals cope with bullying situations. Classes in stress management and counselling have also been supportive methods which have helped individuals cope with bullying.

Equal Opportunities Code of Practice

The code of practice aims to give practical guidance to help employers, employees, trade unions and employment agencies with good practice in the workplace. It emphasises that employees of all racial groups have the right to equal opportunity. The code is not restricted to the requirements of law, but contains recommendations as well.

One aspect of the code of practice relates to the selection of staff. It ensures that criteria which are relevant to job requirements and carefully observed selection procedures not only help to ensure that individuals are appointed according to their suitability for the job but also that this is carried out without regard to racial group. When appointing personnel to health, social care and early years jobs, consistent selection procedures must be in place.

As part of its recommended positive action, good practice is recommended with regard to opportunities for employees to develop their full potential through encouragement, training and careful assessment. It had been noticed prior to the Equal Opportunities Code of Practice that many employees from racial minorities had potential which, because of previous discrimination and other disadvantages, had not been realised. This meant that people from racial minorities were in jobs that did not reflect their qualification and experience. Within the code of practice there is now the opportunity for employers to take advantage of training for their staff to ensure that all have the opportunity to realise their full potential.

When interviewing for new applicants, employers are required to:

- communicate to all employees through notice boards, circulars or written notification

Assertiveness training

Counselling

Ways of supporting individuals who have been bullied

- ensure that no applicant receives less favourable treatment than another on racial grounds
- ensure that no applicant or employee is placed at a disadvantage by requirements or conditions which have a disproportionately adverse effect on his or her racial group
- that employees of underrepresented racial groups are given encouragement to achieve equal opportunity within the organisation.

When an employer advertises a job vacancy it is unlawful for them to publish an advertisement which indicates or could reasonably be understood as an intention to discriminate against applicants of a particular racial group.

This advertisement is not acceptable under the Equal Opportunity Code of Practice.

In order to avoid direct and indirect discrimination it is recommended by the code of practice that selection criteria and tests are examined to ensure that they relate to job requirements and that they are not unlawfully discriminatory. For example, selection tests which contain questions that are irrelevant and on matters that may be unfamiliar to racial minority groups should not be used.

The staff who are responsible for short-listing applicants for interview also need to make sure that candidates are clearly informed of selection criteria and to ensure that these are consistently applied. They must also be made aware of possible misunderstandings that can occur when candidates are being interviewed, particularly if applicants are from different cultural backgrounds and have different interpretations of language.

For interviews, the Equal Opportunities Code of Practice recommends that more than one person should be involved in the interviewing process and that all candidates are asked similar questions.

Much of the guidance within the Equal Opportunities Code of Practice will promote a sense of positive attitude within staff. One way of achieving this is through performance appraisals. Staff who are responsible for performance appraisals should be instructed not to discriminate on racial grounds and to ensure that the assessment criteria are not unlawfully discriminatory.

In order to provide support systems for service users and staff it is recommended that:

- an equal opportunities policy is in place and is communicated to all
- national minimum standards are implemented which form the baseline against which inspections are made
- national service frameworks are in place which describe the standards and treatment for particular conditions or service user groups.

Regulation and inspection bodies ensure that all health, social care and early years services are regulated and inspected against the standards set by the government. Some examples of these are:

- The Commission for Social Care Inspection (CSCI)
- The Healthcare Commission (Commission for Healthcare Audit and Inspection (CHAI))
- OFSTED (Office for Standards in Education).

Activity 11

1. Work in pairs to research one of the inspection teams given above. Give a presentation to the rest of the group about the work they do and how they manage standards.

2. What is meant by the term 'harassment'? Give examples to illustrate the points made.

3. Write a case study to show how bullying could occur in a health, social care or early years organisation.
   Share it with another person.
   Discuss how the person could be helped.

4. Invite a member of staff from a care setting to your Centre to find out how their equal opportunities policy helps to maintain quality practice.

Assessment activity 1.2.5

Situation vacant — CASE STUDY

Dietician – Port Park Community Services

We require a reliable, highly professional individual to work within our team. The successful candidate must be female, aged between 30 and 40 and have had at least ten years' continuous service in a similar role.

1. Identify **two** forms of discrimination in the job advert. Give one example of each.

2. Explain how the Community Service team could ensure that job advertisements are free from discrimination.

3. Discuss ways that the surgery could ensure that the equal opportunities policy is successfully implemented.

4. How could staff from ethnic minorities be motivated to fulfil their full potential?

5. Explain what is meant by the term 'code of practice'. Use examples to illustrate the points made.

6. Explain how an equal opportunities policy could be monitored and evaluated.

7. Identify the different parts of an 'implementation plan' for an equal opportunity policy. Explain what happens at each stage giving the purpose.

8. Give five pieces of advice to a residential home about 'safe working'.

Contents

About this unit

Within this unit you will investigate:

- different types of communication
- factors that support and inhibit communication
- communication skills
- theories relating to communication
- how to interact with a service user.

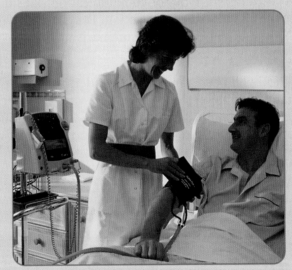

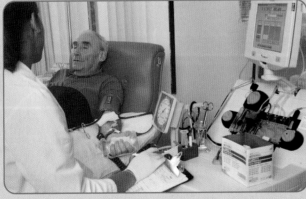

People communicate for a number of reasons

Communicating with others using different forms

Introducing this unit

Think about the number of times that you have communicated already today. You have probably used oral skills more than any other type of communication. You may have spoken to parents, teachers, friends or acquaintances. You may have done this face to face or on the telephone. Some of you will have used the computer today to send an email or to do research using the Internet. Others will have used writing as a form of communication or may have communicated with someone using special methods such as sign language or Braille.

In care settings all forms of communication are used whether it is a health, social care or early years setting. It is very important for care settings that communication is effective whether communicating orally or to a group or to other professional care workers. The skills involved when communicating maximise personal effectiveness because they underpin all other skills when working with people. Knowing ourselves, our attitudes and values will help us to know more about our effect on others.

Some factors that are used when communicating will encourage, for example valuing service users and promoting equality and diversity. Other factors can inhibit communication, for example noise, inappropriate positioning and verbal abuse. Application of factors such as applying the care values can encourage service users to share their problems with care workers.

In this unit you will investigate the different types of communication skills and how they can be used to encourage effective communication. For example, when to use open questions, closed questions, clarifying and summarising and the effects these are likely to have on individuals and groups.

In order to use skills effectively you will need to know and understand some theories relating to communication and interpersonal skills. For example, what theories does Thompson have compared with Burnard and how do they influence the way in which we communicate? Theory can give insight about the best way to use skills and the best situations when they should be used.

Being able to actually communicate with a service user or a care worker effectively is an important feature when working in a care setting. In this unit you will have the opportunity to plan an interaction and to carry it out, evaluating the interaction from your own and from others' perspectives.

2.2.1 Types of communication

Working with people involves interaction. That is the coming together of two or more people who may have common aims but sometimes may have conflicting points of view. Oral interaction can sometimes change people, or increase their awareness or improve their quality of life. It is important, therefore, to use the skills that best suit the individual and their needs.

A variety of different ways will be used when communicating with others, depending on the method of communication used.

Body language
e.g. smiling

Verbal communication
e.g. speaking and listening

Written communication
e.g. care plans

Different ways of communicating

Electronic communication
e.g. emails

Special methods of communication
e.g. Braille, sign language

Oral interaction

Having a meaningful conversation with someone requires the development of skills and **social co-ordination**. It means:

- showing an interest
- being interesting
- having the ability to start conversations and end them.

When communicating orally with others in a care setting we may have several purposes. For example:

Purpose of communication	Examples of where and how used
To give information	At a GP Surgery or Health Centre to tell a service user what services are available and when they are available.
To obtain information	When enrolling a child at a playgroup, nursery school or childminder to make sure that the parents' or main carer's name, address and contact numbers are accurate.
To exchange ideas	At a day care centre when groups of older people are talking about present or past experiences and sharing current news items.

Giving and obtaining information is important because the content must be accurate. If incorrect 'facts' are given, the person who requires the information will be misinformed and this could lead to serious consequences. A good way of '**making a connection**' is by putting people at their ease through taking a genuine interest in a person. This applies whether you are the one giving the information or whether you are receiving the information. If someone is from a different culture from our own it is important as it shows that we value diversity. Being open about what we are trying to achieve and encouraging the other person or persons to do likewise is also important when giving or obtaining information or exchanging ideas.

You can see that we have quite a number of services based here

When talking to people, non-verbal signals, such as gestures or smiles, as well as speech, are often used. This is known as '**body language**' and is a form of giving messages to those with whom we are speaking, for example smiling will **convey** friendliness.

When we communicate with one another we are sending messages and **disclosing** information. When communicating orally, messages are encoded by a sender and decoded by a receiver. The diagram below shows this process:

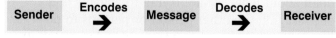

Sending and receiving messages (Argyle 1983)

How would this apply to messages given and received in a care setting? Here is an example:

A care worker (**sender**) puts words together (**encodes**) to say, 'Marcus what do you want to achieve from your session today?' (**message**).

The service user (**receiver**) listens, the brain interprets the signal (**decodes**) and then the message is received. For example, if a social worker is trying to obtain or give information from a service user he/she will:

- help them to feel at ease, e.g. 'Hello! I'm Brian'.
- use an open question, e.g. 'How are you settling in?'
- tell him what he wants to know/find out, e.g. 'I need to check your home address and contact numbers.'
- find out if he wants to know anything, e.g. 'Now, is there anything you need to know about us?'

This is a very simple example, and in an actual interaction the conversation would have more depth, but the principles of giving and receiving messages are included.

Communication in health, social care and early years settings is likely to be of a **complex** nature. This means that it may have several purposes. Care workers will need to be aware that each individual will have their own way of interpreting messages. Effective communication means more than just passing on information. It means involving or **engaging** the other person.

Steve has an appointment with the radiographer at the local hospital. Steve requires a chest x-ray to try to find out about the pains he is having in his chest.

The radiologist just beckons Steve into the room. He speaks very quickly asking Steve to confirm his name and address and the reason for being at the radiography department.

Steve is confused.

The radiologist places Steve in the position he wants him in for the x-ray and then disappears behind a screen. The x-ray is taken and the radiologist moves Steve to a new position and disappears once more behind his screen.

After the x-ray is taken, the radiologist mumbles that the results of the x-ray will be with Steve's GP in ten days.

From this case study it can be understood why Steve was not happy with the situation. For example:

- the radiologist did not tell Steve what he was intending to do
- the radiologist did not put Steve at ease by making some informal conversation or 'small talk'
- the radiologist did not bother to explain to Steve why he needed to take an x-ray of him in two different positions
- the radiologist mumbled and was not speaking clearly or addressing Steve with respect.

Steve needed support and he received none. Steve needed complex information but he was not given any. It is likely that Steve went away feeling very confused, wondering what was happening and worrying about what he was going to learn from his GP in ten days' time. While the radiographer could not tell Steve the results of the x-ray, he could have put his mind at rest by clearly explaining what was going to happen and why and how the x-rays were going to be taken. This is just one example of where a care professional did not provide effective communication.

Bartez | Activity 1

Bartez is attending the local day care centre for the first time. He is very anxious as he does not know what to expect. On arrival he is greeted by a care assistant who makes him feel very welcome and tells him that a social worker will want to talk to him later to obtain some information about his recent history.

The care assistant explains that the people attending are all doing something different. One group is playing scrabble, in another they are preparing items for a sale that the centre is holding while another group are just chatting.

Bartez decides to join the group that is chatting.

1. Why is accuracy important when obtaining personal history from Bartez?

2. Prepare a handout that could be given to a new care worker to explain how people communicate orally.

3. Explain what is meant by the term 'making a connection'.

4. Work with one other person in your group. You are to take the role of the care worker. Plan how you will help Bartez obtain and give information about his recent life history. The plan for the interaction should last for a maximum of five minutes.

5. Carry out the interaction and in discussion with your partner briefly decide how effective you were and why.

Written communication

The written word is very common and is a widely established form of communication. The rules that govern writing are very different from those that are followed for spoken language. In all health, social care and early years settings accuracy of the written word is extremely important. If inaccuracies occur with keeping of formal records, a service user could have the wrong treatment or be given incorrect information with disastrous results. This could lead to a complaint being made or to court proceedings being taken.

False, inaccurate or misleading written records could result in:

- inappropriate actions
- failure to act
- complaints and litigation.

When writing information down it needs to be:

- clear
- accurate
- legible.

In many care settings written communication is used to record personal history. A primary school could use a written record as shown below for this purpose:

Name of child

Address

Telephone number

Emergency contact number 1

Contact address 1

Emergency contact number 2

Contact address 2

Medication

Dietary needs

Previous care and education history

Communicating in writing helps care settings to keep in contact with parents, friends of the organisation and other professionals. It can be a means of:

- giving information
- obtaining information
- exchanging ideas.

In many settings the communication policy will lay down that all written communication must be shown to the manager before it is passed on. Copies of written communication should be kept in case they are required for future reference.

Types of written information kept by a setting could include:

Personal history	Letters	Accident slips
Service users' details about past and current **experience**	Appointments, information about meetings, visits, test results	To inform of minor injury to children

TYPES OF WRITTEN COMMUNICATION

Notice boards		Care plans
These can give reminders or information about group meetings		A plan of the care a service user is to receive

Newsletters	Monitoring medical records	Menus
Giving information about events	Temperature, pulse or, in early years, the progress that is being made	The choices available at meal times

A wide diversity of forms of written communication is used in care settings, as can be seen from the diagram above. Each has its own **characteristics** but the common element relating to all forms is the need for accuracy and clarity. If a person reading the information cannot clearly understand the points that are being made, misunderstandings are likely to occur. The writer needs to clearly establish the purpose of writing, for example:

- who will be reading the written form?
- what points are to be made?
- what does the writer hope to achieve?

Clear, concise writing cannot be done in a hurry. Expressing oneself clearly and effectively in writing is a skilful activity that will need to be mastered by all who work in health, social care and early years settings.

Did you know?

Pascal wrote to a friend saying, 'I have made this letter longer than usual, only because I have not had time to make it shorter'.

Computerised communication

In recent years the development of electronic mail (email) has proved to be quite a significant form of communication. Emails can be both formal and informal depending on their purpose.

An advantage of email is that it provides a very quick way of interacting with another person or organisation as answers can be received in a matter of minutes, rather than having to wait for several days. A disadvantage is that, on some occasions, emails are lost and as a consequence the sender has to repeat the process. Care also has to be taken to ensure that confidentiality is maintained and 'secure' systems are necessary before confidential personal information can be exchanged.

The Internet, too, is increasingly being used as a source of information for a variety of purposes. Computers not only use the written word, this being their primary function, but they can also be used to present information in graphics and sound. Electronic forms of communication are now a well established way of everyday life. In health, social care and early years settings computers can also be used for networking between one organisation and another. A GP surgery could use the computer to send information about a patient to a consultant at a hospital or to send a prescription to a pharmacy. Similarly, an internal network system can be in place so that employees within one setting can be linked with others to share information.

In all situations care must be taken to ensure that the requirements of the Data Protection Act are followed when using the computer. The Act:

- creates new obligations for those keeping personal information
- requires that a service user be given a copy of any information that is kept about them. This is known as your 'right of access'
- requires that any inaccurate information about a service user is corrected or deleted

- a service user has the right to complain to the Data Protection Commissioner if they think someone is keeping data and is not complying with the Act
- allows service users to claim compensation through the Courts if they suffer damage through mishandling of information about themselves
- permits a service user to find out from any person or organisation whether information is being kept about them and, if they do, to be told the type of information kept and the purposes for which it is kept.

People keeping personal information must give individuals access to their personal information and can correct or delete any information found to be inaccurate. Settings must:

- obtain personal information fairly and openly
- use it only in ways compatible with the purpose for which it was given in the first place
- secure it against unauthorised access or loss
- ensure that it is accurate and kept up to date.

A setting must not:

- disclose information to others in a manner incompatible with the purpose for which it was given
- retain information for longer than is necessary for the purpose for which it was given.

Special methods

All health, social care and early years settings need to be prepared to provide for service users who have special needs where communication is concerned. Special needs could include:

- difficulty in hearing or deafness
- poor eye-sight or blindness
- language difficulty, e.g. not speaking English as a first or preferred language.

A variety of organisations can help to provide specialist equipment or specialists to help with such needs, for example:

Makaton · Braille · Special needs support · Sign language · Interpreters

Braille

The communication system known as Braille was first introduced by a blind person called Richard Braille in 1829. The system is one of raised dots that can be felt with a finger. For people who have limited vision or who are blind the system provides the opportunity for independent reading and writing as it is based on 'touch'. It is possible, with the correct computer software, to change the printed word into Braille and to print out using special printers.

Some service users need special methods to enable them to interact with others

Braille can be extremely useful to service users who have poor sight as they are able to read leaflets and handouts which give information about their treatment as well as being able to read books and magazines and satisfy their intellectual needs.

Makaton

Makaton is a large collection of symbols that can help people who have a hearing impairment or who may have a learning difficulty to communicate with others. It is a system that uses signs, speech and symbols. Those using Makaton may use all three methods to help them communicate with others. Makaton uses an established set of hand movements to convey meaning. It is usually taught to children when they are young as soon as it is realised that they have a need.

> **Discussion point**
>
> How can Braille and Makaton help service users with sensory impairment to communicate?

British Sign Language

> **Did you know?**
>
> It is thought that nearly 70,000 people use sign language in the UK.

The British Sign Language (BSL) is used by a large number of people within the UK. The government officially recognised the BSL in March 2003. Children find sign language fascinating and as a result learn the signs quite easily. The BSL has a phrase 'make your fingers count' which appeals to children. Sign language can be taught at any age and is used by those with hearing impairment. It is a language that has developed over hundreds of years and enables interaction between people who otherwise might experience difficulty.

Interpreters

For clients for whom English is not a preferred or first language, interpreters can help with communication. In the past some interpreters have been people who are members of the service user's own family but this has now been discontinued as far as possible. It was

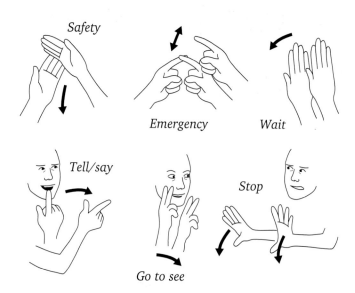

Safety   *Emergency*   *Wait*

Tell/say   *Stop*

Go to see

Using signs to communicate

considered that using family members was not a very good idea as they were then privy to information which the service user may want to keep confidential. For example, a mother whose daughter was interpreting for her may not want her daughter to know that she has cancer.

In many health, social care and early years services, leaflets concerning health topics or health facilities are produced not only in English but also in several other languages so that many in our multi-cultural society can access the information.

> ## Oaklands Day Care Centre   Activity 2
>
> Oaklands caters for day residents who are over 60 years of age. Many of the residents have special needs when communicating.
>
> **1** Sheila has very poor vision. Suggest how her communication needs could be met by the staff at Oaklands.
>
> **2** Grant has severe hearing impairment. How could the staff provide for Grant's communication needs?
>
> **3** The Training Officer at Oaklands wants to raise the staff's awareness of the different types of communication and their purpose. Prepare materials that could be used for a display for this purpose.

2.2.2 Factors that support and inhibit communication

Empowerment is a means of allowing a service user to take control of their lives. This not only means presenting them with sufficient information to allow them to make the correct decisions but also valuing their own views and opinions. Care workers in health, social care and early years settings need to be very supportive when communicating. This will mean applying the care values that help to achieve this.

Care values

Care values are derived from human rights. They are not laws or codes of practice. They are the **values** that people hold that enable service users to be empowered and to be in control of their own lives. They underpin any form of communication whether oral, written, computerised or special methods. They are also applied when carrying out any practical care for service users.

In health and social care settings there are three main care values. These are:

- promoting equality and diversity
- maintaining confidentiality
- promoting individual rights and beliefs.

In early years settings there are ten care values which incorporate those applied in health and social care settings. These care values are often known as 'principles' in early years. Below is a diagram which indicates what these are:

Keeping children safe

Valuing diversity

Upholding the welfare

Maintaining confidentiality

Working in partnership with families

Care values in early years

Fostering anti-discrimination

Providing equal opportunities

Being reflective practitioner

Working with other professionals

Encouraging children's learning and development

How can equality be fostered?

Treating people equally does not mean treating everyone the same. It means treating service users in a way that gives them equal access to their needs, for example communication, services and aids. Care workers need to make sure that their own attitudes, opinions and beliefs are not reflected in their communication with service users. A care worker's communication needs to be **ethically sensitive**, respecting cultural values, cultural practice and cultural needs.

Care settings will have in place **anti-discrimination policies** which will guide care workers in ways to communicate that do not **discriminate** against service users. For example, care workers will need to ensure that within their interactions they:

Give individual help and assistance

Accept dialects – variations in language

Make sure there is full inclusion for all

Are aware of religions, views and spirituality

Communicating in a non-discriminatory manner

Challenge discriminatory behaviour

Celebrate diversity

Do not stereotype

Use a multi-cultural approach

Care workers must make sure when communicating that culture is acknowledged. For example, certain hand gestures are acceptable in this country but would not be in others. To look straight into the eyes of a person, when speaking, is desirable in most conversations in this country, but would be considered rude in others.

How can diversity be promoted?

Diversity is recognising that each person is different. Each of us has different values and because we have different values we have different priorities. Care workers will need to ensure that they recognise the diverse attitudes of those for whom they care and simply because these may be different from their own, they must not be condemned or treated differently.

When meeting a service user, a care worker must not make assumptions. A service user could appear to be demanding simply because they feel insecure or because they are not familiar with their surroundings. A service user may have a same sex partner accompanying them on a visit. They should not be treated differently because of this.

When promoting equality and diversity in any communication, care workers should:

- speak at an appropriate pace so that the service user can understand what is being said
- use language that is appropriate to aid understanding
- treat service users with respect by calling them by their preferred name
- promote the service users' dignity by not patronising or talking down to them.

Discussion point

How can diversity be promoted in a playgroup?

Maintaining confidentiality

Confidentiality means that personal and private information must be kept secret. Information given to a care worker should not be disclosed without the service user's permission. Maintaining confidentiality is a very important aspect of building trust between a service user and a care worker. Without trust, communication is less likely to progress between two or more people. This involves honouring commitments and declaring conflicts of interest. It also means making sure that the policy that relates to ways of communicating with service users is followed.

Within their communication care workers must be sure that they do not abuse service users. This includes not shouting at service users as well as not using unacceptable language. Service users must not be placed at unnecessary risk of worrying about whether what they have told the care worker is going to be spread around the setting to others.

There are occasions when a care worker may have to break confidentiality. Such situations arise when:

- a service user is likely to harm themselves
- a service user is likely to harm others
- a service user is likely to be involved in a crime.

It must also be remembered that other professional care workers will need to have specific information on a 'need to know' basis and in these circumstances information may have to be passed to others.

How can a service user's individual rights and beliefs be promoted?

When communicating, care workers should remember that a service user has the right to say 'no'. They do not have to agree to have:

- the treatment that is recommended
- the food that is suggested
- to join in the activity that is happening
- the views and opinions that are being expressed.

A service user does have the right to complain if they feel they are being coerced into doing or agreeing to something that is against their beliefs or opinions. Service users have the right to make choices: that is to make their own decisions. They also have the right to be consulted. When communicating, service users have the right to effective communication, that is to have things explained in a way that they can understand. They also have the right to be listened to.

The right to confidentiality means that service user's notes must not be left lying around. On the computer, anything relating to the service user should be accessed only by those who have been given the authority to do so, which means that a password should have been given to authorised staff. When speaking, the conversation with the service user should not be so loud that others can hear and if the content of the conversation is personal, the interaction should be in a room where others are not present and where the door is closed. Service users have the right not to be gossiped about or to be spoken about in a way in which they can be identified. Care workers, when communicating, need to make sure that service users' rights are maintained.

Applying the care values when communicating — Activity 3

Meena, who is four years old, is attending a local nursery school. She is taking part in a finger painting activity. You are the nursery nurse on duty with this group.

1. How would you apply the care values when communicating with Meena during the activity?

2. Plan and carry out a role play to show how to communicate effectively with Meena when she is playing in the dressing up corner. Ask your peers to provide you with feedback from the role play about how well you applied the care values during the interaction.

3. Meena's mother has asked for a meeting with you to find out how well Meena is progressing. What rights will you consider when communicating with her?

4. Role play talking to Meena's mother. Ask others to give you feedback on how well you applied the care values during the interaction.

What factors support or inhibit communication?

Communication can be influenced in a positive or negative way by a variety of factors. On some occasions, if factors are not supportive, service users can be **inhibited** from effective communication. For example, if the noise from outside is so great that conversation is drowned out. Alternatively if positioning is correct and environmental factors conducive then communication can be enhanced.

Discussion point

Why is it important for service users to consider themselves to be 'equal' when communicating with care workers?

Positioning

Seating arrangements and positioning should be considered carefully when communicating with others. Positioning between care worker(s) and service user(s) will depend upon the purpose of the communication to be undertaken. For example, if the interaction is informal and between two people, sitting next to

one another, with the care worker mirroring the body language of the service user could be best.

Sitting together comfortably can encourage communication in some situations

If, however, the communication is to be of a more formal nature, then having a table at a higher level, with chairs placed near, but on different sides of the table may be more appropriate. The diagram below shows how a formal setting could be arranged when discussion of a service user's treatment is to take place.

Let's look at the options that are available

If the communication is to be to a large audience then a lecture theatre layout would be more appropriate, as the speaker could be seen and heard by all.

Communicating with a large audience can be challenging

Positioning | CASE STUDY

Case Study 1: Marcus

Marcus is greeting a service user who is visiting the creative activities group for the first time. He sits the service user at a table, which is at waist height with chairs opposite one another. He is very surprised that the service user is unresponsive and that very little 'chatting' occurs.

Case Study 2: Barry

Barry is a consultant at the hospital. He has examined the test results for a service user and now needs to share the information with her. The news he is to share is not good. He decides to use a table set at waist level with chairs either side for the purpose.

Marcus would probably have obtained better results if he had used two armchairs with a low-level table in front. Tea or coffee could have been set ready on the table. The service user would feel less threatened, more comfortable and less formal. The service user would probably have felt more emotionally secure and may have interacted more effectively. If Marcus had used low chairs he could have mirrored the service user's body language, for example crossing his legs towards the service user. On the other hand, Barry's meeting, although using the same table and chairs at the same height, is more formal. By being formal Barry has enabled the service user to feel that they are in control, in a situation where emotional reaction is likely to be a key feature.

Discussion point

Think of other forms of seating arrangement. What message does the arrangement of the chairs and/or tables give?

The height of chairs and tables can influence communication. Sometimes it can enhance, other times the height of chairs or tables can inhibit.

Which is the best positioning to communicate effectively?

Emotional factors that can support or inhibit communication

Effective communication can contribute to forming good relationships with service users. The table on page 51 shows how some emotional factors can support or inhibit communication:

Factor	Supportive	Inhibiting
Fear	Can alert the service user and stimulate response.	Could cause a service user to become withdrawn and not to respond.
Happiness	A positive attitude can help a service user to see things from a different perspective and to look for the good things in a situation.	Some service users could make a biased judgement as they may not see the negative factors involved.
Self esteem	If a service user values themselves and is confident they will not mind trying things out.	A low self esteem could mean that a service user only looks at a situation from a gloomy perspective, lacking in confidence to try something out or do something differently.
Trust	A service user who has trust in a care worker will be willing to accept what is being said. They may ask questions but they are more likely to accept what is being said.	If a service user trusts a care worker there is little likelihood of any inhibiting factors. If they trust the care worker wrongly, they could be hoodwinked into believing that something is acceptable when it is not.
Empathy	A care worker who has empathy is able to put themselves into the same situation as the service user, being able to feel how they feel and to see things from their perspective.	There is a slight danger that a care worker could become too involved with the service user. They could be very critical of care given by others.
Responsiveness	Being able to respond to a service user's questions and needs will confirm to the service user that the care worker is acting in their best interests.	There is a slight danger that the care worker will want to solve the service user's problems rather than letting the service user make their own decisions.
Attentiveness	An attentive care worker will show that they are taking a genuine interest in the service user.	There is a faint concern that a person who is too attentive is being 'nosey', but this is unlikely.
Respect	Calling a service user by their preferred name, not patronising them or treating them as though their opinions are not valued can only contribute to effective communication.	Lack of respect by calling a service user 'dear' or by not valuing their opinions could cause them to cease sharing information.

Discussion point

How can emotional factors inhibit communication between a nurse in a hospital and an inpatient?

Environmental conditions

Space

Care workers need to plan the spacing arrangements to check that eye contact can be made with each person involved in the interaction and to ensure that everyone can see and hear all those involved. Service users do not want to be too close to one another nor too far away. Each will want to know that they have their own space and that **proximity** is appropriate. If they are too near or too far away, communication may be inhibited.

Noise

If a room is too noisy, there is a danger that service users may not hear what either the care worker or other service users have to say. On the other hand, if a room is too quiet, a service user may find the situation is not conducive to talking. Sometimes quiet background music will be appropriate, for example when discussing a personal matter with a client or at the beginning of a counselling session.

Lighting

If a care worker is attempting to explain some information or to take down personal history then full lighting is probably necessary so that the note taker can accurately record information. If, however, service users are being encouraged to relax as part of an alternative therapy session, the lights may need to be dimmed in order to encourage the participant. Lighting needs to be appropriate for the occasion.

Ventilation

Having a room too hot or too cold will be an inhibiting factor to communication. Too much heat is likely to make service users sleepy and feel dreary while, if the temperature is too cold, the service user will be unlikely to be able to concentrate. A room needs to be well ventilated to promote concentration and prevent loss of interest.

Special needs

The use of Braille, British Sign Language, Makaton and interpreters has already been discussed earlier in this unit. Not to provide such aids and services will inhibit communication, whatever the care setting. Making sure that all service users are given access to the facilities and aids that they individually need is a way of promoting equality and enhancing communication.

When communicating with service users who have special needs it is important to:

- face the service user so that they can see your expression and lips if they have a hearing problem
- speak clearly
- not speak too fast
- use language that is appropriate to the user
- pause to allow the service user to respond
- if necessary use aids to help the communication, e.g. hearing aid, spectacles.

Discussion point

How can too much or too little ventilation affect a child in a playgroup?

Rick   Activity 4

Rick has been referred by his reception class teacher to an educational psychologist.

A first visit has been arranged for Rick and his parents.

1. Draw a plan to show the seating arrangements for the meeting. Explain why you would arrange the room in this way.

2. Explain how a 'socio-gram' could be used to find out if the conditions and arrangements were satisfactory during the meeting.

3. Explain how environmental conditions would enhance the communication during the meeting.

4. How could emotional factors affect the communication during the meeting?

5. Role play the first part of the meeting to show how you would consider the positioning, emotional and environmental factors. Ask your peers to provide feedback of the role play.

6. If Rick had a hearing impairment, how would you adapt the communication to meet his needs?

Importance of the content of the communication

We need to make some decisions with these results in mind

It is important to think about what we wish to say to others. A mental plan is always a good idea and sometimes a written plan will be necessary if the conversation is complex. A plan, whether mental or written, will help to ensure that none of the content is omitted. When thinking about having a specific interaction with others, it will be necessary to decide:

What to include	Reason
With whom will I be communicating?	To make sure that the correct person or persons are being spoken with.
What message(s) need to be conveyed?	Clarity of the main points will be required.
What is the aim?	What point(s) are being conveyed?
What are the objectives?	What stepping stones will be needed to achieve the outcome?
Where will the interaction take place?	Is the information to be discussed confidential and not to be overheard by others? Do I need to make special arrangements for the conversation?
How can I be sure that the service user has understood?	What means of checking will I have in place?
Are there any cultural issues to take into consideration?	Should a female have someone to accompany her if a male is giving information? Do I need to remember anything special within the communication?
Does the person with whom I will be communicating have any special needs?	Arrangement of the room so that they can see my face clearly if they have a hearing impairment? Any special aids required?

It is the content of the communication that is of the utmost importance. The way in which we communicate will determine whether the aim has been achieved and whether this has been done so effectively. Many of the points raised within these two sections of underpinning knowledge are points that we do almost automatically. But it is important that we are aware of each, so that they can be a natural part of any communication we may have.

Just occasionally a conversation we have with a service user will cause a dilemma. Should the information be passed on to someone else or not? In such an instance a line manager is a good source of reference and will be able to offer advice.

It must be remembered that if a service user is likely to harm themselves or others then there is no dilemma – the information must be passed on.

Assessment activity (AO1)

Preparing new care workers
CASE STUDY

A group of new care workers who will be working in a variety of care settings, for example nurseries, hospitals and residential homes, are having a combined training session.

The purpose of the training day is to raise their knowledge and awareness of the different types of communication used in health, social care and early years settings. They also need to have knowledge of factors that can support and inhibit communication.

You have been asked to produce a Resource Pack for the training event which will provide the information required during the training. You should give as many examples as possible to illustrate the points being made.

The Resource Pack could take the form of a written report or could contain a mixture of report, handouts, leaflets, etc.

1. Give an in-depth account of the different types of communication used in care settings and their purpose. Remember to give examples of the different types to include:
   - oral
   - written
   - computerised
   - special methods.

2. Explain in detail how the effectiveness of interactions can be increased and the level of personal value and support could be improved. Give examples to illustrate the points made.

3. Explain how communication can be inhibited by inappropriate factors, giving examples to illustrate the points made.

Try to make your evidence as interesting as possible, but remember to meet the depth required.

2.2.3 Communication skills

Interacting formally and informally

Professional care workers interact with a variety of people. These can include:

- other professionals
- service users
- close and extended relatives.

When communicating with other professionals an interaction is more likely to be on a formal basis, although there will be occasions when news of family or holidays, for example, will be exchanged and the interaction will therefore be informal. Formal interactions can be on a one-to-one basis with other professionals or in a group situation. The latter is more likely to occur when several professionals are consulting together or when a case conference is being held.

Interaction with a service user and relatives can be formal or informal. For example, if information is being given to or received from a service user then a more formal approach is likely. If having a conversation about the weather or an exchange of views about an article in the daily paper or on the TV, the conversation is likely to be informal.

When talking with relatives it is important not to give information that is confidential. Only when the service user has given permission can information about his/her situation be exchanged. Some relatives will state that the service user has said 'it is alright for them to know the personal information about their health', but such claims must be verified to ensure that permission has been granted.

Building professional relationships

If communication is to be successful it must be formed on a professional basis. That is, rules must be observed and **boundaries** set. It will be important that the professional knows the framework in which they can work and that they do not cross the 'hidden line'. Good relationships depend on:

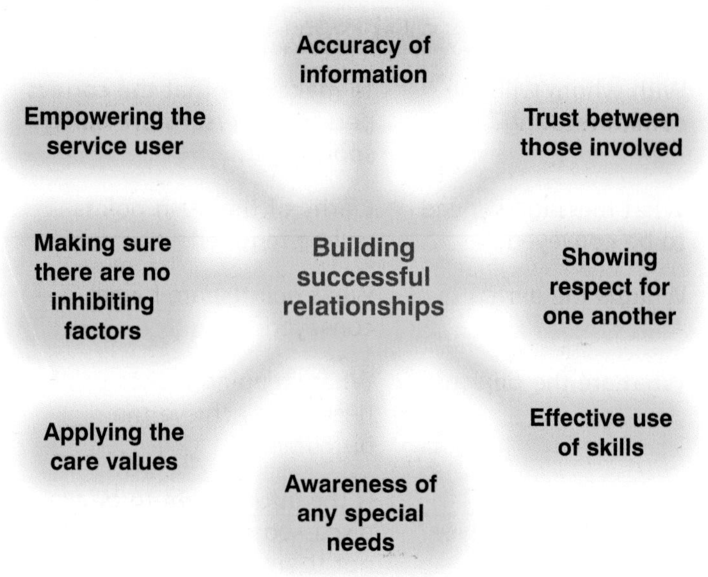

Accuracy of information

Empowering the service user

Trust between those involved

Making sure there are no inhibiting factors

Building successful relationships

Showing respect for one another

Applying the care values

Effective use of skills

Awareness of any special needs

Building professional relationships means using and applying all the points made in the above diagram in every interaction, whether it is with other professional care workers or with service users and their relatives. In any interaction the professional will affect others and will need to be 'tuned in' to what effect they have on those to whom they are speaking. Similarly, other people's attitudes and behaviour will have a significant effect upon the professional care worker, sometimes without the professional realising that this is happening. Freud, in his theories, refers to the process by which feelings for others are 'transferred', reminding us that if we like a person we could be favourably disposed towards them, but if a person has feelings of dislike, then an interaction could become prejudiced. Transference can, therefore, make a significant difference to how we respond to people within an interaction.

When communicating with others it is therefore essential that the professional care worker:

- applies the care values
- remembers that they have a 'duty of care'
- follows any guidelines or **codes of conduct** set out by the organisation for whom they work
- values the individual with whom they are communicating.

Communicating effectively with others

Skills to use when communicating

When communicating with others it will be necessary to ask questions. The type of questions asked and the way in which they are asked will control the effectiveness of the interaction. These will not be the only skills to be used in any interaction but questioning is an art and the skills that govern their use must be learned. There are two main types of question:

- closed questions
- open questions.

Closed questions lead to **monosyllabic** answers, for example, 'yes' or 'no'. They may lead to giving information which is specific such as age, weight or height. They do not give the service user the opportunity to develop or to fully explain their part of the interaction. There are occasions when specific facts are required and so some closed questions are essential, but they do not allow the interaction to move forward. Examples of closed questions are:

- How old are you?
- What is your address?
- Where is the pain?
- Have you been to the day care centre before?

Asking too many closed questions can contribute to a service user feeling burdened and unable to talk freely. They may feel that they are going through an inquisition! Using entirely closed questions would not help the care worker, particularly as they would have a list of facts without any feelings or background knowledge of the service user.

Open questions require a more extended answer, but allow the service user to answer in their own way, giving them the opportunity to develop their responses and to move the interaction on in the direction of their choice. The use of open questions also communicates to the service user that the care worker is interested in what they have to say and wishes to hear and know about the whole range of information. By using open questioning the care worker can develop empathy with the service user and the service user is able to relax and talk more openly. Examples of open questions are:

- How do you feel about…
- Why do you think that?
- How do you think that will help?
- What would you like to see happening?

The use of open and closed questions will be necessary in most interactions and care workers may need to practise both in order to perfect the skills.

Theory into practice

Visit a setting, for example a day care centre, luncheon club, nursery or reception class (or simulate the situation) and hold a five minute conversation in a one-to-one situation using both closed and open questions. Reflect on the use of these skills.

Tone

Talking or communicating with others is part of everyday life. The tone that is used will reflect the content of the conversation. Warmth of tone, for example, can convey friendliness and can help a person to feel at ease. On the other hand, a sharp tone which indicates disapproval or a reprimand could cause the receiver to be uncomfortable and perhaps intimidated. The appropriate use of tone is important. It is not only what is said but the way in which it is said that indicates our feelings, which can quickly be transferred to the listener.

Pace

Varying the pace of an interaction is important as interest is added. A person who speaks at the same pace throughout a conversation can be very boring indeed! When an idea is being shared it is likely that we talk a little more quickly in order to convey excitement. On the other hand, when a point needs to be clearly made and emphasised it is likely that the pace of the interaction will slow down. Appropriate use of pace is a skill that care workers will need to acquire for effective communication.

Direct eye contact

Care workers need to be aware that having direct eye contact with a person can in some instances enhance a conversation and in others inhibit communication. Direct eye contact is recognised in western culture to be a way of conveying interest in a conversation. It indicates to the listener that they are the central focus of the communication and that the environment around them, for example noise or other conversation is excluded. In some cultures, however, having direct eye contact is considered to be rude and should be avoided. Care workers need to be aware of what is and what is not acceptable to the clients in the setting in which they work.

Body language

Body language is also sometimes known as **non-verbal** communication. The **context** of the message can be made clear through the use of body language. In other words it helps the person who is receiving the message to know, for example, whether the person is being welcoming or if they are trying to distance themselves from the situation. Similarly, the care worker can show through their non-verbal communication whether they are friendly and responsive to the needs of the service user.

Positive body language can enhance communication

A face that reflects anger gives out the message 'stay away, you are not welcome'. A face that shows a smile indicates a welcoming approach, warmth and openness and is more likely to encourage positive interaction. Facial expressions can communicate complex messages, for example sadness which could arouse sympathy, or excitement which could convey relief.

Good news can be reflected in facial expression

Examples of body language are:

Facial expressions

Gestures

Body language

Eye contact

Positioning

Gestures involve hand movements. For example, drumming the fingers or twiddling the thumbs probably conveys impatience. Signalling by giving a beckoning gesture could means to come closer. Alternatively, the same gesture could mean that a care worker wanted a child to question what they were doing. It is the accompanying facial language and tone of voice that indicates which message is being conveyed. Some gestures are acceptable in western culture but may be unacceptable in another.

Makaton is a language programme based on a series of signs that represents language and involves the use of hand gestures. Makaton follows a specific teaching procedure and is combined with appropriate facial expressions, body language and speech.

The position adopted by the care worker ensures that the person to whom the care worker is communicating feels comfortable and has their own space. Leaning slightly towards the service user can convey interest but leaning too far forward can intimidate. Individuals like to have their own space around them that others should not invade. This is known as **positive positioning**. If a care worker is exchanging personal information they may sit very close to the person with whom they are speaking. On the other hand, if they are talking generally, the distance could be greater.

Positioning will depend on:

- the person's culture
- the feelings the two people have for one another
- the nature of the information.

This message is acceptable in western culture but not in some others

In western culture having direct eye contact conveys interest in a conversation. It indicates to the listener that they are the central focus of the communication and that all else is shut out. In some cultures, however, having direct eye contact is considered to be rude and should be avoided.

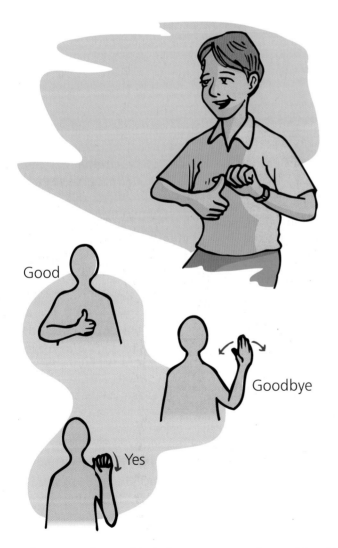

Good

Goodbye

Yes

Makaton can be used to help convey meaning and to aid understanding

Verbal skills

The use of verbal skills that can enhance communication and their purpose are given in the table below:

Skill	Explanation	Example
Clarifying	When clarifying, the care worker will seek to make clearer something the service user has said during the interaction. The service user may have been speaking in a muddled way or may have combined several facts that do not quite fit together. The care worker wishes to be be absolutely clear about the wishes of the service user.	Do you mean that you would like to consider...? Have I understood correctly...? You would prefer not to have a home care assistant because...?
Summarising	Summarising involves the care worker bringing together what the service user has said and in doing so showing that they have understood the situation. The care worker will make links between what has been said and will sum up with understanding what has been reflected within the interaction.	It would seem that you have a problem deciding which approach to use. You like the idea of a quick operation but you have stated that your husband would prefer you to try chemotherapy first.
Paraphrasing	Paraphrasing is a simple way to test understanding. It is a repetition of what a service user has said, possibly not in exactly the same words but words that have exactly the same meaning. Paraphrasing communicates to the service user that the care worker has been listening to what they have been saying and that they are trying to gain a sound understanding.	You have been saying that...? If I've understood correctly you wish to...? So far you have indicated that you would prefer to...?
Empathising	As already stated, this is seeing the service user's situation through their eyes.	You feel very angry that this has happened to you and think that it is unfair when you have always taken care of your health?
Prompts and probes	These are questions that are used in order to obtain deeper answers. They can also be used to keep the communication flowing.	Can you tell me more? How did you feel about that? Did you enjoy the experience?

Assessment activity (AO2)

Oral communication in a care setting

Case Study 1: Bumble Bees Nursery

Amir is working at Bumble Bees Nursery as a nursery nurse. The children who attend Amir's section are between the ages of two and four-and-a-half years old. It is quite a large nursery that caters for over 50 children and is flexible in its hours. Parents and key workers are in and out of the nursery at different times. There are 12 nursery nurses on duty at any one time, a manager, deputy manager, five supervisors and a nurse.

Case Study 2: The Swallows Residential Home

Peter is a care assistant at the Swallows Day Care Centre. Each day between 40 and 50 older adults attend the day care centre, their ages in the main being over 65 years. Most attend because they lack social interaction as they live alone and have health problems such as mobility that mean they are unable to socialise and could become isolated.

Case Study 3: Barnwell Hospital Day Centre

Jackie is a dietician who works at the local hospital.

As part of her duties she attends the hospital day care centre for two hours each day to assist service users who need advice and guidance about their diet, mainly because they are immobile and are putting on weight.

Twenty service users attend each day. There are a manager, deputy manager, health care assistants, nurses and health specialists who visit the day centre throughout the day.

1. Choose **one** of the case studies or a placement of your own. Give background information about the setting chosen.

2. Give a detailed and comprehensive explanation of **four** communication skills used by care workers or service users in the setting. Include a detailed discussion of the reasons for using each skill.

3. Discuss how the care values are applied and appropriate use of communication skills to show how service users are valued in the setting. Try to show a high level of understanding within your work and evidence of synthesis and originality.

2.2.4 Theories relating to communication

Group interactions

When having a group interaction, providing support for all those within the group is very important. Some members of a group may find speaking easy while others may be shy or embarrassed to put forward their point of view. Managing a group interaction requires the application of a variety of skills if the desired outcomes are to be achieved.

Interacting as a group needs good leadership skills

Barriers that can form within group interactions can include:

- not all the group knowing what the aims and objectives are
- lack of trust, which prevents effective teamwork
- clash of personalities
- unknown roles of the members who make up the group
- lack of communication skills of the leader, which could mean that the group will not bind together well.

Groups can have very positive outcomes and can result in an improvement of each member's self esteem as they recognise that they have made a successful contribution to the outcome. It could also mean that through listening to the contribution of others, awareness of a topic has been achieved and behaviour and attitudes have been influenced. Seeing things through the perspective of others can also raise awareness of alternative approaches and ideas that may not have been realised if the communication had taken place on a one-to-one basis. In a group situation it is important to acknowledge the contribution of all and not to disrespect any member's contribution.

Tuckerman's sequential theory

Tuckerman (1965) considers that when a team forms there are usually four stages through which it works in order to be effective.

These are:

Forming stage

Individuals are nervous, quiet, self conscious and apprehensive about what they are doing. Personalities rarely show through at this stage as individuals do not feel sufficiently comfortable to allow others to see their true selves. People are reluctant to give their opinions in case another member of the group does not agree and they may feel 'put down'. It is important for the group leader to find out about the personalities of the group members and perhaps to ask one who is known for their strength of character to start the interaction. This can be achieved by asking for their opinion or view on a specific subject.

Storming stage

At this stage personalities begin to show and opinions are expressed by most group members as they start to relax and let down their defences. Clashes can occur as individuals find members of the group who are very similar to themselves. A leader will need to be flexible at this stage as they will be dealing with a variety of personalities and will need to make the group effective.

Norming stage

Individuals within the group become less tense about what is happening around them and they begin to relax. It is now clearer to members of the group what is expected of them and the group starts to consolidate to achieve their goal.

Performing stage

Each individual knows their role and begins to work independently within the group. There is tolerance of one another and allowances are made for strengths and weaknesses. The group may, however, become less open to new ideas which may lead the group to fail in the task they set out to achieve.

A group, therefore, provides a multiple perspective on a topic as well as adding greater depth and breadth of information. Often a more questioning approach to problem solving and decision making is taken. Groups can be quite small, for example three or four people, or quite large, for example twenty people. A group allows the decision making to be a shared responsibility.

Connor	Activity 5

Connor has to hold a group interaction with a group of seven service users who need to modify their diet as they are overweight and this is contributing to health problems.

1. Explain the four stages involved when interacting with a group.

2. How is a group interaction different from a one-to-one interaction?

3. Choose a topic and in groups of seven (or slightly smaller) role play an interaction in a group.

4. Discuss your thoughts about the role play particularly any improvements that could be made.

The communication cycle

The process of communicating involves various stages within a cycle:

1. Obtaining or giving thoughts
2. Noting body language response
3. Working out what the other person is thinking
4. Listening to responses
5. Understanding the response
6. Talking about new ideas

If a care worker is to be effective in caring he/she must also be effective in communicating. Conversations or interactions usually begin with some form of greeting or welcoming process and proceed until reaching a satisfactory conclusion. Within every communication process the receiver of the communication makes value judgements. This means assigning an overall worth to the message given by the sender. Value judgements can be based upon:

- the receiver's evaluation of the sender
- the receiver's previous experience with the sender
- the message's anticipated meaning.

Care workers must ensure that they do not make value judgements as a result of previous experiences with the service user, as this can result in a service user being misunderstood or their rights being neglected. For example, a care worker may pay little attention to Marjorie as she is making yet another complaint, probably her fourth that week, but the complaint currently being made may have some substance and should not be overlooked. Similarly, a child may lack confidence and often ask for help when working in the reception class. The teacher should not dismiss the requests by making a value judgement based on previous experiences with the sender but should investigate the request to find out more about the type of help needed or if help is required at all.

When having an interaction, a service user needs to feel safe and secure. This does not simply mean from an environmental perspective but also confident that the care worker understands their need and will keep information confidential. Professional care workers need to be confident in what they are trying to communicate, as well as taking into consideration the age of the service user. For example, the language used to speak to a young child would be different from that used with an adult, as a child is likely to have a limited vocabulary.

Care workers' 'professionalism' must be maintained during any communication. This means that at all times the professional care worker must remember that they are not conversing with a friend but with a service user. They must be able to recognise the difference in that this is a 'working relationship' with structures imposed that have regard for legislation, regulations and standards relating to their particular organisation.

In any interaction there are three core features that are fundamental to effective communication. These are:

- feeling and communicating empathetic understanding
- offering **unconditional positive regard**
- being genuine or **congruent**.

Empathy, as already discussed, is a conscious effort to see the situation as the other person sees it. It is thought that empathy can be achieved in three different ways:

- understanding the service user from his/her own point of view, including the feelings surrounding their point of view
- understanding the service user in and through the context of their own lives
- gaining an understanding of any disagreements between the service user's thoughts and the point of reality.

Empathy is not passive but takes an active interest in the service user's concerns. Gerald Egan (2002) states that there is 'a basic formula' that expresses empathetic understanding:

- **You feel** – guilty (emotion expressed by the client)
- **Because** – you are ill (experiences and behaviour that cause the feelings).

Unconditional positive regard, or acceptance, means valuing the service user and recognising their individuality without making assumptions about them. Assumptions are more often than not incorrect and mean that people tend to misjudge others and get the wrong idea about them or about what they are trying to express. An example of making an assumption or **stereotyping** would be to assume that because a service user has Alzheimer's disease they are unable to make choices, or that they need to be spoken to as though they are a child. It is important for a care worker to convey warmth through the use of friendly words, reassurance about confidentiality and by expressing a desire to help and understand.

Being genuine or congruent is an essential skill when communicating with others. Sincerity is achieved through being open, honest and truthful about what is being said and the way in which it is said. When communicating with a service user, for example, a care worker will not use set phrases or

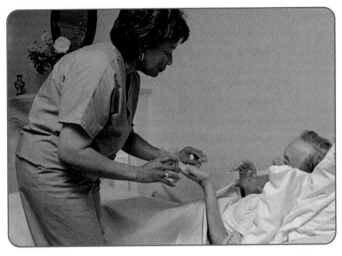

Congruency between nurse and patient is an essential ingredient

professional styles. Egan (2002) believes that genuine and sincere care workers do not use their role to hide behind or to protect themselves. Understanding and helping a service user should be the natural part of a care worker's approach and not 'part of their role'. Congruency can be achieved through using verbal and non-verbal responses consistently and through making sure that these reflect the care worker's inner feelings.

Care workers should not be afraid of silence or long pauses. Silent pauses often mean 'let us have time to think'. This may be a necessity for both the service user and the care worker to enable them to reflect and analyse what has been said and to decide on the direction they wish to move to within their next piece of conversation. Silences can show that both are listening and thinking about what has been said.

Service users will bring with them their individual needs when involved in interactions. If a service user is in pain or worried, they may not be able to communicate effectively. Emotional distress can create a communication barrier as the service user may lack concentration and may not speak clearly. Emotional differences, too, can create communication barriers, for example if a care worker is feeling happy, the service user may think that their concerns are not being taken seriously.

Shyness and embarrassment are also considerations that a care worker must be aware of when communicating. A service user who is shy may struggle to express themselves as they may not want another to know how they feel or may be embarrassed about their feelings. A person's **self** image will play an important role in any communication. Self image is the way a person sees themselves. This will affect the individual's self esteem. It is likely that if a person has a poor self image and self concept they will have a low self esteem and this will more than likely limit their opportunities. People who have a low self esteem consider that others will have a poor opinion of them and that they have a low expectation of their performance. As a result they may suffer from depression and withdrawal. Maslow considered that 'the goal of living is self actualisation'. That means that you need to fulfil your full potential. Self actualisation is at the top of Maslow's hierarchy of need. A person cannot reach this point unless all their other needs are met.

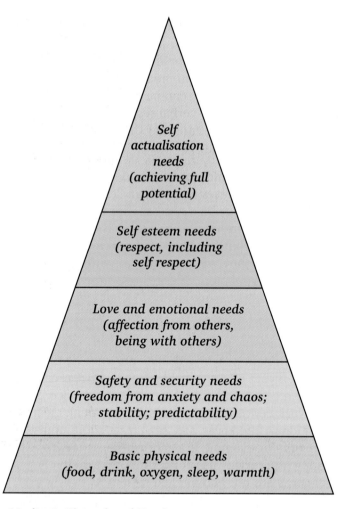

Maslow's Hierarchy of Need

Service users can be very distressed and vulnerable and as a consequence any communication with the service user should not confirm a low self esteem but should have a positive outcome.

Michaela — Activity 6

Michaela is preparing patients for an appointment with the orthopaedic specialist at the hospital. She also has to talk to the patients after they have their consultation. Some are upset about the information they have received.

1. How can Michaela establish good relationships with the patients when she is preparing them for their consultation?

2. Explain what Michaela should remember, to encourage a successful outcome when she is communicating with a patient?

3. How can Michaela maintain a professional attitude when having a one-to-one interaction with a service user?

4. Why is it important to maintain a professional attitude when having an interaction?

The structure of interactions

Introduction

The preparation of the environment to encourage conditions conducive for communication will have already taken place prior to the communication. Environmental factors such as heating, lighting, ventilation and positioning will have been considered and appropriate arrangements made.

During any introduction some form of greeting will take place whereby the service user will be welcomed. Finding out how the service user wishes to be addressed, for example their preferred name, is an important aspect of this stage. First impressions are very important. If the service user feels that they are not valued or respected, the communication will be inhibited.

Body language will play a very important role during the introductory part of any communication. Moving towards the person, extending a hand in a gesture of welcome and smiling are components of body language that will enable a service user to feel at their ease.

Mrs Grant? I am so pleased that you could make this meeting

In this part of the communication it will be important that the care worker has established in their mind, if not on paper:

- the overall aim of the communication – the desired outcome
- the objectives – the steps that will be taken to ensure the outcome will be achieved.

A common purpose will be established which will enable those who are communicating to share the topic agreed.

Main content

Within the main content effective communication skills will be established. The steps within the objectives will be applied at a pace appropriate to the service user. Communication skills such as open and closed questions will be used to encourage the service user to open up and to discuss the situation which has to be considered. It is using open-ended questions appropriately and the skill of applying prompts, probes, summarising and paraphrasing that will directly contribute to successful outcomes.

The content of the communication will need to have been well thought through prior to the communication taking place. It is important that during the main content part of the communication:

- a logical sequence is followed
- jargon or professional language is not used unnecessarily
- congruence is established
- discrimination does not occur which could affect self esteem
- cultural needs are considered
- confidentiality is maintained
- trust is established
- pace and tone are appropriate
- any special needs such as sign language are used.

Reflecting and winding down

This involves reflecting on what has been said during the interaction. The purpose is to ensure that the participants have understood the content of the interaction and have agreed the outcomes. The interaction should not be ended abruptly otherwise the trust that has been created while interacting is likely to be destroyed. Also the participant(s) will be left feeling as though they are unsure and not in control. The 'winding down' is as important as the introduction and the main content.

SOLER

Gerald Egan in his book *The Skilled Helper* recommended using an **acronym** to help build all the components into communication with others. The acronym he used was:

SOLER

S	O	L	E	R
Sitting attentively at an angle	Open posture	Leaning forward	Eye contact	Relaxed body language

> **Discussion point**
>
> How could Gerald Egan's theory be applied when talking with
> - a service user who is being told that they have to have a foot amputated?

What is happening in this situation?

SOLER can help to guide professional care workers when discussing sensitive information

- the teacher is sitting across from the parent at a slight angle
- he/she is leaning towards the parent
- he/she can look directly at the parent when this is appropriate
- he/she is listening attentively to the parents' questions and responses
- he/she does not look as though they are in a hurry.

Within the main content active listening will be essential. When actively listening, flexibility is needed. Active listening does not just mean listening and hearing, it involves trying to understand the meaning of the words being used by the service user and the context from which they originate. Active listening is developing an interaction with the service user that helps to identify the real issues and to provide a meaningful dialogue in exchange.

When listening, individuals can operate at three different levels. These are:

- Partial listening – this is where some of what the service user has said registers with understanding on the receiver. This is often termed as Level 1 listening.
- Well tuned in listening – the majority of what is being said is accepted and understood by the listener. This is often known as Level 2 listening.
- Global listening – the receiver is able to identify fully with the person speaking and has established empathy and congruence. This is often known as Level 3 listening.

receiving a message, analysing the content, reflecting on what has been said, matching with previous experience are all part of the communication cycle

Listening involves a cycle

The main purposes of active listening are:

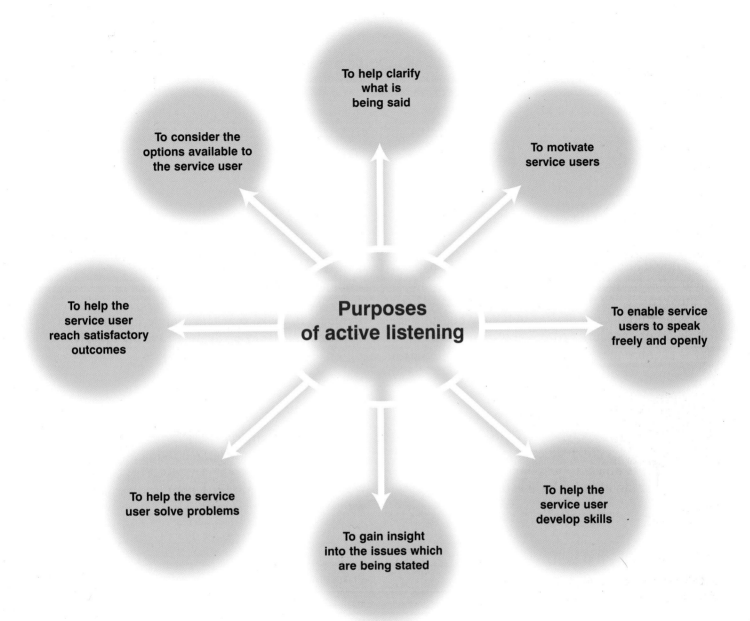

Theories of Burnard

Burnard has discussed, through a number of his books, some of the difficulties experienced by people who wish to communicate, as well as suggesting ways in which care professionals can be helped to improve their communication. Burnard believes that self awareness is one of the keys to effective communication. By acquiring very good awareness of self, Burnard suggests that it is possible to forget about self and unconditionally

focus on others, therefore being objective and able to help. This is an essential quality for all health professionals as within their role, objectivity is central when dealing with others.

Discussion point

How could having full knowledge of self awareness assist a nurse who is dealing with a patient who is recovering from a stomach cancer operation?

Burnard also discusses group formation within his works and identifies some processes that can occur as groups begin to work together. His explanation of group dynamics is given below:

Working with one other

To work effectively there must be a 'bonding' within a group. When 'pairing' occurs, two people may work together excluding all others from any interaction. Other people in the group are left out.

Selecting a victim

This is one or more people 'picking' on someone and displaying threatening behaviour towards them. This is often a method used when a person is feeling uncomfortable or unable to cope. Such behaviour will not encourage effective group response to a task.

Directing own feelings

Trying to force ones own feelings on the whole group is a method of projecting. Sometimes this can happen when an individual within the group is feeling angry or ineffectual. The person who is upset tries to get everyone to think that these are the feelings of the whole group, not just pertaining to themselves.

Forming a sub-group

A sub-group that line themselves up against other members of the group is formed. The group are often antagonistic and derisive to the others within the group. They often try to 'belittle' the other members or make sarcastic comments. Such behaviour needs to be dealt with fairly quickly.

Making trouble

A member of a group, who feels they have been forced to attend a group meeting, may try to disrupt the meeting as much as possible. Through such action the group may not be able to achieve its goal.

Blotting out the issue(s)

Not contributing in any way or introducing an unrelated topic can be an emotional action that is part of the 'taking flight' process. This can happen when individuals are distressed or they are afraid of the issues being discussed.

Silent approach

When this happens in a group interaction the individual chooses to remain completely silent. This can have quite an adverse effect on members.

Protecting

One person protects another or rescues them so that the protected individual does not have to take responsibility for their actions.

Behind the scenes

This may be introducing a topic that is not listed on the written agenda that the group has been given. A 'hidden agenda' can arise from the discussion that is taking place or because one or more members of the group have issues that they wish to have discussed and which are causing them concern. Such an approach can cause difficulty to the group as it prevents coverage of the topic(s) on the formal agenda.

Discussion point

How could the 'blotting out' of the issues affect a group of nursery nurses who were discussing the importance of safety and security of a nursery school after a child had managed to let themselves out of the building?

Thompson

Neil Thompson's interest in language and communication stems from his early years, where he realised that language shaped identity, and from his social work, where he spent a great many years helping people with their problems. Thompson recognises that the caring professions such as medical, counselling, social work and alternative therapies all need communication and language as building blocks to good practice. He states that 'communication is not simply a matter of transmitting information but also involves transmitting a relationship'. Thompson recognises that communication is part of every individual's social and working life and the power relationships that accompany these aspects of our lives.

Because communication has such a strong link with powers it is important that those in the caring world have at least a basic understanding so that the positives can be used effectively and the negative aspects or barriers can be avoided as much as possible. A high level of competency is needed in order to communicate effectively. Thompson states, 'I am not just a unique individual, I am also socially located'. This means that within all interactions we will reflect:

Thompson considers that when interacting with others we should not:

- make judgements about others
- try to take control of others through manipulative use of language
- be overpowering but should try to respond to people spontaneously
- be fixed in our ideas but should be open to other people's ideas
- consider ourselves to be superior but should try to develop congruence and empathy.

Thompson considers communication in terms of being enhancing or supportive and inhibiting or defensive. For example, if an individual simply states the facts rather than making evaluative statements about a person, they are more likely to be supportive. If, however, a person is inflexible and really defensive in their approach, they are more likely to inhibit communication. Thompson believes that 'high quality work without high quality communication is not really the order of the day'. Commitment to a high standard of communication is necessary if care practice is to be effective.

Discussion point

How is making judgements about a person likely to inhibit communication?

Bales

Bales theory concentrates on the behaviour of members of a group. Some of his theories are based on observation of the behaviour of small groups in a laboratory setting, which provided a way of measuring group dynamics and structure. Bales considers that verbal and non-verbal behaviour can be listed under two broad headings. These are:

- the task area
- the socio-emotional area.

In the 'task-based area' some group members are more interested in getting the task completed. Therefore they will try as quickly as possible to clarify what is required and to move forward towards a successful conclusion. To achieve this they will:

- ask questions
- provide opinions and information
- suggest ideas
- seek direction
- repeat and clarify.

If this is the approach being used, group members are not concerned about other people's feelings. They are not being deliberately insensitive to others but their prime role is to 'get the task done'. The group leader needs to recognise that members who take this role can be valuable, as they ask questions from which all members can benefit.

Bales considers that socio-emotional behaviour can be divided into two headings:

- positive
- negative.

Those individuals who make a positive contribution to the group make contributions that:

- show solidarity
- say things that encourage laughter enabling people to relax
- show satisfaction when giving help
- demonstrate the ability to show understanding and acceptance.

By using such approaches the members foster a sense of bonding and cohesion within the group. They also reduce the amount of tension through humour and they acknowledge the importance of people's emotional feelings not just considering the role or task that has to be undertaken.

The negative aspects of socio-emotional behaviour can include:

- becoming withdrawn
- rejection of others
- demonstrating aggressive behaviour
- patronising others or putting them down
- strongly disagreeing.

Any group will need both the positive and the negative contributions of members if they are to view topics from different perspectives and to successfully achieve tasks.

Discussion point

How can negative reactions help a group conversation whose focus is to plan the way forward after an accident in a residential home for older people?

Assessment activity (AO3)

Research   CASE STUDY

Case Study 1: Bumble Bees Nursery

Amir is working at Bumble Bees Nursery as a nursery nurse. The children who attend Amir's section are between the ages of two and four-and-a-half years old. It is quite a large nursery that caters for over 50 children and is flexible in its hours. Parents and key workers are in and out of the nursery at different times. There are 12 nursery nurses on duty at any one time, a manager, deputy manager, five supervisors and a nurse.

Case Study 2: The Swallows Residential Home

Peter is a care assistant at the Swallows Day Care Centre. Each day between 40 and 50 older adults attend the day care centre, their ages in the main being over 65 years. Most attend because they lack social interaction as they live alone and have health problems such as mobility that mean they are unable to socialise and could become isolated.

Case Study 3: Barnwell Hospital Day Centre

Jackie is a dietician who works at the local hospital. As part of her duties she attends the hospital day care centre for two hours each day to assist service users who need advice and guidance about their diet, mainly because they are immobile and are putting on weight. Twenty service users attend each day. There are a manager, deputy manager, health care assistants, nurses and health specialists who visit the day centre throughout the day.

1. Choose one of the case studies above (the same one chosen for AO2). The manager of the setting has asked you to undertake research, using a range of appropriate resources (books, Internet, previous research), to provide a comprehensive analysis showing how **two** theories could provide the care workers with guidance about the effects of communication on service users and care workers.

   You should include information about the effects of appropriate and inappropriate communication.

2. Present the result of your research as guidance for the care workers.

2.2.5 Interaction with a service user

Before communicating with a service user it is often best to prepare by:

- making a plan – this enables a systematic approach to be used
- arranging the area to be used, e.g. seating arrangements, ventilation, lighting, etc.
- deciding what you are going to talk about with the service user(s), for example what information will you give or obtain or what ideas need to be exchanged?

Making a plan

A plan is important because it will help to organise thoughts and to put them in the correct order or sequence. It will also enable the person who is collecting information or exchanging ideas to think about what information they will need, the skills that they will need to use, how body language may help the communication and how to ensure that active listening is encouraged. Factors that can influence communication will also need to be thought about.

Planning will involve:

- Who will the interaction involve?
- What is the focus of the communication to include?
- What are the aims and objectives?
- Where is the interaction to take place?
- How do I need to prepare the environment?
- What communication skills will I use?
- What body language am I likely to use?
- How can I apply the care values?
- Do I need to consider any cultural issues?
- Which theories will enable me to be effective in the interaction?

Discussion point

Why is planning an interaction important?

Thinking about the environment for the conversation

Care workers will need to decide whether the one-to-one or group communication is going to be formal or informal as the arrangements will need to reflect these needs.

Ruth 1   CASE STUDY

Ruth is an older person who has just arrived at a residential home. She is very nervous so she will need lots of reassurance. Ruth does not know any of the other residents, so it is likely that she will be lonely. It is hoped that through communicating with Ruth, the care worker will be able to meet some of her social needs and to give her someone to confide in. It is known that Ruth is worried that she will lose some of her independence by becoming a resident at the residential home, so she will need a great deal of reassurance that this will not happen. The care worker wants to share with Ruth how her needs will be met. She will also need to know about the activities offered by the residential home so that she will have the opportunity of socialising and making friends.

Preparing the environment for Ruth

It is important that the care worker ensures that Ruth has *privacy*. This means making sure that there are no interruptions during the interaction. If the interaction were to be interrupted Ruth is unlikely to feel safe and secure. Also she would feel that she could not speak freely as she may be overheard. A note on the door indicating that the room is in use should deal with this possibility.

The care worker needs to ensure that the *lighting* is appropriate. If the room is too dark the service user is likely to feel uncomfortable and may not communicate effectively. It is also difficult to focus on a person's face if the light is poor. If Ruth has a visual or hearing impairment, poor lighting may prevent lip reading or sign language if these need to be used.

The *temperature* of the room needs to be appropriate for the weather conditions. The care worker needs to be aware that older people feel the cold a little more and may feel cold if they are sitting still for a long time. The window could be opened to help ventilation but *noise* levels will also need to be considered. Too much noise can inhibit communication, especially if Ruth has any hearing impairment.

The arrangement of the seats and table will also need to be considered. Sitting side by side may be a good idea with a low table in front with tea/coffee available. This will help Ruth to feel welcome and comfortable.

Plan of a correctly prepared room

Discussion point

Why is it important to prepare a room correctly before having an important conversation?

In the plan shown above, the chairs have been arranged alongside each other, but with sufficient room to allow for personal space. They have not been placed one each side of the table to make the communication less formal. The table will be helpful when the care worker is making notes and to put refreshments on. The window is open very slightly to make sure the room is well ventilated, but not draughty.

Communicating with a service user

Before communicating with a service user it will be important to know what the aim or purpose of the interaction is.

Previously in this AO Ruth's needs have been stated. Look back and remind yourself of these. The aims or purpose of the communication between Ruth and the care worker are:

- to gain Ruth's confidence and to build up a relationship
- to encourage Ruth to confide in the care worker
- to reassure Ruth and to make her feel welcome and to assure her that she will not lose her independence
- to provide information about how her rights will be met
- to provide information about the social events organised by the residential home
- to empower Ruth.

A plan outlining the order in which events will take place and what will be included in the various parts of the conversation would be very helpful.

A plan could look like the one given below although planning can take various different forms:

Timescales	Order	Reason
Wed 9.00 am	Write outline transcript of greeting: words, body language...	To make Ruth feel welcome
Wed 9.15 am	Write outline of main content...	
Wed 10.00 am	Write outline transcript of winding up	
Thurs 10.00 am	Arrange room...	
Thurs 10.30 am	Prepare drinks....	

Any cultural issues that affect Ruth will also have to be considered during the preparation. For example, Ruth is an older adult and, therefore, may prefer a more formal or traditional approach. She is also quite independent and care must be taken not to patronise her.

All interactions or conversations, however long, have three main parts:

- the first contact or initial introduction
- main content and maintaining contact with the service user including discussion
- reflection and winding up or ending the interaction.

The first/initial contact with Ruth

As Ruth enters the room the care worker will walk over to meet her and ask her to sit down. The care worker is not going to extend her hand for a 'hand shake' as she has met Ruth previously.

The care worker will lean slightly forward and her facial expression will show a warm smile, showing warmth and friendship. The outline transcript of greeting could include:

Care worker: Hello Ruth, I'm pleased you were able to join me. I've set out two chairs for us here. Which would you prefer to have?

Ruth: I'll sit at this one as it will give me more leg room.

Care worker: Would you like a tea or a coffee Ruth?

Ruth: Tea please.

Care Worker: I know you have only been here for a few hours but how do you feel now that you are actually here?

Ruth: I like my room very much. It has lots of space and I don't feel crammed in. I don't know the routines yet, but I do hope I'm not going to have to do everything at set times!

Care worker: Lunch time and tea times are at fixed times, Ruth, but we can accommodate some changes for you if the need arises, for example if you go out or have visitors.

Ruth: That's reassuring.

Care worker: I am going to be your key carer Ruth. That means that I will be here to try to meet any needs you have. I hope that we will get to know each other well. I want to assure you that conversations we have will be confidential. Information will only be passed to other carers on a 'need to know' basis, for example if they are providing additional care or if I am on holiday. How do you feel about that?

Ruth: I am very reassured that my business will not be known by everyone who lives here. I value my privacy.

Care worker: Your independence is as important to us as it is to you Ruth. We...

From this outline transcript of the initial/first meeting it is possible to see that the care worker has:

- used closed questions to obtain specific answers
- used open questions to draw information from Ruth
- has given information to Ruth.

> **Discussion point**
>
> Which were the open questions asked by the care worker? What was their purpose?

Main content

The care worker will want to address a number of key points within the main content of her talk with Ruth. These will include:

- finding out how Ruth would want to maintain her independence
- her role as a key worker and what this involves
- giving information about how the care plan will be devised and Ruth's role within the care plan
- obtaining information about what Ruth likes doing as far as activities are concerned
- giving information about the activities available within the residential home
- allowing time for exchanging ideas on how Ruth would like to proceed as far as activities are concerned or about any concerns she may have.

From the outline transcript of the first contact it can be seen that the care worker has skilfully reached a point where the topic of independence has been introduced. Her outline transcript notes will have helped order her thoughts to develop this theme. For example:

Care worker: How would you like to see your independence being maintained Ruth?

Ruth: Well, I don't want to have to change my GP. Mine only lives a couple of miles away and I want to stay with him.

Care worker: That's perfectly acceptable Ruth. Many of our residents choose to have the GP they have always had. Yours lives close so there is no problem with that. We can take you to see him or we can ask him to come and visit you here if there is a need. Are there any other ways you would like to be able to make choices?

Ruth: Well, yes there are. I want to be able to take a bath when I want and also to go for short walks when I feel like it.

Care worker: Let's take the bathing issue first. Of course you can take a bath whenever you wish. You have 'en suite' facilities, so there is no problem with that. We do ask that you just ring down before getting into the bath to let us know you are doing so. This is so we can just check that you have been able to get out alright and that nothing has happened to you. We would not come into your bathroom while you are in the bath, we would just call through the door. This is for safety reasons.

The care worker is giving factual information during this part of the conversation. She is not being emotional, but is reassuring Ruth throughout that everything will be done to ensure her independence. She is, however, pointing out to Ruth that some measures must be taken to ensure safety and security and that these measures are in Ruth's interest but will not be an invasion of her privacy. She is also showing Ruth that she does have the right to choose.

Reflection and winding up

In this part of the conversation the care worker must take the responsibility for reflecting. That is she must make sure that Ruth has understood correctly what has been said and give Ruth the opportunity of asking further questions. Reflecting and winding up is 'ending a conversation'. This must be done appropriately so that the service user feels valued and that needs have been met. Examples of winding up are:

- Let's think about what we have agreed...
- Do you think what I have said is a fair summary of what we have been talking about...
- Let me just go over the notes I have made to be sure that I have recorded all the points you want followed...
- Is there anything else that you would like to ask?
- Perhaps in a couple of days we could have another chat to see if there are any other issues you would like to talk about?

In these examples, all the topics discussed are summarised, the opportunity to ask questions is given and a move forward is suggested by offering another meeting, the latter providing security to Ruth as she knows that if she has missed anything she can bring the topic up in another meeting which

is to take place in the near future.

Within the interaction there will be the opportunity to:

- give information
- obtain information
- exchange ideas and opinions

– what the procedures are, what social activities take place
– how Ruth wants to maintain her independence
– what Ruth likes doing in comparison to what is available.

Evaluation

Reflecting

Planning for improvement   **Evaluating**   Analysing

Drawing conclusions

Reflecting

Reflect means thinking about the whole conversation from start to finish. Here is an example of reflection by the care worker who has communicated with Ruth at the residential home. She is thinking or reflecting on the first part of the conversation she had with Ruth:

'I think I showed understanding of Ruth's needs and I did this in different ways. I ensured that the interaction was entirely focused on Ruth by asking her how she felt that she could maintain her independence. I asked an open question and allowed Ruth to answer how she wanted, making sure that I listened actively. I did not dismiss anything that Ruth said, but tried to clarify by making sure that I understood her meaning. In this way I communicated back to Ruth what she had said, sometimes clarifying in order to make points clearer. I also showed empathy, by making a 'conscious effort to see the world as another sees it.'

Empathy-building statements, such as, 'are you worried that you will not be able to make your own decisions?' helped Ruth to explain how she felt. In this example, the care worker is thinking about the aims and objectives, what she actually did, how well she did it. She is going over in her mind what actually took place. It often helps if we make notes at this stage to remind us of what was actually said.

How do we analyse?

When the care worker has clearly reflected on all the parts of the communication she had with Ruth she will begin to **analyse**. That is thinking about particular things such as skills used and how well she has used them. To do this the care worker will need to make **judgements** or decisions. For example, she may want to make judgements about the skills used and how they were used. An analysis of the skills is given in the example below:

'I think my tone of voice was appropriate because I did not have a raised voice, also I allowed Ruth to speak at her own pace. If I had rushed the conversation Ruth may have thought that I was not really interested in what she had to say. I made frequent eye contact so that Ruth knew I was interested in what she had to say and that I was focussing on her and not on others. I used quite a number of open questions, for example, one I used was, "What else would help you to maintain your independence?" This gave Ruth the chance to talk about her feelings and what she wanted to continue doing for herself and showed that I wanted to listen to Ruth.

I also reassured Ruth about confidentiality and how the information she had given would be kept. I made sure that she realised that other care workers would only be told information on a "need to know" basis. This probably helped Ruth to trust me and to build an effective working relationship with Ruth.

I carefully observed Ruth's body language and by the end of the conversation it appeared to me that Ruth was much more relaxed than at the beginning. She was not so nervous and her body language became more relaxed and less tense.'

The care worker has considered the skills she used in his conversation with Ruth and has given examples to illustrate the points she was making. She had theoretical information or knowledge about skills and how they should be used and so she could make decisions. She was able to think about the skills against the 'theory'. Thinking about each component part within the task or activity is part of the analysing process.

What is drawing conclusions?

When making decisions there is a need to make 'informed judgements'. That is, measuring something against the knowledge we have of the subject.

If we are making decisions and explaining them we will be making 'reasoned judgements' as we will be examining the facts and knowledge supplied by others who may be experts, and we will make decisions against the facts, opinions and views of others. This could be the views of 'theorists', or other people who have knowledge and opinions of the subject or we could be using the feedback we have received from our assessor or peers, or we could include our own opinions. An example of the care worker drawing conclusions from the conversation with Ruth:

'In my opinion I used prompts very successfully as Ruth moved the conversation forward as a result of my saying "so, which do you think you would like to join?" If I had not done this it is likely that Ruth would have continued to talk around the subject without making any decisions. In her feedback my assessor confirmed that this was appropriate.

I was not afraid of silence. Ruth had several silent periods during the conversation. I think she was thinking back over past activities that she had done. Jan Sutton and William Stewart in their book Learning to Counsel *state "silence can be threatening but it can also be constructive". In Ruth's case I think it was constructive because she was recalling memory of pleasurable activities which helped her to arrive at a decision.'*

In this example, the care worker is expressing her own opinions and referring to the opinions of others. In a full evaluation the care worker would discuss a range of skills used, drawing conclusions about their effectiveness.

What decisions can I make? What can I learn from this experience?

Planning for improvements?

Having drawn conclusions, good practice is to think about factors that may have contributed or influenced the communication. For example:

Purpose	Reasons for use	Effectiveness
Was the aim fully achieved? If not, then why not?	Were the skills used appropriate? Could others have been used which would have been more effective?	Was the outcome achieved? How did the service user react? How did the service user leave the interaction?

If we do not think about how we could improve, it is not possible to get any better in the communication we have. Care workers should always be thinking about their own 'professional development'. In other words 'how to do things better'. When planning for such improvements we need to think about:

- which skills need improving?
- could the sequence of events be improved?
- were the timescales appropriate?
- could the environment used be improved?

Assessment activity (AO4)

Communication　　　　　　　**CASE STUDY**

Case Study 1: Bumble Bees Nursery

Fahmida is a nursery nurse at Bees Nursery. She has been asked to supervise four children who are making birthday cards using card, paint and a variety of stick-on materials. She has been asked to explain the task to the children and to talk to them about what they are doing while making the cards.

Case Study 2: Swallows Residential Home

Winnie is working at Acland Court residential home as a supervisor. She has been asked to talk to Rosie who is a resident at the home. Rosie has suddenly become withdrawn when a few weeks previously she was full of life and joined in all the activities. Winnie has been asked to find out if anything is bothering Rosie as she is also not eating very much.

Case Study 3: at the local hospital

Kev is a dentist working in his own practice. He has as one of his patients, Molly, who is not very good with oral hygiene. Kev needs to talk to Molly about the state of her teeth and about what she could do to promote good oral hygiene.

1　Choose **one** of the case studies given above or **one** of your own.

2　Draw up a plan for preparing a room to have the conversation with the service user, explaining the actions taken.

3　Prepare an outline plan for the conversation, including an outline transcript of the initial contact, main content and winding up.

4　Draw up a checklist of the skills you will use during the interaction, making sure it can be used for assessment purposes.

5　Have the one-to-one interaction with the service user. Make sure you arrange for the assessor to assess you.

6　Evaluate in-depth your own performance making realistic recommendations for improvement.

Unit 3 Promoting Good Health

Contents

About this unit

Within this unit you will investigate:

- perspectives of health and well being
- preventative measures and job roles
- factors affecting health and well being
- health promotion.

Introducing this unit

This unit investigates the range of lifestyle choices and societal factors which influence health and well being. Health and well being are affected not only by an individual's lifestyle choices, but also by societal and environmental issues.

Government policies and resulting legislation have a big part to play in the promotion of good heath. The introduction of screening programmes to prevent ill health has been a useful tool. Even so, many personal factors affect health – some of them over which a person has little control.

Health promoters, too, have a significant role to play in helping service users to make the right decision about their health. Their choice of presentation approach can make or mar a health promotion campaign. Presentation methods have to be well chosen to ensure the message is successfully put over to the individual to whom it is directed.

3.2.1 Perspectives of health and well being

The concept of ill health differs according to medical and social needs.

In 1948, the World Health Organisation (WHO) defined health as a 'state of complete physical, mental and social well being and not merely the absence of disease and infirmity'.

Discussion point

Do you think that this is a realistic definition of health? Is anyone completely well across physical, mental and social areas of their life? How would you define your own health? Are there any areas of your life where you are not completely well?

If you were a person with a disability how would you feel about this definition?

In 1984, after much criticism about their original definition of health, the World Health Organisation (WHO) produced an updated definition of health:

'The extent to which an individual or group is able, on the one hand, to realise aspirations and satisfy needs, and on the other hand, to change or cope with the environment. Health is therefore seen as a resource for everyday life, not the objective of living: it is a positive concept emphasising social and personal resources as well as physical capabilities.'

Discussion point

Do you think this is a better definition of health? Do you think this definition would be more acceptable to a person with a disability?

Explain why.

As suggested by both WHO definitions, being healthy is more than just feeling physically well. Healthiness is connected to people's ability to reach their full potential, therefore all aspects of a person's being must be considered:

- physical health
- mental health
- social health
- spiritual health
- societal health
- emotional health.

These are not alternative models of health but together they form a holistic concept of health.

Different aspects in the concept of health

Aspects of health	Explanation
Physical health	This is how the body functions, probably the easiest aspect to see and to measure.
Mental health	Strongly linked to emotional health, this is the ability to think clearly and coherently.
Emotional health	It is the ability to recognise and to express emotions such as joy, anger, fear, etc., appropriately. Emotional health means being able to cope with depression, stress and anxiety.
Social health	The ability to make and maintain relationships with other people.
Spiritual health	This could be connected with religious beliefs for some people but for others it would be their own personal beliefs or principles.
Societal health	A person's health is linked to everything in the society that surrounds that person, e.g. if living in an area with war or famine, their finding food would be their main priority not health.

Holistic concept of health

The word holistic comes from 'whole'. Therefore a **holistic** concept of health considers the whole person rather than just the separate aspects of health. It recognises that each one of the aspects of health impacts on the others. For example, if you are emotionally upset, your mental and physical health can be affected. So, too, could your social and spiritual health. It is very difficult to separate the aspects of health as they are interrelated and interdependent.

Hasim	Activity 1

Hasim is a 33-year-old man who is well educated. He runs a successful business and has a comfortable lifestyle with his wife and family in a good neighbourhood. Physically he looks after himself as he watches his food intake, he does not smoke or drink alcohol. He goes to the gym three times each week. Sometimes he feels worried about his business but he does not discuss this with anyone as he was brought up to be self sufficient and independent. He has lots of friends and he is very popular. He believes in looking after his immediate and his extended families. His parents and his parents-in-law come to his house for Sunday lunch twice a month. As they are retired he often brings them gifts and pays for them to go on holiday.

1. Applying the concept of holistic health to Hasim, decide if he is healthy.

2. Explain your answer.

Definitions of health

Definitions of health come from two main sources, the professional definition from nurses, doctors and health care professionals and the lay definitions from the ordinary person in the street. Both definitions are important as they help people to see health from two different perspectives. On one hand the professional definition helps people to see how health care professionals view health, whereas the lay version encompasses the beliefs that influence ordinary people and how they think about illness and health. Some professional definitions of health are negative in that they view health as an absence of illness or disease. Positive definitions of health would concentrate on health rather than ill health.

An example of a negative model is the biomedical model of health.

The biomedical model of health (also known as medical model)

This model looks at people as if they are machines. The various body systems are seen as systems which can be repaired, replaced or tinkered with rather like a washing machine, car or other piece of mechanical equipment. If someone feels ill, they will go to their doctor who will diagnose the problem then provide some medication or recommend a minor operation or general overhaul depending on the severity of the symptoms. According to this model, health is an absence of disease.

Parallel with machine – biomedical model of health

Key features of the biomedical model of health:

- disease is caused by bacteria, virus or genetic factor. Looks for biological process rather than social or emotional process
- person is a type of machine, other aspects of life do not count, e.g., living under strain of unemployment would not be a contributory factor to ill health under this model
- deals with illness and ill health rather than promotion of good health
- health professionals can deal with ill health using a range of medical advances such as surgery, medicines, transplants
- person receiving treatment does not participate in the medical procedure designed to repair their malfunctioning part.

Generally, the biomedical model of health is satisfactory when dealing with acute or short-term illness. For example, appendicitis will cease to be troublesome once the offending appendix is removed. However, treating someone with alopecia might be more complicated for the medical professional, as this is a chronic condition.

Bill and Barney   Activity 2

Bill

Bill is 64 years old. Over the past two years he has had an increasing number of minor accidents while driving his car. Twice recently he tried to reverse into a parking space which was far too small for his car and he managed to damage both cars. He has forgotten to meet his wife to go shopping – this has happened several times. He was always good at remembering birthdays but he has started to forget them. He does not seem to be interested in anything. He was an active man but now sits in his chair gazing into space. When his wife asks him if anything is wrong, he loses his temper.

Barney

Barney is a 24-year-old man who has been diagnosed with malaria after a safari in Africa.

1. Discuss the above case studies in light of the medical model of health.

2. Which patient would be easier for the doctor to treat? Explain why.

Although the biomedical model of health dominated medicine in the Western world for two or more centuries, it began to fall out of favour in the twentieth century. This was for three reasons:

(i)   decline in number of deaths due to infectious diseases;
(ii) dramatic increase in medical technology and its cost;
(iii) growing emphasis on quality of life.

(i) Decline in number of deaths due to infectious diseases

This was through medical science which cut the number of deaths from infectious diseases such as tuberculosis, pneumonia, influenza and so on. These diseases were all caused by micro-organisms

and were the most common causes of death. In 1880 tuberculosis (TB) killed 80,000 people in the UK – this had dropped to 440 people in 1997. This was due, in part, to the development of antibiotics. However, in 1997 cancer and heart disease were the most common causes of death in the UK. With 43% of deaths from cancer and 26% from circulatory disorders this had increased greatly from 1880 when cancer and circulatory deaths combined only accounted for 10% of deaths. Neither cancer nor heart disease had a simple known cause and medical treatments were limited in their success. Chronic disease, such as cancer, had replaced infectious diseases, such as TB, as the biggest killers.

(ii) Dramatic increase in medical technology and its costs

Although there was a dramatic increase in medical advances, some of the costs associated with treating illness and disease also rose prohibitively. Prevention of illnesses became of paramount importance: prevention was cheaper than cure.

(iii) Growing emphasis on quality of life

People want more out of life and they expect to have an active, healthy and enjoyable life.

The above three factors changed the accepted view of life where illness would be dealt with to one where good health is promoted and encouraged.

Research   Activity 3

Visit www.parliament.uk – 'A Century of Change: Trends in UK Stats since 1900.'

Find out how lifestyle change has affected quality of life.

Social model of health

This model of health, in direct contrast to the biomedical model, recognises the important influence of factors such as housing, poverty, education and lifestyle on health. This model does not look for a single physical cause of ill health or illness but instead recognises that there could be several factors which could contribute to a person's state of health.

A social model of health recognises that ill health issues can sometimes be cured by addressing social conditions. For example, damp, unsuitable accommodation could lead to bronchitis and repeated chest infections for an older person. Moving them to a dry, comfortable environment could alleviate their physical symptoms thus making them feel better.

Model of health	Features
Biomedical	• health viewed as absence of disease • disease caused by virus, bacterium, toxic or genetic factor • doctors diagnose disease and decide on treatment • medical advances responsible for patient recovery.
Social	• lots of complex factors in society can contribute to ill health • must address origins of ill health in order to improve health • people's own lifestyle choices can make them healthier.

Summary of biomedical and social models of health

It must be recognised that the eradication of some diseases at the beginning of the twentieth century was not due entirely to medical advances. Social improvements, too, played their role. Public Health Acts 1848 and 1875 ensured that sewerage, drainage and water supply were controlled by a Local Board of Health. Health improvements in the UK at this time were due largely to social policy that reformed public health provision.

Health and well being are affected not only by an individual's lifestyle choices but also societal and environmental issues. Health and well being can be affected by:

• personal responsibility for health
• health as an absence of illness
• illness–wellness continuum
• concepts of ill health
• government policies on health.

Edward Chadwick   **Activity 4**

Edward Chadwick was a nineteenth-century social reformer who had an impact on the public health policy in the UK.

1   Find out how he contributed to social policy.

2   Why did some people feel disinclined to support Chadwick?

Personal responsibility for health

This is a positive concept of health. In this model people feel responsibility for looking after themselves and thereby ensuring they are well. They will be careful to eat a sensible intake of nutritious healthy food such as lots of fresh fruit and vegetables, wholegrain cereals, lean protein foods and few processed or take-away meals. Alcohol will be limited to the recommended guidelines and regular exercise will be a must. Such individuals will feel the onus is on them to keep themselves healthy. Screening guidelines will be followed, for example regular smear tests every three to five years, this in the belief that actions, such as screening, have to be a positive action in maintaining their own health. Recently, in line with this way of thinking, the government recognised that people want to have choices in regard to their health. In the white paper 'Choosing Health: Making Healthy Choices Easier' people set the agenda, not the government.

People who subscribe to this positive view feel that they are responsible for their own health and see others who do not look after their own health as unhealthy. They would almost blame the 'unhealthy' person if any symptoms developed.

People who feel responsibility for their own health are more likely to survive serious diseases. Their positive outlook will enable them to adopt the correct beneficial mental view which could help them on their way to recovery. Positive thinking and mindset can help a person to overcome disease rather than someone who adopts the fatalistic view of 'I've got this disease I'm going to die – there's nothing I can do'. People with a positive view tend to think along the lines of, 'yes there is something I can do – I will defeat this illness'.

Health as an absence of illness

This is a negative view of health. In this view, absence of any symptoms of illness, such as aches or pains, is seen as good health. Anyone subscribing to this view would take good health for granted and feel they did not have to take any measures in order to stay healthy. They would not view themselves as ill if they had a hangover or if they were suffering from a cold. People with this negative view of health are more likely to ignore health advice as they feel it does not make a lot of difference anyway. 'Binge drinking every weekend will not do me any harm as we all have to die some day.'

Nagging symptoms, which do not cause too much trouble, tend to be ignored allowing diseases, such as cancer, time to develop to advanced stages. Once diagnosed this person is likely to play a passive or non-participatory role in his/her treatments. He/she may feel ready to give in to the disease as they may feel they are being punished or victimised.

Gian, Eddie and Micky   Activity 5

Gian

Gian is 42 years old. He is overweight and takes little exercise. He exists on take-away and ready meals. He does not smoke or drink alcohol.

Eddie

Eddie is also 42. He is the correct weight for his height. He takes regular exercise. He smokes forty cigarettes every day and drinks alcohol regularly.

Micky

Micky is 72. He is the correct weight. He regularly works out and does not smoke. He looks after himself but his family has a history of heart disease.

1. All three men need a heart transplant. Which person do you think should receive the one available donor heart?

2. Should age and unhealthy lifestyle be a barrier to a transplant? Explain your reasons.

Marilyn and Kim   Activity 6

Marilyn

Marilyn is 59. She walks her dog every day for at least two miles. She eats a healthy diet, does not smoke and has the occasional glass of wine. She watches her health carefully and takes supplements when she feels it is necessary, e.g. extra vitamins, if she feels she is going to get a cold and zinc for a sore throat. Recently, a mammogram showed an irregularity and the early stage of breast cancer was diagnosed. Since this diagnosis Marilyn has read everything she can about breast cancer and has been impressed by some of the alternative/complementary therapies that her doctor has told her about. She is prepared to make any necessary changes to her lifestyle which will help her to fight this disease. She feels she will defeat it and is very positive for the future.

Kim

Kim is 58. She, too, has been diagnosed with breast cancer. She did not go for her mammograms as advised and ignored repeated requests for her to do so. She discovered a small lump on one of her breasts and after waiting for a few months 'for it to go away' she realised it was getting bigger so she visited her GP. She feels very depressed and sorry for herself. She does not think that changing her diet after all these years will help her – after all she has the disease now. She dismisses the alternative/complementary therapies suggested to her, as a help for her stress, as new age rubbish. She tells her husband not to book a holiday for her for next year as she 'won't be here'.

1. Which concept of health did Marilyn adopt?

2. Which concept of health did Kim adopt?

3. Who do you think would be most likely to recover from breast cancer? Why?

4. How does a positive attitude help Marilyn?

Illness–Wellness Continuum

This model shows that there are various degrees of illness as well as wellness. This continuum shows us that most people could improve their health to optimum wellness. Conversely, everyone could also deteriorate to premature death.

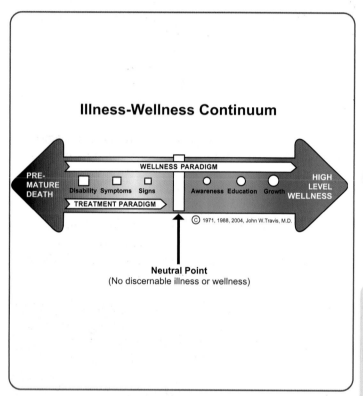

Illness–Wellness Continuum

Theory into practice

Looking at the illness–wellness continuum diagram, where would you put yourself in this particular moment in time? Why? How do you think you could reach optimum health?

According to the diagram, the further left you go, the nearer you are to premature death. It is possible for a person to exhibit signs of a disease but go to the doctor for treatment causing the signs to be eradicated. This enables the person to return to the neutral point. However, if untreated, the signs can go to the next stage of symptoms which, if then untreated, could disable the person's wellness. As demonstrated by the diagram, the earlier the treatment, the easier it is for the patient to return to health. Signs and symptoms will have been alleviated therefore returning the patient to the neutral point.

Once at the neutral point the person can then build up to optimum health or wellness. As shown in the diagram the person must have awareness of all that contributes to wellness. This includes physical, emotional, intellectual, social and spiritual aspects of health. For example, for physical health you need:

Components needed for physical health

Theory into practice

Look at the components for physical health in the diagram. What do you think each one means? Some are self explanatory. For example, balanced diet means ensuring you eat a variety of foods which will give your body all the protein, complex carbohydrates, vitamins and minerals it needs. Physical activity means exercising regularly – twenty minutes each day is better than one long session each week at the gym. Managing stress levels means that you employ a method of relieving stress which works for you. It could be walking the dog, going to a yoga class or listening to your favourite piece of music.

Awareness of safety could have lots of different meanings such as not taking risks when driving or crossing the road. It could be walking home with friends rather than alone, etc.

Medical self care could be finishing the course of medicine given to you by the doctor therefore ensuring the infection has cleared up. Or it could be reporting symptoms.

1 Explain each component as applied to you.

2 How healthy are you physically?

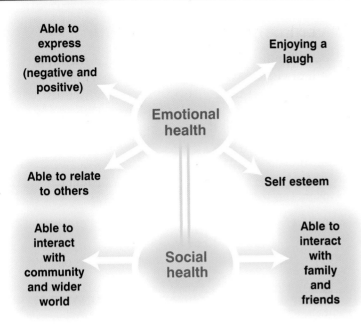

Components needed for emotional and social health

Social and emotional health are linked because if you have low self esteem (emotional health) you are less likely to be able to interact with others. Social health is primarily about interacting with others.

Theory into practice

Looking at the diagram of emotional and social health – how healthy are you? Do you relate well to your family and friends but not to the community and/or wider world? Do you find it difficult to express emotions, whether positive (e.g., happiness) or negative (e.g., anger)?

Intellectual health

In order to be intellectually healthy you should experience:

Curiosity

Active role / employment

Intellectual health

Keeping up with current events

Updating knowledge

Components needed for intellectual health

Discussion point

Are you intellectually healthy? Do you keep up-to-date with what is going on in the world around you? Do you take advantage of opportunities to update your knowledge? Do you take an active role in life? What is your purpose?

Finally, you should be aware of the spiritual side of health. Do you have a set of values or beliefs which you use as a guide in times of trouble or difficulty? Research has shown that people who have spiritual beliefs and a code of moral behaviour are generally happier and healthier than those who do not.

Education, too, plays a part in wellness. If a person is well informed then s/he is well placed to make a balanced judgement about the issue that may concern them. Education helps to keep a person intellectually stimulated and encourages them to think and to work to continually update their knowledge and understanding. With awareness coming through education a person can reach their ultimate goal which is optimum health.

Advice · Activity 7

What advice would you give to the following people to allow them to reach optimum health?

1. Charlie who has a high powered job which makes him feel stressed and unable to sleep at night.

2. Hassam who is physically fit, enjoys a healthy diet and drinks in line with government guidelines. He only goes out with members of his family.

3. Dennis who has been plagued with severe headaches over the last four months.

4. Ahad who finds his job so easy he is bored and finds time at work passes very slowly.

Concepts of ill health

The concepts of ill health refer to the following:

i. Ill health as a disease
ii. Ill health as a disorder
iii. Ill health as a subjective feeling of illness.

(i) Ill health as a disease

This involves a member of a medical team examining a patient after discussing the patient's symptoms. The symptoms could be bleeding, pain, discomfort, problems with breathing, lumps and so on. The doctor will then diagnose the medically named disease based on the observable symptoms. However, it is possible to have a disease and for the patient not to feel unwell. Some diseases are well advanced before the patient begins to feel ill.

(ii) Ill health as a disorder

This is related to an organ, tissue or body system which does not function correctly. An example of this could be if the heart misses a beat then there is a specific fault in the cardiovascular system.

(iii) Ill health as a subjective feeling of illness

Illness is that subjective feeling that a person has when they feel unwell. Sometimes it could be that there are no symptoms to see or describe yet the person does not feel well. Other times people feel unwell and yet they do not have any known disease. It is the person's own definition of their lack of health.

Sometimes, if a person is seriously ill, all three concepts of ill health will happen. Firstly, they will feel ill then symptoms may appear and they will have a body system which does not function correctly. For example, in the weeks before a heart attack a person may feel tired then s/he could find it difficult to breathe then comes the heart attack.

Concepts of ill health | Activity 8

Which concept of ill health would the following fit into?

1. Magda – feels fine, no symptoms, she has breast cancer which has not been detected.

2. Pete – feels ill, no symptoms, no tissue, organ or system disorder detected.

3. Mal – feels ill, has symptoms of fatigue and anaemia, has malfunction of circulatory system.

Government policies on health

In the mid-nineteenth century, because of the rapid growth of cities with their poor physical conditions, there were major outbreaks of infectious diseases such as cholera, typhus and diphtheria. The government recognised that in order to improve public health there had to be major reforms. Some of the reforms were the state provision of health and social welfare services which were brought about by the following Acts of Parliament:

1848	Public Health Act
1875	Public Health Act
1906	The Education (Provision of Meals) Act
1907	The Old Age Pensions Act
1911	The National Insurance Act
1919, 1923, 1924	Subsidised Housing Acts
1920	The Unemployment Insurance Act
1929	The Local Government Act
1934	The Milk Act: The Unemployment Assistance Board

Theory into practice

Research one of the above Acts. Producing your materials in the form of a presentation for the rest of your group, explain the purpose of the Act. Did it achieve its aims? How far did it help the working people of this country?

In 1941, Sir William Beveridge investigated the welfare provision of the time. His ideas of improvement led to the development of the National Health Service. Beveridge wished to tackle five 'evils' within British society.

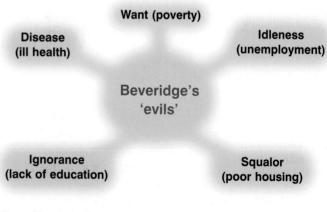

Beveridge's 'evils'

Acts which were passed after Beveridge's investigation were related to the five evils he identified in his report.

Acts designed to help eradicate Beveridge's 'evils'

Current national government initiatives

After the emergence of the welfare state there was a period of development and expansion for health and social care services. Already in the 1970s community services were beginning to take on a preventative role.

Although Beveridge aimed to remove his targeted five 'evils' his policies did not remove inequality. The Black Report (August 1980) showed that although the NHS had been running for 30 years, purporting to offer equal care for all, there were marked differences in the number of deaths according to class.

Occupations within social class groupings	Social Class		Occupation
	I	Professional	accountants, engineers, doctors
	II	Managerial & Technical/ Intermediate	marketing & sales managers, teachers, journalists, nurses
	IIIN	Non-manual Skilled	clerks, shop assistants, cashiers
	IIIM	Manual Skilled	carpenters, goods van drivers, joiners, cooks
	IV	Partly Skilled	security guards, machine tool operators, farm workers
	V	Unskilled	building and civil engineering labourers, other labourers, cleaners

Classification of jobs
Source: www.archive.official-documents.co.uk/document/doh/ih/list.htm

Black concluded that good health related to a decent **income**, good quality housing, good well balanced nutrition, access to the NHS and access to healthy food. The NHS alone was not totally responsible for good health. People's standard of living was. The solutions suggested by this report were so expensive that they were ignored. However, in 1997 the newly elected Labour government commissioned an 'Independent Inquiry into Inequalities in Health 1998'. Donald Acheson was the architect of this report which found that although death rates had fallen in all social groups, the gap between Class I and Class V had actually widened.

Mortality rates

European standardised mortality rates, by social class, selected causes, men aged 20–64 England and Wales, selected years.

All causes rates per 100,000

Social class	Year		
	1970-72	1979-83	1991-93
I Professional	500	373	280
II Managerial & Technical	526	425	300
III (N) Skilled (non manual)	637	522	426
III (M) Skilled (manual)	683	580	493
IV Partly skilled	721	639	492
V Unskilled	897	910	806
England and Wales	624	549	419

Lung cancer rates per 100,000

Social class	Year		
	1970-72	1979-83	1991-93
I Professional	41	26	17
II Managerial & Technical	52	39	24
III (N) Skilled (non manual)	63	47	34
III (M) Skilled (manual)	90	72	54
IV Partly skilled	93	76	52
V Unskilled	109	108	82
England and Wales	73	60	39

Coronary heart disease rates per 100,000

	1970-72	1979-83	1991-93
I Professional	195	144	81
II Managerial & Technical	197	168	92
III (N) Skilled (non manual)	245	208	136
III (M) Skilled (manual)	232	218	159
IV Partly skilled	232	227	156
V Unskilled	243	287	235
England and Wales	209	201	127

Stroke rates per 100,000

	1970-72	1979-83	1991-93
I Professional	35	20	14
II Managerial & Technical	37	23	13
III (N) Skilled (non manual)	41	28	19
III (M) Skilled (manual)	45	34	24
IV Partly skilled	46	37	25
V Unskilled	59	55	45
England and Wales	40	30	20

Accidents, poisoning, violence rates per 100,000

	1970-72	1979-83	1991-93
I Professional	23	17	13
II Managerial & Technical	25	20	13
III (N) Skilled (non manual)	25	21	17
III (M) Skilled (manual)	34	27	24
IV Partly skilled	39	35	24
V Unskilled	67	63	52
England and Wales	34	28	22

Suicide and undetermined injury rates per 100,000

	1970-72	1979-83	1991-93
I Professional	16	16	13
II Managerial & Technical	13	15	14
III (N) Skilled (non manual)	17	18	20
III (M) Skilled (manual)	12	16	21
IV Partly skilled	18	23	23
V Unskilled	32	44	47
England and Wales	15	20	22

Source: www.archive.official-documents.co.uk/document/ doh/ih/list.htm

Mortality rates in social classes — Activity 9

Transfer the tables onto graph paper so you can see the marked difference in deaths between the social classes. In 1970–72 deaths from strokes in Class V were nearly twice as many as Class I: by 1991 they were more than three times. Explain why.

Coronary heart disease has decreased greatly for Class I but has decreased minimally for Class V since 1970. Can you explain why?

Acheson, like Black, concluded that the biggest killer was poverty. However, he produced a list of 39 recommendations which would impact on health inequalities. He highlighted three areas which were deemed to be essential if inequalities were to be addressed:

• high priority must be given to the health of families with children;
• all policies likely to have an impact on health should be evaluated in terms of their impact on health inequalities;
• further steps should be taken to reduce income inequalities and improve the standard of living for poor households.

Although the Conservative government, who had commissioned the report, ignored Black's suggestions due to cost in 1980, in 1992 they produced the first ever national strategy for health improvement in the White Paper, 'The Health of the Nation'. This document set out to shift the form of the NHS from treating sickness to promoting health. There were 27 targets over five key areas which would try to persuade individuals to follow healthier lifestyles. 'Health of the Nation' wished to see an improvement in health in the five chosen areas:

Coronary heart disease and stroke

Cancers (breast, lung, cervical and skin)

Accidents

Decrease deaths

HIV / AIDS and sexual health

Mental illness

Five key areas for improvement in health – 'Health of the Nation'

The Labour government produced 'Saving Lives: Our Healthier Nation' in 1997. This White Paper built on the success of the 1992 'The Health of the Nation'. However, for the first time it was stated that health depended on social, economic and environmental policies as well as on individual lifestyles and health services. Again, the government targeted the main killers:

• cancer
• accidents
• mental illness
• coronary heart disease/strokes.

Theory into practice

HIV/AIDs and sexual health do not appear in the 1997 White Paper. Why is this?

In the areas chosen the government set themselves measurable targets.

Main killer	Reduction in death rate by 2010	Number of lives saved
Cancer	20%	100,000
Coronary heart disease	40%	200,000
Accidents	20%	12,000
Mental health	20%	4,000

Better health for everyone, especially for the worst-off, was the key of this White Paper. To help meet the targets the government needed to:

Demand high standards of health for everyone

Put extra £21 billion into NHS

Tackle smoking as biggest preventable cause of ill health

In order to implement 'Our Healthier Nation', the government needed to

Stress key role of improvement for NHS

Check government and local government working together to improve health

Measures needed to reach targets set by 'Saving Lives: Our Healthier Nation'

There was to be a partnership between: 1. people; 2. communities; and 3. the government, which would be used to improve people's health.

Saving lives: our healthier nation suggested partnership

1. People + 2. Communities + 3. Government = improved health

Saving Lives: Our Healthier Nation suggested partnership

1. People could improve their health by:

- more physical activity
- better diet
- giving up smoking.

Suggestions for better health from Saving Lives

2. Communities could address community factors which cause ill health:

- unemployment
- poor education
- poverty
- substandard housing
- polluted environment
- crime and disorder
- low wages.

3. The government could take on health inequality with a series of initiatives on:

- education
- housing
- neighbourhoods
- welfare-to-work
- transport
- environment.

All of these initiatives would improve health. Specific health issues to be addressed would be:

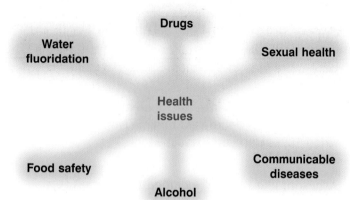

Health issues to be addressed by the government

Two important initiatives came out of 'Saving Lives: Our Healthier Nation'. In March 1998 Health Action Zones (HAZ) were set up in areas of the country which suffer from social deprivation. The idea behind HAZ was that root causes of ill health would be addressed. HAZ also funded local organisations and communities so they could take forward their own projects. For example, Gateshead HAZ funded a scheme which allowed mothers to borrow safety equipment (e.g. safety gates). This project was set up because of the number of accidents recorded in the local hospital. The scheme was means tested and after five years had significantly reduced the number of accidents to children aged under three years.

The second initiative was Health Living Centres. As the name suggests, these were Centres which would provide people with information on health living. People would be provided with information, advice and support so they could make informed decisions about health matters. People struggling with health problems, such as trying to give up smoking, would be given support and helped to seek the best method of cessation to meet their needs. Courses, too, would be available which could include budgeting, cooking meals, first aid or keeping fit.

Like HAZ, Health Living Centres would involve statutory and voluntary organisations working together. The local community would be involved in the planning of any projects. They would be funded with money from the Lottery.

Health Action Zones — Activity 10

Do you live in a Health Action Zone? If you do what has HAZ contributed to lessening the effects of social deprivation in your area? If you do not live in a HAZ, find out where the nearest one is and invite a member of the HAZ team along to your school/college. Prepare a list of questions for the HAZ representative to answer. You might want to ask if health (in relation to Saving Lives: Our Healthier Nation targets) has improved since HAZ was set up. How do they know?

Is there a Health Living Centre near you? See if you can visit if there is one close by. What services do they offer?

Choosing Health: Making Healthy Choices Easier

Following on from 'Saving Lives: Our Healthier Nation' the government produced 'Choosing Health: Making Healthy Choices Easier' in November 2004. This White Paper recognised that public interest in health was increasing and that people wanted more say in choosing for themselves. They wanted to set the agenda and decide when and if the government intervened. Again, emphasis was placed on the government's role in tackling social inequality and the causes of ill health. The new public health approach would have THREE core principles:

(i)   Informed choice
(ii) Personalisation
(iii) Working together.

(i) Informed choice

People want to make their own decisions so they need to be well informed with up-to-date reliable information which will enable them to make the correct decisions. This informed choice was qualified by two pointers.

a) Children who are too young to make their own decisions must be protected by the parent/carer who will make an informed decision on their behalf. For example, the parent/carer will weigh up the pros and cons regarding the vaccine for whooping cough.

b) Another person's choice must not cause harm to someone else's health, e.g. in the instance of someone smoking next to a non-smoker.

(ii) Personalisation

Any support or help given to a person must be fitted to that person's needs. It should be flexible and convenient to the person receiving the support. For example, if an older person is receiving help with getting out of bed in the morning then a suitable time must be arranged – it should not be an automated effort geared to fit into a helper's slot. There should be negotiation so the older person feels happy about the arrangements.

(iii) Working together

Agencies need to work together across the community as an effective partnership is the key to success.

Examples of organisations working together

The main health priorities of this 2004 White Paper were to:

- reduce the number of people who smoke
- reduce obesity and improve diet and nutrition
- increase exercise
- encourage and support sensible drinking
- improve sexual health
- improve mental health.

Health priorities — Activity 11

1   Look at the main health priorities of the 2004 White Paper. Has the government started to tackle these priorities?

2   Research figures for under-age drinking. Have numbers risen or decreased? How does this fit into sensible drinking?

3 Has the number of people treated at GUM clinics decreased? What is the most common sexually transmitted infection today?

4 If you were a government minister in charge of tackling these issues how would you approach the problem?

The NHS Plan (2000)

This government policy paper was a plan to radically reform the NHS in the biggest reorganisation since the NHS was established in 1948. This was a plan to modernise the NHS and make it fit for the twenty-first century. The NHS would require investment and reform. Some of the proposals set out were:

- Cut waiting time to 3 months for out-patients, 6 months for in-patients by 2005;
- Expand cancer screening programmes to cover more patients and more cancers;
- Further cut waiting time for cardiac surgery;
- GP appointments within 48 hours by 2004;
- Provide extra
  7,500 consultants
  2,000 GPs
  20,000 nurses
  6,500 health professionals;
- Create 7,000 extra hospital beds;
- Medical nursing in care homes would be free, etc.

Discussion point

Log on to www.nhsia.nhs.uk or www.dh.gov.uk and check out the remainder of the proposals for the NHS Plan 2000. Do you think this policy will address inequality? Do the proposals meet the needs of the population of the twenty-first century?

Quality in the NHS

Traditionally, medical staff were not questioned on the services provided as they were thought to know best. However, measuring the quality of the services became one of the issues of public services including the NHS. A government paper 'A First Class Service' in 1998 led to the introduction of:

- NICE
- Clinical governance
- Commission for Health Improvement
- National Service Frameworks.

NICE – National Institute for Clinical Excellence

- Began in 1999;
- Provides advice for all health professionals in NHS on cost effectiveness and clinical effectiveness of all drugs, medicines, surgical procedures and diagnostic tests;
- Needed because of advances in technology and medications;
- NICE appraises drugs and technologies and then makes decision on whether costs justified in terms of improved health.

Clinical governance

- Began in 1999;
- Frameworks through which professionals deliver highest possible level of clinical care;
- Medical staff must be regularly retrained and updated to maintain the very highest standards;
- NICE will advise as will Commission for Health Improvement.

Commission for Health Improvement

- Independent body set up in 1999;
- Accountable to Health Secretary;
- Monitors health care quality and standards;
- Can interfere in hospitals if health care is not up to standard (in England and Wales);
- Scotland has Clinical Standards Board.

National Service Frameworks (NSF)

- Series of national standards for doctors and other health workers;
- Sets guidelines and examples of best practice for a selection of illnesses;
- Cancer, diabetes, coronary heart disease are amongst those covered by National Service Frameworks;
- All patients countrywide should have high standard of treatment.

Local Government Initiatives Health Improvement Programmes (HImP)

Health Improvement Programmes came into being as a result of the 1997 White Paper 'The New NHS – Modern Dependable'. They are local health strategies developed by health and local authorities and other key stakeholders such as Primary Care Groups and

NHS Trusts. They would give a description of how national targets would be met by local actions.

HImPs aim to:

- give a clear description of how the national aims and targets will be tackled locally
- set a range of locally determined priorities and targets with particular emphasis on addressing areas of major health inequality
- specify agreed programmes of action to address national and local health improvement priorities
- show that the action proposed is based on evidence of what is known to work (from research and best practice reports)
- show what measures of local progress will be used (including those required for national monitoring purposes)
- indicate which local organisations have been involved in drawing up the plan, what their contribution will be and how they will be held to account for delivering it
- ensure the plan is easy to understand and accessible to the public
- also be a vehicle for setting strategies for the shaping of local health services.

Through the Health Improvement Programme Performance Scheme, health authorities which made good progress in meeting their targets would be rewarded.

HImP have now changed their name to Health Improvement and Modernisation Plans (HIMPs). This is to reflect their high status in bringing together planning for health improvement within the modernisation process of the NHS.

HIMPs — Activity 12

1. Find out about the HIMPs for your local area. Which organisations and agencies were responsible for drawing them up?

2. From what you know about your area do you think the HIMPs are realistic and attainable?

3. Invite a selection of people from the organisations/agencies involved in drawing up the HIMP to a 'Question Time' type of event at your Centre. Before the event, prepare a list of relevant questions for your guest panel members. It is courtesy to send them a copy so that they know in advance what they are going to be asked about.

Healthy Schools Award

This was launched in October 1999. The idea behind it was to improve the health and well being of school-aged young people, in particular those who were socially and economically disadvantaged. Schools play a well recognised role in promoting physical, social and emotional well being of pupils, staff and other members of the school community. A healthy school is one that is successful in helping pupils do their best and empowers them to build on their achievements. The Healthy Schools Award is based on the holistic approach to health.

Citizenship — Emotional health and well being — Alcohol education — Physical education — Healthy Schools Award — Safety — Drugs education — Sex and personal relationships — Healthy eating

Healthy Schools Award covers all these areas

Discussion point

Does your school run a 'Healthy Schools Award' scheme? Has it made a difference to your school community? Visit www.wiredforhealth.gov.uk to see what the programme involves.

Assessment activity (AO1)

Health and well being — CASE STUDY

Case Study 1: Jasbinder

Use a range of information to answer the questions below. You must use both **primary** and **secondary** information if you are aiming to achieve the higher mark.

Jasbinder, 46, eats a healthy well balanced diet and always takes the recommended amount of exercise. She does not smoke or drink alcohol. She always visits her GP for screening, e.g. smear tests. Ten weeks ago Jasbinder was rushed into hospital as she had appendicitis. She is now recovering, but cannot understand how she got this illness. In order to improve her health and well being, she has asked the practice nurse for advice.

Assessment activity (AO1)

Continued...   **CASE STUDY**

Case Study 2: Andi

Andi is 48, eats and drinks what he likes, when he wants. He is overweight because of his overeating, which began over two years ago when he was made redundant. Unable to find another job, he feels worthless. Although he has applied for job after job, he has had no luck. He believes that employers think he is too old. Before he lost his job, the flat he lived in was passable, but since he lost his job he could not afford it and had to move. His current flat is cheaper, but is in a deprived neighbourhood. He feels depressed and has had a troublesome cough for eight months. He has not been to his GP as he does not feel this would help him. Andi is emotionally unstable as well as having physical problems.

Read the above case studies.

1 Using the case studies as a basis, demonstrate your knowledge to explain the **two** different concepts of health and well being which apply to Jasbinder and Andi. The account should be detailed and demonstrate a **high** level of understanding.

Use primary and secondary information to complete this task. You will need to produce a questionnaire or interview questions to obtain the two different perspectives, for example care workers and service users.

Try to include detailed information about personal responsibility, health as an absence of illness, etc.

2 Draw clear and accurate conclusions about the medical and social models of health and well being to explain Jasbinder's and Andi's responses to health education advice.

3 Describe thoroughly, the implications of **one** government initiative.

3.2.2 Preventative measures and job roles

According to Tannahil (Naidoo and Wills, 2000) there are three different yet overlapping approaches in the model of health promotion:

- Health education – this includes campaigns and formal health education programmes. It also includes education, advice and information given to people by health practitioners, e.g. doctors, health visitors, etc.
- Prevention – this includes all preventative medical services, such as screening and immunisation.
- Health protection – this involves the government and other agencies working together to ensure health is safeguarded. This may be through passing legislation to look after social and physical environments. Public health measures and safe working conditions are examples which fit into this category. This model is useful for showing the health promotion perimeters.

The seven areas suggested by Tannahil, as numbered 1–7 in the table below, may be recognised within health promotion.

1.	Preventative measures	e.g., immunisation, breast screening, cervical screening, screening for hypertension.
2.	Preventative health education	e.g., aims to discourage misuse of alcohol – could be in school's health education programme.
3.	Preventative health protection	e.g., fluoridation of water supplies.
4.	Health education for preventative health protection	e.g., providing education to support number 3 could be for health visitors.
5.	Positive health education	e.g., promotion of low-alcohol drinks.
6.	Positive health protection	e.g., government legislation, e.g. banning sale of alcohol to under 18s.
7.	Health education for positive health protection	e.g., lobbying to ensure alcohol is not sold to under 18s.

Source: Tannahil's Model of Health Promotion
Reproduced from Naidoo and Wills, Health Promotion

Education

Health education is about giving people information to make them more informed about choices they take regarding their health. Being informed can lead towards individual attitude and behaviour changes. As shown in the diagram on the next page there are many people involved in health education albeit informally. For example, parents reminding their young children that too many sweets will ruin their teeth, or a wife mentioning to her husband that he is starting to drink too much.

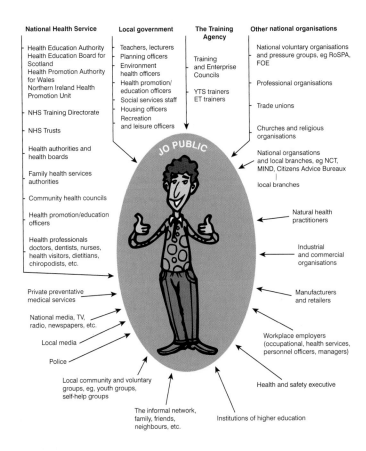

National Health Service

Health Education Authority
Health Education Board for Scotland
Health Promotion Authority for Wales
Northern Ireland Health Promotion Unit

NHS Training Directorate

NHS Trusts

Health authorities and health boards

Family health services authorities

Community health councils

Health promotion/education officers

Health professionals doctors, dentists, nurses, health visitors, dietitians, chiropodists, etc.

Private preventative medical services

National media, TV, radio, newspapers, etc.

Local media

Police

Local community and voluntary groups, eg, youth groups, self-help groups

The informal network, family, friends, neighbours, etc.

Local government

Teachers, lecturers
Planning officers
Environment health officers
Health promotion/education officers
Social services staff
Housing officers
Recreation and leisure officers

The Training Agency

Training and Enterprise Councils

YTS trainers
ET trainers

Other national organisations

National voluntary organisations and pressure groups, eg RoSPA, FOE

Professional organisations

Trade unions

Churches and religious organisations

National organsations and local branches, eg NCT, MIND, Citizens Advice Bureaux local branches

Natural health practitioners

Industrial and commercial organisations

Manufacturers and retailers

Workplace employers (occupational, health services, personnel officers, managers)

Health and safety executive

Institutions of higher education

JO PUBLIC

Agents and agencies in health promotion
(reproduced from Ewles & Simnett 'Promoting Health')

As you can see from the diagram, there are many formal health educators ranging from health promotion officers to environmental health to teachers, media and so on.

As well as Tannahil's model of health there are others such as Beattie's model (1991) which charts the ethical and political tensions faced by practitioners. There are four approaches suggested in this model:

- Health persuasion – this is a traditional health education approach including preventative measures such as screening.
- Personal counselling – this is where service users can have one-to-one sessions where they and not the health practitioner set the issues. It could also be as part of a service user-led group in which people are provided with the means to find their own solution to their health issues.
- Community development – practitioner acts as a facilitator to groups of people who are encouraged to identify and meet their own needs through support and education.
- Legislative action for health – activities designed to protect the public's health, in which the practitioner is involved in lobbying or policy work.

As already stated, traditional health education aimed to change people's behaviour and lead them towards a healthier lifestyle. However, this has sometimes led to a culture of blame, i.e. blaming people for their own ill health. This is one of the ethical issues associated with health education. Practitioners should not judge the service user as sometimes they may not be in a position to take responsibility for themselves because they are too ill or too young. Whilst giving information, practitioners must be careful to respect other people's beliefs and not to impose their own views on the service user. People need to feel in control of their own health and the more in control they feel, the more likely they are to take an active part in it. Success is likely to be achieved if a service user has identified his/her own health needs and the practitioner acts as a facilitator rather than an authoritative figure.

To help practitioners decide if their health promotion is ethically sound they should ask themselves the following questions:

- Will I be allowing the service user the freedom of their own choice?
- Will I respect their choice even if I do not agree with their decision?
- Will I respect all people equally?
- Will I be non-judgemental?
- Will I be telling the truth?
- Will I be doing good and preventing harm?

- Will promises and agreements be honoured by me?
- Will harm be minimised in the long term?
- Is there a degree of risk involved?

Molly   Activity 13

Molly, aged 63, has just been diagnosed with lung cancer. Her GP feels annoyed with Molly as he has been trying to encourage Molly to stop smoking for years, as she has had one chest infection after another. However, although many years ago Molly tried to stop smoking, she found she could not stop. She needed cigarettes to calm her down when she was dealing with her son who is severely disabled. He has temper tantrums through frustration and Molly finds these difficult to deal with. Her husband died suddenly eight years ago and Molly now has to do all the physical tasks of caring for her son. Sometimes she feels she would not have survived without her cigarettes.

Molly is very upset at the diagnosis but fortunately the cancer is in the earliest stages and the prognosis is good. However, when Molly goes to her GP she feels bullied into giving up smoking. She had thought she would try to give up but now feels pressured and rebellious. She feels reluctant to approach her GP for advice as she feels he is not supportive.

1. Look at the list of questions that practitioners should ask themselves to decide if their health promotion is ethically sound.

2. Do you think Molly's GP acted ethically when dealing with Molly?

3. How would you have advised the GP to handle the situation?

Prevention

Health education programmes can be categorised into three different concepts.

- Primary health education is aimed at healthy people to prevent ill health happening. Children and young people are the targets of this category with hygiene, nutrition and contraception being some of the topics covered. Primary health education also sets out to improve the quality of life by improving the quality of health.

Concepts of health education programmes

- Secondary health education is directed at people who already have health problems to try to prevent their ill health moving on to the next stage. The idea is to return people to their former state of full health. Restoring their good health could mean that the service user has to make a change in his/her lifestyle, e.g. drinking less alcohol, eating a healthier diet or taking some exercise.

- Tertiary health education is educating service users with chronic or serious health problems about how to make the most of their remaining potential for healthy living. An example of this would be teaching someone who has been paralysed in a road accident to manage their symptoms in order for them to be as self sufficient as possible. It would enable the person to get the most out of their situation and allow them to live a more 'normal' life. Rehabilitation programmes are included in this category.

Health education	Aim	Examples
Primary prevention	To prevent ill health problems arising.	Discouraging children from starting drinking, taking drugs or smoking. Advice on contraception, safe sex. Immunisation.
Secondary prevention	To prevent ill health moving on to chronic stage. To change service user's bad health habits.	Advice for drinkers to cut down on alcohol. Advice on how obese service users can lose weight. Screening programmes.
Tertiary prevention	To help people with chronic or serious health problems.	Advice for service users with chronic conditions. Advice on rehabilitation.

Summary of health education programme concepts

Case Studies — Activity 14

It is not always easy to fit service users into the primary, secondary or tertiary framework.

Examine the following case studies and decide where the service users would be best placed.

Anoushka, aged 16, very overweight, nevertheless she goes to the gym and seems fit.

Bharti, aged 42, who has been diagnosed with Multiple Sclerosis (MS).

Phil, aged 23, who binge drinks every Friday and Saturday night.

Jasper, aged 60, who has been feeling ill and leukaemia is suspected.

John who has repeated chest infections not helped by his heavy smoking.

Preventative legislation

There are many laws which help to promote good health in the UK. Many agencies, too, work hard to ensure people's health is maintained. Environmental health departments, for example, are involved in control of air pollution and they are involved in training caterers in the handling of food. They ensure the enforcement of laws relating to health and safety legislation.

Legislation, policies and charters are designed to protect the public from harm. Examples of recent Acts are:

- Manual Handling Regulations 1992;
- Health and Safety at Work Act 1974 (HASAWA);
- Control of Substances Hazardous to Health 2002 (COSHH);
- Reporting of Injuries, Diseases and Dangerous Occurrences Regulations 1995 (RIDDOR);
- Health and Safety First Aid Regulations 1981;
- Management of Health and Safety at Work Regulations 1999.

All of the above place mandatory safe practice responsibilities on both the worker and the employer. The aim is to improve the safety record thereby reducing the incidence of injury and illness. These Acts help to reduce time lost at work through injury and encourage good worker/employer relationships. Other legislation related to the

prohibition of sale of alcohol and cigarettes to minors and the wearing of seat belts also provides help. So, too, does the banning of smoking in some public areas such as shopping malls or on trains.

The National Health Service and Community Care Act (1990) also helped service users as it gave people in need the right to an assessment to see if they could be supported to live in their own homes. Being assessed as capable of living in their own home helped some service users to stay happy, therefore helping to maintain their emotional and social health.

There are various charters that set out what people can expect from, for example, the NHS – The Patients Charter. Individual hospitals, care homes, etc., have produced their own charters setting their own targets for the delivery of their services based on other previously published charters.

GP contracts are agreements between the government and General Medical Council to encourage GPs to increase their provision of screening and health promotion activities. Target payments were set for childhood immunisations and pre-school boosters, cervical cytology (smear tests) for working with patients in areas of high deprivation, for child health surveillance and for working with patients aged 75 and over.

Discussion point

Do you think it is a good idea to ban smoking in ALL public places?

At Newcastle's Royal Victoria Infirmary smoking shelters outside the main hospital building are to be dismantled as there is to be a total ban on smoking on the premises. Do you think this is a good idea?

Screening

This can be a useful preventative tool. The idea behind screening is that a disorder can be detected before any outward signs or symptoms are shown. Early detection can mean quicker recovery for the service user and because of the early treatment, the disease will not be so far advanced, therefore it should be less expensive to treat.

Antenatal screening

Screening is carried out before birth during antenatal tests:

- Amniocentesis and chorionic villus sampling for genetic disorders such as Down's syndrome, muscular dystrophy, sickle cell disease or haemophilia;
- AFP test to measure alpha-fetoprotein in blood of mother for spina bifida;
- Cross matching of blood group for ABO and rhesus + or −;
- Ultra sound scan – to show normal rate of growth.

Theory into practice

Patricia is 42 and is pregnant for the first time. Her husband's youngest brother suffers from Down's syndrome.

Which antenatal tests will Patricia need to have? These websites may be useful for you – www.babycentre.co.uk and www.babyworld.co.uk.

Baby and child screening

Babies are screened after birth and this continues through childhood:

- Blood test for thalassaemia;
- The Guthrie test for phenylketonuria;
- Ortolani-Barlow test for dysplasia of the hip;
- Hearing tests such as squeaking a toy behind the child to see if they turn towards the sound – for deafness;
- Looking at gums and teeth – for dental caries;
- Eye tests for vision using Snellen wall chart of decreasing sizes and for colour vision. Also to see if child uses eyes to follow moving object.

The Health Visitor   Activity 15

Ask a health visitor to come into your school or college and ask her about the screening tests such as hearing, vision, and general health tests she carries out on babies. Have her early detection skills ever spotted any serious problem?

Adult screening

Adults, too, can be screened:

- Blood pressure test for hypertension;
- Smear test for cervical cancer – log on to www.bbc.co.uk to see development of new vaccine which may prevent cervical cancer.

Cervical smear test

This is a test to detect abnormal changes in the cells of the cervix. If detected and treated early this can prevent cervical cancer. Smear tests should first be carried out within six months of having sexual intercourse, with a second smear test carried out within the next year. Thereafter a woman should have a smear test every three years for the rest of her life. If a woman has regular changes of sexual partners then she will require more frequent tests.

The vagina is held open with a speculum and cells are removed by a spatula and placed onto a microscope slide. They are examined and if the cells are normal, no further treatment is required. However, if there are some abnormal cells, a second smear test will be requested. If abnormal cells are still detected the person may need a colposcopy (examination of cervix using a viewing instrument) or a biopsy (removal of sample of suspect tissue).

Mammography

Mammography is an x-ray procedure for examining the breast. It is used to investigate breast lumps and to screen women for breast cancer.

Mammography allows the detection of breast tumours that are too small to be found during a physical breast examination. Successful treatment of breast cancer depends upon early detection and research has shown that mammography can significantly increase the early detection rate of cancer and can therefore reduce the death rates.

Mammography is free to women over 50 and anyone over 40 who has a family history of breast cancer. It is a simple process. It is safe as low dose x-rays are used. The breast is placed on the machine and flattened onto the x-ray plate below so as much tissue as possible may be photographed. The breast is x-rayed from different angles – above, below and from the side. Experts examine the x-ray photographs for irregular, dense masses of tissue which could indicate that a tumour is present, in which case a biopsy will be needed to determine whether the tumour is benign or malignant.

Other tests

- physical examination for testicular cancer;
- tonometry (pressure test) for glaucoma;
- other eye tests for visual defects;
- dental checks for tooth cavities and decay.

Immunisation

Immunisation, which is also called vaccination or inoculation, was one of the most successful developments in medicine. It was responsible for a drastic reduction in the number of deaths of people from potentially fatal infectious diseases such as polio and diphtheria.

A vaccine stimulates our immune system to produce antibodies without having to become infected with the virus. No vaccine gives a guaranteed 100 per cent lifelong immunity to the disease.

There are two types of immunity:

| Passive immunity | Types of immunity | Active immunity |

Types of immunity

Active immunity – this is when a vaccine triggers the immune system to produce antibodies against the disease as if the body has been infected with the disease. It teaches the person's immune system to recognise the disease and to produce the antibodies needed to fight it.

Passive immunity – this is when the body is given antibodies rather than having to produce them itself. This happens to newborn babies when antibodies are passed to them from their mother via the placenta. A baby is protected from mumps, measles and rubella for up to a year after birth.

That is why the MMR is given to a child just after his/her first birthday.

Vaccine production is monitored by the Health Protection Agency.

Vaccines are made by producing a **pathogen** which is an organism that produces the disease. Most bacteria can be cultivated on **agar** plates. **Viruses** are made by infecting cells grown in tissue culture.

The pathogen must then be altered so it does not cause the disease. This could be achieved by:

- Weakening or **attenuating** the pathogen by growing it repeatedly to select a strain which would not cause complications of the natural disease. Polio and MMR vaccines are **attenuated**;
- Removing the part of the pathogen that causes the immune response and using this in the vaccine. The Hib vaccine is made this way;
- Killing the pathogen by heating it or by using **formalin**. The whooping cough virus is made in this way. The treated pathogen can then be mixed with other components (the **adjuvant**, stabilisers and preservatives) to produce a dose of vaccine.

Information on immunisation was from the NHS website.

Full immunisation schedule

When to immunise	What is given	How it is given
2, 3 & 4 months old	Diphtheria, tetanus, pertussis (whooping cough), polio and Hib (DTaP/IPV/Hib)	One injection
	MenC	One injection
Around 13 months old	Measles, mumps and rubella (MMR)	One injection

When to immunise	What is given	How it is given
3 years and 4 months to 5 years old	Diphtheria, tetanus, pertussis (whooping cough) and polio (dTaP/IPV or DTaP/IPV)	One injection
	Measles, mumps and rubella (MMR)	One injection
13 to 18 years old	Diphtheria, tetanus, polio (Td/IPV)	One injection

Health promotion is designed and implemented for a variety of reasons including:

- to prevent disease
- to improve health and well being
- to ensure people are well informed and able to make choices
- to change behaviour
- to encourage the use of preventative methods
- to increase the skills and confidence required by individuals to take control of factors influencing their health
- to change policies and environments to facilitate healthy choices
- to address the determinants of health such as housing, poverty, etc.

As you observed from the diagram earlier on in this unit, there are many different health and care professionals who have a duty to develop and provide health education messages for their individuals. Some of those that have a major health promotion responsibility are:

- **Health education specialists** – this is probably your local health promotion team who will work as part of the Public Health department. Health promotion teams strive to improve health for people who live and work in their areas with the specific aim of reducing inequalities in health. This is achieved by working in partnership to meet national and local health targets. The team will use specialist knowledge good skills to lead and co-ordinate health promotion programmes in conjunction with their PCT and other partners across their area. They will also provide advice, training

courses and displays on health initiatives. Clinics, schools and other interested organisations will be able to borrow resources such as health education books, CD/DVDs, posters and leaflets free of charge. The health promotion teams will often have health screening such as measuring blood pressure and testing fitness, etc., in local shopping centres. This is to alert people to possible problems, e.g. being overweight or unfit – advice would then be given if the service user wanted it.

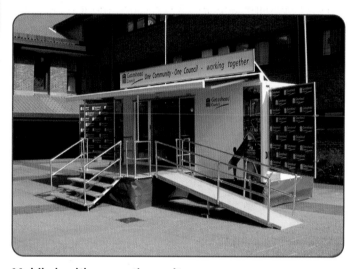

Mobile health promotion unit

- **Health visitors** work within the Primary Care Team. Their main role is one of providing health education to the people they advise. Most of their work is with families, babies and young children and they are often the main source of health information for these groups. Health visitors often provide advice on feeding and weaning to parents but also to a wider audience during campaigns. Health visitors concentrate on well people and their work is concerned with the prevention of illness rather than treating it. Health visitors visit service users on their own initiative, even if they have not had a request for help. They work as part of a multi-disciplinary team along with the GP, community nurse, practice nurse and community midwife.

- **Community nurses** are an important part of the Primary Care Team. They are responsible for assessing, implementing and evaluating the nursing requirements of service users, who are supported, to live in their own homes. They have an important role in the health education of people in the community.

- **Environmental health officers** are responsible for environmental health, that is, they deal with the physical elements in the environment which could threaten health. They have far-reaching roles from running food hygiene courses to checking over commercial restaurants, takeaways, etc., to ensure the kitchens are following legislation to meet food safety. Pollution, too, is part of their remit, as is pest control, e.g. rats, mice and cockroaches. They will investigate air and noise pollution. Legislation gives power to Environmental Health departments to take advisory and legal action on behalf of people who live or work in the area. They have the power to close down food businesses that operate outside the law and endanger people's health with their unhygienic practices. The scope for health promotion by these departments is very wide. As new threats to the environment appear, their portfolio becomes even more diverse.

- **GPs** are part of the Primary Care Team. GPs are encouraged by the government and General Medical Council to increase their provision of screening and health promotion activities. They have targets (with payments) for immunisations, cervical cytology, for working with patients in areas of high deprivation, for child health surveillance and for working with patients over 75. Most GPs work in partnership with other GPs in a Health Centre where they run antenatal clinics, family planning clinics, coronary risk clinics and well-woman/man clinics.

Skills used by professional care workers

- Communication skills
- Interpersonal skills
- Problem solving
- Listening
- Skills used by professional care workers
- Mathematical skills
- Practical skills
- Scientific skills

Discussion point

How would each of the care professionals given above use each of the skills? What other skills could they use?

Skills can be acquired or learnt. It is often helpful if an individual has some of the skills at a basic level as these can be developed to a higher standard with training and experience.

Qualities

Qualities are often part of an individual's genetic make up and are inherited from parents or grandparents, for example. Qualities can also develop as a result of factors that have influenced an individual's development, for example income, social class or size of family.

Each individual is unique and has qualities that contribute to their character. Qualities reflect the things that are important to an individual and the things they value. For example, a person who is patient and willing to share may have been part of a large family and may have spent time with siblings helping them with dressing, learning and leisure activities.

caring reliable honest sharing patience cheerful calmness understanding, etc. flexible

Discussion point

How can skills and qualities work together to help a professional care worker to be effective in their role?

Theory into practice

Invite an Environmental Health Officer into school/college to talk about the various aspects of his/her job. What impact does s/he feel s/he has on the local area? Does s/he feel that s/he makes a contribution to health education?

Assessment activity (AO2)

Key workers
CASE STUDY

1 Choose **two** key workers from the following list:
- Health education specialist
- Health visitor
- School nurse
- Community nurse
- Environmental health officer
- GP.

Seek an interview with the chosen key workers or invite them to the centre. Ask them for a thorough description of their job role in promoting health.

2 Ask the chosen professionals about the skills and qualities they require in order to meet the needs of service users.

3 a Question the professionals about **two** preventative measures they use. Analyse the measures given.

   b Explain the reasons for the preventative measures which are applied and see how each measure meets the needs of the individuals within their setting.

3.2.3 Factors affecting health and well being

Socio-economic conditions Cultural conditions Environmental conditions

Health Work Housing

Agriculture Social and community networks Education

Living and working conditions Lifestyle factors Unemployment

Age Sex Constitutional factors

Many different factors affect health and well being, it is not just luck. Who your parents are, the genes you have inherited, country you were born in, etc.,

will all contribute to you and your health. For example, if you were born to a poor family in Ethiopia in times of a famine you would be very lucky to survive.

Attitudes and prejudices can affect health as service users are sometimes too afraid to go to see their GP. It could be because they are scared they will be told that the lump they have found is an inoperable tumour. Or another reason could be fear of removing their clothes because the lump is in an 'embarrassing' place. They may also feel that they are creating a fuss about nothing and if they ignore it they think it might disappear. Another person may feel that if they go to the doctor about a skin lesion, they will be lectured to give up the sun bed. A lot depends on our attitude to health.

Lifestyle choices are a big factor in health. With diet it is not always as simple as choice. Some people would love to have the money to buy 'healthy' foods but if they are on low incomes they tend to buy foods rich in fat and carbohydrate which have a high satiety level. The Acheson report noted that people in the lower socio-economic groups:

- were more likely to be obese which would give them a higher risk of poor health
- had lower birth weights than in the higher groups which is linked to cardiovascular disease in later life
- were less likely to breast feed their babies thereby denying them protection from infection
- tended to eat more processed foods containing more salt and fat which could increase the risk of cardiovascular disease
- ate less fruit and vegetables and less food rich in dietary fibre therefore having a lower intake of anti-oxidant and other vitamins.

But Acheson also noted that 'healthy' food was more expensive. Perhaps if 'healthy' food was available at reasonable prices, more people in lower socio-economic groups could afford to buy it. People often have to keep to a strict budget for food and can only buy what they can afford. Bigger packs of foodstuffs, which are better value for money, are not an option because of the amount of money which would be removed from that week's budget. Poor nutrition has a direct link to health.

Substance abuse such as smoking is again prevalent in the lower socio-economic groups. According to the Acheson report the poorer the person the more likely they are to smoke. In 1996 Acheson found that 26% of men and 28% of women smoked. However, only 2% of professional men and 11% of professional women compared to 41% of unskilled men and 36% of unskilled women smoked. Richer people also smoked fewer cigarettes and were less likely to be addicted. This could be because richer people may not have as great a need for an escape from their problems. Sometimes, people in the lower socio-economic groups find that smoking relieves stress and helps people cope with their lifestyles. They feel that smoking is all they have got.

Drinking, too, can help people forget and feel happy for a while. This is why some homeless people drink, 'as it helps you forget you're sleeping on the streets'. Substance abuse such as glue sniffing can also help people to forget. However, any substance abuse is dangerous and can lead to bigger problems within a short period of time: ill health certainly and lack of food and money as people struggle to find their next fix.

Health practices can be as straightforward as brushing your teeth thoroughly and making sure you visit the dentist every six months for a check up. All screening procedures should be taken up as they can prevent pain and ill health in the future. Again, Acheson noted that it was the poorer communities, who were at most risk of ill health, who had the worst access to prevention services such as screening programmes, health promotion and immunisation.

Recreational activities are essential for good health. Some activities are free of charge, for example walking. Others such as joining a gym, golf club or squash club need money. However, not all recreational activities are physical activities – going to the cinema or out for a meal can be recreational, as could any hobby. If money is tight it can be very difficult to afford any recreational pastimes. Recreational activities help people to relax and de-stress. People who cannot afford to enjoy any recreation could feel that they are never allowed an opportunity to get 'away from it all' thereby denying them the opportunity to 'recharge their batteries'.

Social factors include family, social class and culture. A family has a lot of influence over an individual – a person could be born having inherited a genetic disease. A person born into a single-parent household could be in a low socio-economic group. If born into a deprived background the person could live in substandard housing with poor quality food through lack of money. A family will socialise a child: the way a person thinks and

behaves will be related to the way they have been brought up. Attitudes to health are usually learned, e.g. if parents are afraid to go to the dentist it is very likely that their child will be afraid also. The physical health of an individual is related to their family's economic situation, eating habits and type of housing.

Social class – As already observed in current government initiatives, the higher the social class the fewer the deaths from diseases such as lung disease, CHD and so on. It has been argued (by Argyle in 1987) that middle-class people have made more use of preventative health services such as cervical screening and vaccination programmes than the lower socio-economic groups. Acheson's report highlighted the fact that access to health care and ill health prevention was also related to class. Obviously nutrition and housing conditions, too, would be better for the higher socio-economic groups and this would contribute as would education, size of family and amount of disposable income. Money for recreation and holidays would improve the quality of life for the higher socio-economic groups creating the 'feel good' factor.

Culture refers to the beliefs, values and ways of behaving shared by members of the community or a particular group or society. Obviously culture can affect people's views of health. For example, in his report Acheson commented that Asian women were not taking up the opportunity to have cervical screening as there was a lack of access to female practitioners. A person's culture can forbid him or her to drink alcohol, have sexual intercourse before marriage or demand that the person wears certain items of clothing.

People from certain cultures can impose certain behaviours on others in their group. For example, young people growing up in a binge drinking culture think that they have to do the same to be accepted by the others.

Research has shown that there are 6.4 million people making up the black and ethnic minority in Britain. South Asians have the largest ethnic minority group representing just over 4% of the population (2001 Census):

Indian (1.8%)	Pakistani (1.3%)
Bangladeshi (0.5%)	other Asians (0.4%)

Disadvantage and discrimination characterise the treatment these people receive, especially in health and health care. They experience poorer health, have reduced life expectancy and have greater problems accessing health services than the majority of the white population. There is very little research into the health problems, e.g. sickle cell or the lassaemia of people from different ethnic groups. Health promotion campaigns tend to emphasise the need for people of ethnic origin to adapt to British culture in order to improve their health. The availability of information about health services is sometimes presented with lack of cultural sensitivity. Communication can also be a problem.

Theory into practice

Find out which other cultural practices could have some bearing on a person's health.

Environmental factors – these can be:

Pollution – the Department of Health recognises that pollution causes ill health and this is reiterated in the Acheson Report (1998). Smog disappeared with the Clean Air Acts but exhaust fumes from cars, buses, etc., cause problems especially for people with respiratory difficulties. Power stations, factories and waste products from gas fires and central heating also cause air pollution.

Of course, pollution is not just air pollution, there is also noise pollution, land pollution and water pollution, which can all be just as injurious to health. Noise pollution, e.g. very loud music or a dog barking continuously day and night, can cause stress. Landfill sites, too, can cause water and land pollution especially if toxic or clinical waste is buried. Opencast mining can cause noise and air pollution.

Discussion point

Have you experienced pollution of any type? Have you tried to sleep when there has been a lot of noise outside? Imagine if this went on for weeks! Is there a landfill site near you? If so, did people object to its presence?

Housing – obviously housing makes a big difference to health, especially if it is damp and poorly heated. Acheson reports that such housing 'increases the prevalence of allergic and inflammatory lung diseases, such as asthma'. He goes on to say that such households also have higher incidences of accidents. Such housing is likely to be inhabited by the lower socio-economic groups. People will probably be in built-up areas where the air is polluted by factories or a build-up of traffic. If the area is run down there could be fear of crime. Several families could share the house to cut costs and this would lead to overcrowding and possible insanitary conditions. Also there could be vandalism in the area. All of these factors could lead to stress, especially if someone was bringing up a child in this environment.

In 1995 the Rowntree Report stated that because of high levels of crime, unemployment, poverty and vandalism, some areas were especially stressful to live in.

Think it over

See if you can watch the film 'Cathy Come Home' which examined how people became homeless and the type of accommodation they were offered. If there is a Big Issue office in the town nearest to you ask if the Officer-in-Charge would be willing to talk to your group about homelessness.

Workplace health – The Health and Safety at Work Act (1974) states that it is the duty of every employer to ensure, as far as is reasonably practicable, the health, safety and welfare at work of all his/her employees. This Act did not replace existing legislation so there are a number of Acts such as The Factories Act, The Office, Shop and Railway Premises Act and The Shop Act which try to ensure employees are kept safe and healthy. The Health and Safety Commission (HSC) is responsible for putting the principles of health and safety law into practice. The Health and Safety Executive (HSE) is the enforcement body appointed by the HSC to help with carrying out duties. Employees, too, have to look after their own health and safety, for example by wearing hard hats if they are advised to do so.

Control of Substances Hazardous to Health 1988 (COSHH) applies to every workplace. The Reporting of Injuries, Diseases and Dangerous Occurrences Regulations 1985 (RIDDOR) also applies to every workplace. See Unit 4 for more information.

It must be recognised that the lower socio-economic groups are more at risk from accidental death than people in the higher groups. They are more likely to work with toxic chemicals, up scaffolding or have jobs which are injurious to health.

Financial factors especially **income** play a big part in the quality of life available to that person. Whatever a person earns each week will be used to feed, clothe and house the family. According to 'Opportunity for All' (2004), a Department of Work and Pensions paper, between 1998/99 and 2002/03, the number of children in low-income households fell by 600,000 after housing costs were taken into consideration. The proportion of children living in workless households has fallen by around 300,000 since 1997. The level of financial support has increased significantly as a result of tax and benefit reforms, with families in the poorest fifth of the population an average of £3,000 per year better off in real terms. All this is good news as living on a low income has an impact on the development of children and their health. Often parents are stressed because they are struggling to pay bills, to buy food and to maintain their poor standard of living.

Physical factors – additional needs could be a physical or learning disability which affects the way the person with disability is treated. Some people would view a person with a disability as unhealthy because they would believe that there is no cure for most disabilities. People with disabilities are often categorised by their disability. Although a person with a disability may feel fine, they may need assistance in getting out of bed and getting dressed. This could impact on their mental health as they may feel disempowered by their inability to be independent. Similarly, if it is a lot of effort for them to go to the cinema or go onto a train, they could feel that it is not worth the effort involved. People sometimes stereotype and treat all people with a disability as if they were children. People who have disabilities have often had their disability since birth, so they do not feel unhealthy because of it. However, they may feel unhealthy because they cannot exercise because of their disability. People with learning difficulties may not be able to make choices about their health or lifestyle. Sometimes they have to rely on carers to make choices for them.

Will   Activity 17

Will is 42 years of age. He has severe learning disabilities and has recently moved into residential care as his father died and he has no one to look after him. His key worker, Susie, has decided that Will is overweight and needs to cut out sweets, chocolate, etc., which he loves. Portions of puddings and cakes are reduced. Will is very upset and does not understand what has happened as nothing has been discussed with him. Susie did give Will a booklet to read.

1 Should Will's key worker have acted in the way she did?

2 Did she act in an ethical manner?

3 How would you approach the matter of Will's weight?

Sometimes people with learning disabilities have difficulty reading and understanding the information given to them. There are some specific resources available for people with learning disabilities. Carers should ensure these resources are available to their service users and be prepared to discuss them and ensure they understand the information.

Health promotion   Activity 18

1 Go to your Health Promotion Unit or Health Centre and pick up some health care leaflets. How accessible do you think these are for someone with a learning disability?

2 Ask if there are any leaflets available for someone with a learning disability.

3 If available, is this leaflet easier to understand?

Try this out

How physically accessible is your local Health Centre or chemist?

Borrow a wheelchair from a local residential home and see if you can manoeuvre your way around. Whilst you have the wheelchair, see if a person with a physical disability who wants to keep fit could have access to your local gym.

Assessment activity (AO3)

CASE STUDY

1   Choose two factors which can affect health and well being. Research each one thoroughly using both primary and secondary evidence. The evidence should include a bibliography, and should be referenced within the text.

2   Explain **two** ways in which an individual's quality of life can be affected by ill health.

3.2.4 Health promotion

It is essential to understand the different approaches (models) that can be used when planning and carrying out health promotion campaigns, to include:

- the preventative model – probably the most common method
- the empowerment model – seeks to encourage individuals to take control of their own health, and occasionally the environment, as well as the choices they make. Also known as client-centred approach
- the educational approach – seeks to inform and educate to promote health practices
- the medical directed approach – used to work with individuals to identify if the service user is free from medically defined disease
- the use of fear as an approach – increasing in popularity, particularly when used on television, e.g. using vivid images of the consequences of unhealthy lifestyle choices to instil fear into those who watch.

All of the above models are used for health promotion – the list is not exhaustive as there are other approaches. Each model has its own value and no one is any better or worse than the others. The choice of approach depends on various factors such as the audience targeted for the health promotion and also their perceived needs. The health promoter's experience, too, needs to be taken into account, e.g. it is no good deciding to adopt the medical model of health, if the health promoter is not in the medical profession, as the service user has to be declared free from a medically defined disease!

The preventative model

Behaviour change is an alternative name for this model. The idea behind it is to change people's behaviour and their attitudes so they will adopt a healthier lifestyle. Individuals would be taught how to give up smoking, how to follow a healthy eating plan, take more exercise or cut down on the amount they drink. Service users would be encouraged to follow healthy guidelines. This model is used by health promoters who feel they have people's best interests at heart. They also feel that the service user's health would benefit as a result of following their advice.

The empowerment model

Another name for this model is the client-directed approach. Service users are given information about the health topic in which they express an interest. On the basis of this given information they are then able to make a decision. The decision will be made independently as the service user now feels well informed and well able to make a judgement.

Health promoters using this model will be facilitators who will help service users to identify their worries and help them to gain the knowledge and skills necessary to bring about change. Self empowerment is crucial to this model. Health promoters treat the service users as people who have worthwhile skills and experience different but equal to their own. It is their right to make health decisions and to be in charge of their own lives. Service users are seen as the main change agents and are more than equal partners in the process.

The educational model

This is sometimes called the informative approach. The idea behind this model is that if the service user is given enough information about a health issue, it will allow them to make an informed decision about their lifestyle.

Service users' rights to make their own decisions are respected but if the health promoter feels any issues need to be tackled to raise awareness then they will bring that issue to the service users' attention. Their aim is to inform in order to promote health practices which are in the service users' best interests.

The medical model

This is also known as the interventionist model. The emphasis of this is upon the detection and prevention of a medically defined disease. Service users are encouraged to take advantage of medical prevention services such as smear tests or immunisation. A doctor or a nurse would persuade the service user to have the test best suited to their needs.

As this method relies on medical intervention the health promoter would be medically trained.

Use of fear as an approach

As the name suggests, this model uses fear to try to scare service users to adopt a healthier lifestyle. Sometimes the fear is overwhelming for some of the targeted audience and some service users may switch off their television and so miss the message.

An example is the driver who stays for an extra drink and although not drunk loses control of his vehicle and kills a child. Television seems to be the latest preferred medium.

Scare tactics will be used by the health promoter with the message of 'this could happen to you if you have an extra drink'. No details are spared – viewers see the child being hit by the car and the devastating effects on the driver and the child's family.

Approach	Aim	Example
Educational/ Informative	To inform and educate to promote health practices.	Service user is given information about obesity. They have to decide on what they are going to eat.
Medical/ Interventionist	To check service user is free from medically defined disease, e.g. CHD.	Freedom from diseases such as CHD or cancer by seeking medical intervention early on.
Use of fear	To show images of consequences of unhealthy lifestyle to frighten service user into choosing a healthier lifestyle.	Television is used as a medium to show someone dying from lung cancer as a result of smoking.

Theory into practice

Watch one of these 'fear as an approach' adverts. Do you think they are effective in delivering their message?

Approach	Aim	Example
Preventative/ behaviour change	To encourage service users to change their behaviour.	Encourage service user to lose weight by eating more fruit and vegetables and taking more exercise. Encouraging children into healthy eating at an early age.
Empowerment/ client-directed approach	To encourage service users to take control of their own health.	Service user is advised to give up eating chocolate to help lose weight but decides to take up exercising and walking. Decision empowers service user but is still improving health and is supported by health promoter.

Different methods of communication in health promotion campaigns

Health promotion campaigns can succeed or fail depending on the method of communication chosen to get the message across to the service users.

Mass media methods of transmitting health promotion materials

The above diagram gives the main methods mass media can employ when promoting health.

Theory into practice

Examine some current health promotion campaigns (such as 'Breast is Best'). Which health promotion approaches do they use? Are they effective? Would another approach have been more effective?

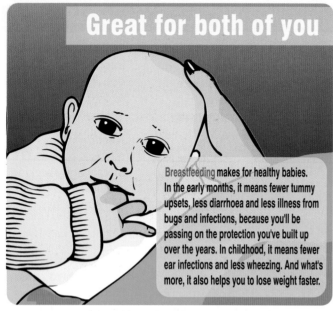

Great for both of you

Breastfeeding makes for healthy babies. In the early months, it means fewer tummy upsets, less diarrhoea and less illness from bugs and infections, because you'll be passing on the protection you've built up over the years. In childhood, it means fewer ear infections and less wheezing. And what's more, it also helps you to lose weight faster.

Breast is best

Mass media is used widely for promoting health but it does have its limitations. Although many people might see them; because there is no interpersonal communication, some people ignore the message. In the case of television they might switch off. With any written message there could be a problem with language barriers or literacy. However, if the message is simple and is repeated often enough it can be persuasive, e.g., 'Breast is Best' was a successful campaign on television.

The following chart lists advantages and disadvantages of the various presentation methods.

Method	Advantages	Disadvantages
Videos	• Suitable for small/medium audience • Can be stopped and started to facilitate discussion • Can convey reality • Educational programmes can be recorded for later	• Requires power supply • Can break down • TV/Video needed • Small screen could limit audience
Whiteboard	• Cheap and usually available • Good for highlighting main points • Can be re-used • Cannot break down	• Limited – can be used for groups up to 20 • Must have correct pens or could damage board
Posters	• Cheap, easy to make • Can give other help to people, e.g. phone numbers • Can raise awareness of health issues	• Easily damaged • Soon loses impact
Flipcharts	• Can be prepared in advance • Easily portable • Nothing to break down • Cheap	• Limited to max 20 people • Easy to damage paper
Computer slides	• Can be projected onto large screen • Can be prepared in advance • Can have sound effects and be animated	• Equipment is expensive • Can break down • Requires electricity supply
Overhead projector transparencies	• Equipment widely available • Can be prepared in advance • Can be used with any sized audience • Cheap to buy and hand produce	• Can break down • Requires electricity supply
Leaflets, handouts and other written materials.	• Reduce need for note taking • Information can be shared with others later • Cheap to produce • Service user can read afterwards at own pace • Can refer service users to other information, e.g. phone numbers or websites	• Can end up thrown away if not read • Easily lost • Not durable • Need literacy skills

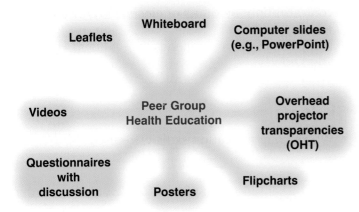

Peer group methods of transmitting health promotion materials

Peer group education can be highly effective because of the personal touch. Campaigns are designed for a particular group and are therefore individualised for that chosen group. People can ask questions, receive answers and hear other people's ideas. There is interpersonal interaction. Peer group health presenters must be well rehearsed and aware of their limitations – if they do not know the answer to a question it is better to be honest and say so. Young children are often very keen to listen to students from 'the big school'.

Planning a health promotion campaign

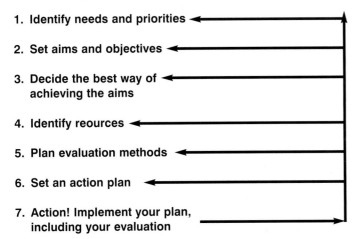

Planning and evaluating health promotion. (Reproduced from Ewles & Simnett, 'Promoting Health')

Ewles and Simnett produced a seven-stage plan which is very useful when planning any health promotion campaign. When identifying the needs and priorities, the local health promotion team could make some suggestions which could link into the national targets. Or needs and priorities could

link into the school/college's health promotion targets. If a recent campaign is chosen then the health promotion unit will be able to help with promotion materials such as posters, badges, etc.

Each campaign must have a definite focus – safe sex could be chosen if there is a high proportion of under age pregnancies in the area.

Aims and objectives must be set. These are often confused as people find it difficult to differentiate between them. The aim is the overall purpose or mission whilst the objectives set out quite clearly how the aim will be met. For example, if the aim was to reduce teenage pregnancies some of the objectives could be to:

- raise awareness of number of teenage pregnancies in the area and the part individuals could play in reducing the risk of teenage pregnancies
- raise awareness about the risk of STI as well as pregnancy
- inform students about the different ways of accessing advice about contraceptives and how to obtain them.

Aims and objectives

Objectives set must be SMART

Specific	must be clear and not vague
Measurable	at end of campaign has objective been achieved or not?
Achievable	must have achievable target
Relevant	focused on aim within broad aims
Timed	must have agreed timescale to deliver objectives

The model of delivery must meet the service users' needs.

Intended and unintended outcomes

Were the intended outcomes achieved? For example, if you were hoping to educate Year 5 about how to deal with bullying (trying to prevent mental health problems), did they understand your message? How do you know?

Unintended outcomes could be that at the end of the health promotion session a child comes to you for help because they are being abused at home by a parent.

Preset criteria

This can be judged by what you have achieved (outcome) and whether the aims and objectives you set were achieved. For example, if your campaign was to educate students on the different methods of contraception, could they work out which methods would be suitable for them and why? How do you know this?

Evaluation

This involves:

- Reflection – you need to review all areas of your work from the beginning of the planning stage to the end of the campaign.
- Analysis – all aspects of your performance need to be looked at in great detail. What did you do well? Which areas could stand some improvement?
- Make informed decisions – this is using your understanding and knowledge to help make a judgement.
- Plan for improvement – what would you do differently next time? How would you go about changing your original plan to allow for your improvements?

You must evaluate:

- your own performance
- the benefits to the individual
- skills used
- quality measures, e.g. time and cost.

The following points are NOT a definitive list.

Own performance

- What did you do well? Look for positive aspects.
- What would you change the next time? Look for constructive ways forward.
- How could you improve?
- What advice would you give someone who was going to repeat your campaign?

Benefits to the individual

- Did you extend the individual's knowledge?
- Would individuals leave the session feeling more confident about the topic delivered, e.g. bullying,

contraception, amounts of alcohol in a double whisky, etc.?
- Did you succeed in engaging individuals? How do you know?
- What was the impact of the campaign?

Skills used

- Which communication skills were used?
- Was personal interaction satisfactory?
- Was presentation well rehearsed?
- Was presentation imaginative and geared towards service users' needs?
- Were ICT skills deployed?

Quality measures

- Did campaign offer good value in terms of time and money spent?
- Did outcomes justify the cost?

Assessment activity (AO4)

CASE STUDY

1 Choose a topic for the small-scale health promotion campaign. It is a good idea to choose a topic which is from the Department of Health's Health Promotion Events. To check, go to www.dh.gov.uk/news. If the topic is current it will be easy to pick up health promotion materials such as posters, leaflets, etc.

2 a Produce a detailed plan which breaks down each main task into smaller parts. There must be aims, objectives, intended and unintended outcomes, cost, time, etc.

   b Name and explain the approach to be used when planning and carrying out the health promotion campaign.

3 Carry out the health promotion campaign independently.

4 Evaluate own performance, showing the ability to reflect on achievements in the health promotion campaign. Analysis will include evidence of the success of the campaign, measured against preset criteria.

Unit 4 Health and Safety in Care Settings

Contents

About this unit

Within this unit you will investigate:

- the influence of current legislation on safe practice in care settings
- safety and security
- safe moving and handling techniques
- contribution to infection control.

Introducing this unit

Providing a safe and secure environment is important in any setting. However, in a setting which offers care, it is especially crucial as vulnerable service users could be placed at risk. Vulnerable service users include babies, young children, people with additional needs and older service users. The Health and Safety at Work Act 1974 is the main act which covers health, safety and security in all places where people work including all care settings.

It is essential to understand the importance of maintaining safety and security in health, care and early years settings. Staff need to be aware of how accidents and breaches of security can happen. Accidents and breaches of security can be reduced if staff keep to any policies and procedures which may be in place within their setting.

An employer has the responsibility to examine and assess all procedures which take place in the working environment and involve risk. All risks must be minimised. Moving and handling service users involves risk. The Manual Handling Operations Regulations 1992 were introduced to reduce the numbers of injuries due to moving and handling.

When working with vulnerable service users in care settings, it is vital that procedures are followed to prevent the spread of infection. If you look in a recent newspaper you will find reports of deaths due to the spread of the 'Superbug' or MRSA (methicillin-resistant staphylococcus aureus). Simple 'standard precautions' if followed correctly, could prevent deaths caused by 'cross infection'.

Toxic material

Warning sign

Smoking and naked flames forbidden

Prohibition sign

Safety helmet must be worn

Mandatory sign

First-aid post

Safe condition sign

4.2.1 Current legislation on safe practice in care settings

In the UK the Health and Safety Executive (HSE) is the main body responsible for enforcing legislation and providing guidance on health and safety in the workplace. HSE covers offices, factories, building sites, mines, quarries, fairgrounds, railways, chemical plants, offshore and nuclear installations, schools and hospitals (see below).

Fairgrounds

Railways   Offices

Chemical plants

Offshore installations

Factories

HSE   Building sites

Schools   Mines

Hospitals   Quarries

Nuclear installations

HSE covers all the above workplaces

The HSE employs health and safety enforcement officers who can:

- enter premises
- conduct investigations
- take samples and photographs
- ask questions
- give advice
- issue instructions that must be carried out by law
- initiate a prosecution
- inspect documents
- take photographs
- take measurements
- issue Improvement and Prohibition Notices.

Until the formation of the Health and Safety Executive for Northern Ireland in 1999, enforcement in the province was undertaken by the Health and Safety Inspectorate and the Health and Safety Agency.

The main Act relating to health and safety at work is the Health and Safety at Work Act 1974 in England, Wales and Scotland and the Health and Safety at Work Order 1978 in Northern Ireland. These Acts cover health and safety in places of work and lay down the minimum standards required by law. They provide the framework for a safe working environment.

An Act is a law passed by parliament and you can be prosecuted if you do not comply with it. If you are found guilty you can be fined or sent to jail.

The Health and Safety at Work Act is the umbrella legislation under which other regulations are made. These regulations relate to specific activities such as the management of health and safety, lifting and handling, reporting of accidents, etc. Laws which will most likely affect care provision feature in the diagram below.

Health and Safety (First Aid) Regulations 1981

Management of Health and Safety at Work Regulations 1992

Control of Substances Hazardous to Health 1994 (COSHH)

Health and Safety at Work Act 1974

Manual Handling Operations Regulations 1992

Fire Precautions Regulations 1999

Safety Signs and Signals 1996

Reporting of Injury, Disease and Dangerous Occurences Regulations 1995 (RIDDOR)

Lifting Operations and Lifting Equipment Regulations 1998 (LOLER)

Health and Safety at Work – related Acts

Under the HASAWA/HSW (Health and Safety at Work Act 1974) EMPLOYERS must:

- ensure the health and safety of their employees
- provide and maintain equipment and work systems which are safe
- deal with substances such as chemicals safely
- provide a written health and safety policy statement when employing five or more people
- provide adequate information and training to enable employees to carry out work safely.

They must also ensure that visitors, outside workers and members of the public are not put at unnecessary risk.

EMPLOYEES must:

- take care of their own health and safety at work
- take care of the health and safety of others
- co-operate with their employer
- not misuse or interfere with anything provided for health and safety purposes.

However, both employer and employee must work together to safeguard the health and safety of anyone who is visiting or working on the premises.

Residential premises are workplaces as well as home to vulnerable service users. Employers in residential settings must be careful to ensure that meeting the legal requirements does not override their duty to provide a pleasant home for the service user.

Summary HASAWA

Designed to reduce the number of accidents to employers, employees and members of the public in the workplace, this Act is the key piece of health and safety legislation.

You can see from HASAWA that the intention was to make places of work safer for everyone. However, service users, too, are protected by this Act as employers should assess the vulnerability and competence of each service user on a regular basis. Failure to update assessments could endanger the service user and constitute a breach of legislation.

Another important Act is the Management of Health and Safety at Work Regulations 1992 amended in 1994 and 1999. These regulations stated that employers had to carry out risk assessment (which will be explained fully in AO2 on page 118). The main points of the regulations are:

EMPLOYERS must:

- assess risks to staff and visitors
- take action to eliminate or minimise risks
- appoint a competent person(s) to help meet the requirements
- establish procedures to deal with imminent danger
- provide all staff (including temporary staff) with any health and safety information/training which may be required
- have written procedures for appropriate health and safety arrangements.

In accordance with these regulations EMPLOYEES must:

- work to any training, instructions, policies and procedures given by their employer
- report any situations which they believe to be unsafe. For example, reporting an extractor fan that is not working in a bathroom, which means there is excess condensation which has pooled on the tiled floor causing danger of slipping for both care workers and service users.

As you can see, the main purpose of the Regulations is to ensure that employers carry out regular risk assessments thereby taking care of employees, service users living in the home or anyone entering the home. If an employer can see a hazard which could lead to an accident then s/he has a duty to deal with it. Failure to do so could lead to prosecution as the employer would be in breach of the Act. An example of this could be a loose handrail which could cause an older infirm service user to lose balance and fall down the stairs.

Summary of Management of Health and Safety at Work Regulations

These Regulations were designed to add risk assessment to employers' duties.

Reporting of Injuries, Diseases and Dangerous Occurrences Regulations 1995 (RIDDOR)

There is a requirement to report major accidents and incidents which have happened in the workplace. **Notifiable** diseases, too, have to be reported.

Reporting accidents, injuries, ill health and dangerous occurrences is a legal requirement. You must report these to the Incident Contact Centre (ICC) in Caerphilly (if you are in the UK).

RIDDOR states that EMPLOYERS must report:

- deaths
- major injuries
- accidents resulting in more than three days off work
- diseases
- dangerous occurrences.

Reportable major injuries covers a wide range including:

- amputations
- loss of sight
- fracture other than to fingers or toes
- dislocation of shoulder, hip, spine or knee
- injury resulting from electric shock or burn leading to unconsciousness or admittance to hospital
- chemical/hot metal burn to eye
- unconsciousness caused by **asphyxia** or exposure to a harmful substance or biological agent
- acute illness arising from absorption of any substance by inhalation, **ingestion** or through the skin
- acute illness due to exposure to biological agent, toxins or infected material.

Examples of accidents to service users:

Reportable	Non-reportable
A confused service user walks through a single pane glass door, assessed as needing warning stickers. Severe cuts result.	An active service user falls down outside and breaks an arm. No obstructions or defects were to blame.
An unattended frail service user falls whilst trying to get out of the bath and hits head on bath, causing loss of consciousness. Care plan stated service user must be attended when in bath/shower.	Service user pushes another service user over when walking in garden.

Reportable diseases include:

- poisonings, e.g. by contact with chemicals
- skin diseases, e.g. skin cancer, **dermatitis**
- lung disease, e.g. asthma as a result of working with dangerous substances or asbestosis as a result of working with **asbestos**
- other conditions such as certain musculoskeletal disorders, e.g. repetitive strain injury.

As well as the above, the final category of reportable diseases includes infectious diseases. The diseases given in the following diagram are examples of reportable or notifiable diseases. It is important that such diseases are reported to the relevant medical authorities so that carers, service users and the wider community can be protected.

Examples of diseases:

Typhoid
Plague
Anthrax
Whooping cough
Measles
Mumps
Examples of reportable infectious disease
Diphtheria
Meningitis
Food poisoning
Tetanus
Scarlet fever
Smallpox
Tuberculosis
Viral hepatitis

Reportable infectious diseases

In a care setting with vulnerable people it is essential to identify, monitor and manage possible epidemics of infectious diseases.

Examples of diseases:

Reportable	Non-reportable
A nursery nurse contracts meningitis after caring for ill children in nursery.	A nursery nurse catches flu, which is widespread in the nursery.
A care assistant develops dermatitis after wearing rubber gloves whilst washing bedpans in the sluice.	A care assistant has developed dermatitis that is unrelated to work.

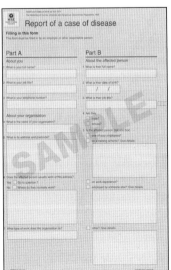

Report of a case of a disease

Report of an injury or dangerous occurrence

If a reportable disease, the records should include:

- date of diagnosis of disease
- name and occupation of person affected
- name and nature of disease
- date and method of reporting to enforcing authority.

Under RIDDOR a dangerous occurrence must be reported immediately even if it does not result in a reportable injury, e.g. a hoist, which should bear the weight of a service user, topples over. Fortunately, the service user is unhurt.

Examples of HSE injury and dangerous occurrence reports can be found on the previous page.

Record keeping

A record must be kept of any reportable injury, disease or dangerous occurrence for three years from date of the incident. If a reportable injury, this should include:

- name and occupation of employee affected
- name and status (e.g. service user, visitor) of non-employee affected
- brief description of circumstances
- date and method of report to enforcing authority.

Person involved	Accident details	Type of injury	Reportable under RIDDOR
Service user	Died in sleep		Natural causes – not reportable
Visitor	Slipped on icy step – broken leg	Major injury to member of public	Contact Incident Contact Centre (ICC)
Service user	Slipped in bath – unconscious. Head wound, taken to hospital – kept in 48 hours.	Major injury	Contact Centre (ICC)
Care worker	Hurt back whilst lifting service user. Off work 5 days.	Over 3 day injury.	Contact Centre (ICC)

It is necessary to have an accident report for the following reasons:

- to meet the requirements of the law
- in case further information is required by professional care workers
- in case service user/employee's condition worsens
- in case legal action is taken
- to inform relatives.

The Health and Safety (Safety Signs and Signals) Regulations 1996

The main purpose of these Regulations is to advise employers on the minimum requirements for the provision of safety signs at work. Safety signs have been standardised throughout the European Union so that wherever a particular sign appears it carries the same message. Signs are therefore easy to recognise and understand.

The main category of safety signs are:

- Warning signs – which are triangular in shape with a black picture on a yellow background with black edging.

Flammable material or high temperature

Explosive material

Toxic material

Corrosive material

Radioactive material

Overhead load

Warning signs

These signs are for hazards such as toxic materials, examples being flammable material, toxic, corrosive, radioactive, general danger, danger electricity, and laser beam.

- Prohibition signs – which are round in shape with a black picture on a white background, red edging and diagonal line.

No smoking

Smoking and naked flames forbidden

No access for pedestrians

Do not extinguish with water

Not drinkable

No access for unauthorised persons

Prohibition signs

Eye protection must be worn

Safety helmet must be worn

Ear protection must be worn

Respiratory equipment must be worn

Safety boots must be worn

Safety gloves must be worn

Mandatory signs

First aid post

Stretcher

Safety shower

Eyewash

Emergency telephone for first aid or escape

Safe condition signs

These signs prohibit certain actions such as smoking.

- Mandatory signs – which are round with a white picture on a blue background.

These signs tell people they must do something such as wear safety goggles.

- Safe condition signs – which are rectangular or square with a white picture on a green background.

These signs give information about safety features such as fire exits.

Signs must be clearly displayed and kept in good condition.

Health and Safety Law poster

'The Health and Safety Law – What you should know' poster should be displayed in a location which is accessible to all employees. The poster informs the employees of their rights and responsibilities regarding health and safety. Employer's duties are also explained. The appointed person(s) for the management of health and safety within the organisation should be named. One appointed person should be an employee representative and the other should be a management representative. There is also a space for the name, address and telephone number of the enforcing authority whose health and safety inspector covers the workplace.

The Health and Safety (First Aid) Regulations 1981

The Health and Safety (First Aid) Regulations 1981 state that places of work should have first aid provision. The extent of the provision is based on various factors such as:

- the number of people
- working with hazardous materials or dangerous equipment
- categories of risk; i.e. lower risk, e.g. shops, offices; or medium risk, e.g. care homes.

A risk assessment should be carried out to determine the level of first aid provision required. The minimum required is a suitably stocked first aid kit and an 'appointed person'. That is someone with specific duties relating to first aid. First aid is essential as it will prevent the injury from becoming worse and could save lives.

Every employee in the workplace must be made aware of first aid procedures. They should have access to a first aid box which should be easily identifiable and well stocked. There should be a clearly visible notice stating where the first aid box is located and who the appointed person is. A trained first aider and a first aid room should be made available if the workplace gives rise to special hazards.

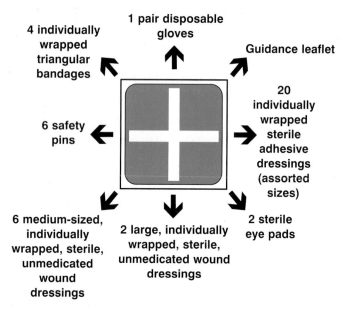

1 pair disposable gloves

4 individually wrapped triangular bandages

Guidance leaflet

6 safety pins

20 individually wrapped sterile adhesive dressings (assorted sizes)

6 medium-sized, individually wrapped, sterile, unmedicated wound dressings

2 large, individually wrapped, sterile, unmedicated wound dressings

2 sterile eye pads

Minimum requirements for a first aid box

All first aid cases dealt with must be recorded by an appointed person. Records should include the name of casualty, date, time, circumstances of accident, details of injury and treatment given. These records should be retained.

Risk category	Numbers employed	Suggested number of appointed persons
Lower risk, e.g. offices, shops	Under 50	At least ONE appointed person.
	50 – 100	At least ONE first aider*
Medium category, e.g. most care homes	Under 50	At least ONE appointed person.
	50 – 100	At least ONE first aider* for every 50 employed

*NB. First aiders must be trained and certificated by organisations approved by the Health and Safety Executive.

An employer must have a policy/procedure in place for recording accidents: either an accident book or

report form. RIDDOR requires the recording of an accident and so do the Registered Homes Inspectors, if the accident occurs in a residential or nursing home. Employees should know the location of the accident book and how to fill it in. If an accident happens, complete an accident report ensuring any witnesses to the accident also complete a report. You must ensure your report contains:

- date, time and place of accident
- people involved
- details of what you saw
- comments from any persons involved
- condition of person after accident.

Example of an internal accident report (e.g. for use in a school):

ACCIDENT REPORT

In the event of a person being injured in an accident at work or related to that work , or in the event of a dangerous occurrence, this form must be completed and copies sent to the Administration Headquarters of the Function involved.

1. FUNCTION: _____
   SECTION / PREMISES _____

2. COMPLETE THIS SECTION IN ALL CASES

Injured Person:

Surname _____ Forename (s) _____

Address: _____

_____

Age: _____ Sex: _____ Occupation _____

State: Whether Employee or Non-Employee: (Delete as necessary)

DATE OF ACCIDENT: _____ To Whom Reported _____

Place of Accident _____ Time of Accident _____

Date/Time Accident Reported: _____ Date of Ceasing Work: _____

STATE CIRCUMSTANCES OF ACCIDENT: _____

_____

_____

_____

Precise Nature of Injury: (where applicable state left or right) _____

_____

_____

Name and Address of Witnesses: _____

_____

ACTION TAKEN TO STOP RE-OCCURRENCE _____

_____

Signed: _____ Position _____

FOR OFFICE USE ONLY:

If any of the following apply, a copy of this form must be forwarded to Safety Section and Finance -also Form F2508 to be completed and sent within 10 days to the Health and Safety Executive.

Fatality ☐   Major Injury ☐   Over 3 day Injury ☐   Flammable Gas Incident ☐

Example of an accident report form

Health and safety policy document

Every workplace with five or more workers MUST have a written document of their health and safety policy. This policy must include:

- name of person implementing the policy
- name(s) of other person(s) responsible for specific health and safety hazards
- list of identified health and safety hazards and procedures to be followed in relation to them
- statement of intention to provide a safe place of work
- evacuation of the premises procedure
- recording of accidents procedure.

The health and safety policy must be reviewed as often as appropriate.

Care settings must have their own health and safety policies which reflect current legislation. There will be policies relating to moving and handling, first aid, food hygiene, reporting of injuries and dangerous occurrences (RIDDOR) and waste control policy (COSSH).

It is essential to have a health and safety policy:

- to set standards, so that everyone knows what is expected
- to know who is responsible, so that it is easier for staff to talk to a named person
- to ensure all staff know the correct procedures, so there is consistency
- to maintain the law, so that legal proceedings will not be taken against the care setting
- to provide a safe environment, so that both staff and service users will feel secure.

The Control of Substances Hazardous to Health 1994 (COSSH) revised 2002

This Regulation requires employers to control exposure to hazardous substances at work. Employers must meet essential requirements for the storage and use of hazardous substances. Care settings must have a COSSH file, which is kept up to date, listing all the hazardous substances stored on their premises. Hazardous substances used in care settings include some cleaning materials, disinfectants and micro-organisms from soiled laundry and clinical waste.

As stated above, all care settings must have a COSSH file which lists all the hazardous substances

used in the workplace. Employers must assess the health risk faced by their employees, service users and visitors and decide on the action needed to control exposure to hazardous substances. The assessment results should be recorded in the COSSH file. The file must:

- identify and name the hazardous substance
- state where each hazardous substance is kept
- state how the hazardous substances are labelled
- describe the effects of the hazardous substances
- state the maximum amount of time it is safe to be exposed to them
- describe how to deal with an emergency involving the hazardous substance.

COSSH assessments should be relatively easy in a care home. Firstly, establish what products and biological hazards (for example soiled linen) are in the home. Identify if less harmful products could decrease the risk. If the product cannot be replaced then staff and service users must be subjected to minimum exposure by providing precautions such as good ventilation.

All cleaning materials, for example bleach, should be kept out of the reach of vulnerable service users. This can be achieved by keeping the substances in a locked cupboard when not in use. There have been deaths in care homes where service users have swallowed hazardous substances through mistaking them for soft drinks.

When working with any hazardous substances the care worker should ensure precautions listed in the COSSH file are followed. Guidance for storage of hazardous substances is also given in the COSSH file. Containers should be correctly labelled and have safety lids. Always follow manufacturers' instructions.

As stated earlier, in the Health and Safety (Safety Signs and Signals) Regulations 1996, a yellow triangle denotes a hazardous substance. If you see a yellow triangle on any substance, this is a hazard symbol and you must check the COSSH file for the precautions you need to take with the substance. Ensure you follow the procedure.

Hazardous substance	Effect
• Substances used directly in work activities, e.g. cleaning materials.	• Skin irritation or dermatitis as a risk of skin contact.
• Biological agents such as bacteria and other micro-organisms.	• Infection from bacteria and other micro-organisms.

Assessment activity 4.2.1

Current legislation on safe practice in care settings
CASE STUDY

Patricia is the manager of a residential care home. She is very careful to ensure the care home follows the requirements of the Health and Safety Executive. The accident book is always completed after any incident.

Read the above text and use the information to help with the following questions.

1
  a Describe **three** roles of the Health and Safety Executive in ensuring regulations are followed in the workplace.

  b Explain, using **three** examples, why accident books/reports are necessary in health, social care and early years settings.

  c Analyse, using **three** examples, why it is important for a care setting, such as a residential home, to have a health and safety policy.

2

Find the Health and Safety Law poster in your school/college:

  a Where should the health and safety poster be displayed?

  b Who is your 'appointed person'?

  c Why is the health and safety poster important?

  d What is the main content and purpose of the poster?

4.2.2 Safety and security

Carrying out formal risk assessments

Maintaining safety and security in health, social care and early years settings is of paramount importance especially as some of the service users will be vulnerable due to age, disability or medical condition. A risk assessment must be carried out by law. The Management of Health and Safety at Work Regulations 1999 require employers to assess risks within their buildings. Significant risks should be concentrated on, not minor ones. The aim of a risk assessment is to ensure no one is hurt or injured. Risk assessment involves examining what could cause harm to people and deciding whether enough has been done to prevent a possible injury. If it is felt that enough has not been done then more action should be taken to lessen the risk.

Stage 1
Look for hazards

↓

Stage 2
Assess who may be harmed

↓

Stage 3
Consider risk – are precautions adequate?

↓

Stage 4
Document the findings

↓

Stage 5
Review the assessment and revise if necessary

There are five stages in a risk assessment

Stage 1: Look for hazards

This is where significant hazards are identified. The person carrying out the risk assessment will walk around the premises of the nursery, residential home, etc., and look at things which could cause serious harm or could affect several people. Employees can contribute their views. It could be the equipment, physical environment, people's behaviour or tasks which are potential hazards. The accident book and ill health records could help identify hazards. In the case of equipment, manufacturer's instructions could also provide guidelines.

Hazards — Activity 1

1 Examine your work experience placement and look for hazards which could cause serious harm. Record your findings.

2 List five possible hazards and explain which safety features could be introduced to improve safety. Explain how each would help.

3 Why are risk assessments made? How regularly should they be made?

Hazard assessment

Stage 2: Assess who may be harmed

All employees including full, part-time and maintenance staff must be taken into account when making a risk assessment. Service users and visitors, too, must be considered.

Stage 3: Consider the risks and decide whether more should be done

The aim here is to minimise risks. More needs to be done if the risk remains medium or high. Priority should be given to any risk that remains high or affects most people. The first consideration should be if the hazard can be removed or disposed of. For example, a worn carpet in a main thoroughfare could be replaced or a loose handrail in the corridor could be tightened. If the hazard cannot be removed,

the risk from it needs to be controlled by taking extra precautions. The following principles should be applied, preferably in the order they are listed:

- try a less risky option, e.g. if there is a full-length glass window in the lounge of a residential home, place a sideboard across it so that no one will get near enough to fall through;
- prevent access to hazard, example from above also applies here;
- organise work to reduce exposure to the hazard, e.g. share moving and handling tasks among staff and throughout the day;
- provide personal protective clothing, e.g. disposable plastic aprons and latex-free gloves;
- provide welfare facilities, e.g. washing facilities to ensure the removal of contamination;
- provide first aid facilities.

Once measures to avoid or control risks found in the assessment have been identified they must then be implemented. Not all precautions need to be expensive, some could be a change of working practice. New and existing precautions must be checked to ensure effectiveness.

Stage 4: Document the findings

If there are five or more employees then significant findings (hazards and conditions) from the risk assessments must be recorded or documented. Staff must be told about the findings. An example of a significant finding could be a 'badly worn carpet in the residents' lounge due to be replaced in three months time'. This would need to be covered with tape to prevent anyone tripping over it but would need to be checked on a regular basis until the carpet was replaced.

Stage 5: Review the assessment and revise if necessary

Records to demonstrate that all necessary aspects have been covered are very useful. They make a useful reference point for when assessments need to be reviewed.

Health and Safety Audit Checklist

	Yes	No	Comment on possible risk
Name of care setting:			
Address:			
Telephone No:			
Date of Audit:			
Politics and records			
Does care setting have up-to-date...			
• health & safety policy?			
• moving & handling policy?			
• equipment policy?			
• accident policy?			
• staff training policy?			
Is there an accident book?			
Do staff know where it is?			
Are all reportable accidents reported to Incident Contact Centre?			
Are all following assessments up-to-date?			
• COSHH			
• Manual handling			
• Personal protective equipment			
Are the results implemented in working procedures/practices?			

Health and Safety Audit

	Yes	No	Comment on possible risk
Procedures			
Are they up-to-date?			
Has there been a review of safety policy and management policies?			
Are there procedures for consulting with staff and union safety representatives?			
Are working time issues resolved?			
Staff training			
Are all staff trained?			
Is refresher training provided?			
Are agency staff/contractors informed about policies and procedures?			
How is effectiveness of training evaluated?			

	Yes	No	Comment on possible risk

First aid

Is first-aid box fully stocked?

Do staff know where first-aid box is?

Are there named first aiders?

Is staff training up-to-date?

COSHH (Chemicals)

Are health hazards from all substances assessed?

Are staff trained about safe procedures?

Are staff trained about use of protective clothing?

Are control measures implemented?

COSHH (blood-borne diseases)

Have assessments been made, including contaminated/soiled laundry?

Are staff trained in safe working procedures?

Are safe procedures implemented and followed?

Are staff given appropriate protective equipment/clothing and is it used?

Are cuts covered with waterproof dressings?

Are basic hygiene procedures in place?

Are there procedures for cleaning up spillages?

Are staff offered hepatitis B immunisation?

Do staff know what to do in the event of an accident?

Clinical waste

Is all clinical waste:

* bagged up in yellow bags/containers?
* segregated from general waste?

Are needles, syringes and cannulas (sharps) disposed of at suitable facilities?

Are there procedures to deal with spillages?

Drugs

Are cupboards locked?

Are service users' drugs in locked cupboard in bedrooms?

Moving and handling

Is moving and handling avoided where possible, e.g. by providing lifting aids?

Have manual handling tasks been assessed for risks and preventative measures been implemented?

	Yes	No	Comment on possible risk
Are appropriate aids available?			
Is equipment adjustable?			
Are all staff trained in use of equipment and handling techniques?			
Are there sufficient staff to carry out work?			
Stairs			
Are they well lit?			
Is stair covering in good condition?			
Are there obstructions?			
Floors			
Are there slippery surfaces?			
Have spillages been cleaned up?			
Are carpets frayed, flat, even?			
Are floor surfaces suitable, non-slip, flat, properly maintained?			
Are there obstructions, tripping hazards?			
Lighting			
Are all bulbs working?			
Are lighting levels sufficient?			
Ventilation			
Are there odours?			
Are there draughts?			
Is there sufficient fresh air?			
Have chemicals, fumes, steam/condensation been removed?			
Windows			
Are restraints in place?			
Is glazing in good condition?			
Is glazing material appropriate?			
Violence			
Is there a reporting system?			
Do staff know how to report incidents and are they encouraged to do so?			
Are preventative measures implemented?			
Stress			
Is there a policy?			

	Yes	No	Comment on possible risk
Have risk assessments been completed?			
Were staff involved?			
Protective equipment			
Is protective equipment (e.g. gloves, aprons, etc.) suitable, safe, and comfortable?			
Are staff trained to use it?			
Is it appropriate, properly stored, cleaned and maintained?			
Display screen equipment			
Has work station been analysed and assessed to reduce risk?			
Are eye and eyesight tests needed?			
Are staff trained to use and set up their VDU work station safely?			
Water and surface temperatures			
Are thermostatic mixing valves operating at required temperature?			
Are hot water temperatures regularly tested (using thermometer)?			
Are pipes and radiators in excess of 43°C?			
If yes, has remedial action been taken to protect vulnerable service users?			
Is temperature comfortable?			
Laundry			
Are machine interlocks working?			
Is there separation of soiled laundry?			
Electrical safety			
Have the electrical systems (lighting and power circuits) been checked?			
Are appliances in good condition?			
Are plugs, sockets, leads in good condition?			
Are there trailing leads?			
Are appliances correctly fused?			
Are there enough sockets?			
Are regular checks carried out?			
If faulty, is equipment repaired or replaced promptly?			
Are staff trained in safe use of equipment?			
Welfare			
Are there adequate toilet and washing facilities?			

	Yes	No	Comment on possible risk
Are facilities clean and well maintained?			
Is storage provided for staff belongings?			
Are staff provided with sufficient rest breaks?			
Are smoke-free areas provided?			
Is home regularly cleaned, in good repair and decorative order?			
Kitchen safety			
Are machines guarded?			
Are floors clean, slip resistant and dry?			
Is there room to move around freely?			
Is ventilation sufficient?			
Are staff trained in kitchen hygiene, use of equipment, etc.?			
Is food correctly stored?			
Outside			
Are paths and steps in good condition and well lit at night?			
Is there adequate risk assessment of falls from balconies?			
Are pesticides locked away?			
Are staff trained to use outdoor equipment safely?			
Do they have suitable protective equipment?			

Safety audit — Activity 2

1 Examine the safety audit checklist. Can you think of any other questions which could be asked under the various headings?

2 Visit your choice of care setting and carry out a health and safety audit, using the sample audit checklist. Were the 'other questions' you thought of relevant? Was there anything missing? How did your care setting do? Is it a safe place to be?

Reducing risks in different types of care settings

There are many different types of care settings.

Different types of care settings

As already mentioned in 4.2.1, the Health and Safety at Work Act 1974 lays down the rule that employers have a general duty to ensure the health and safety of employees, service users, visitors, etc. Residential homes differ from the others on the above diagram because they are usually the permanent home of the service user. Although health and safety is important, they also need to be maintained as pleasant places to live. Service users have different degrees of independence and as a result different needs. There should not be strict guidelines across the range. A service user living in a rehabilitation hostel will have different needs to an older service user living in a residential home. The differences will be reflected in the design of the home, the facilities and the safety features provided. Having a flexible approach leads to appropriate provision which is tailored to the needs of the service user.

In any care setting there are hazards which could cause injury to the service users, especially if they are older, disabled, ill or very young. Types of hazards which could be encountered can be categorised into:

- hazards associated with equipment and materials
- hazards associated with people
- hazards associated with environment.

Hazards associated with equipment and materials

There are many different examples such as:
- broken or ill-fitting tops/lids on top of containers
- gas or electric appliances in poor condition
- worn or damaged lifting equipment
- incorrectly labelled substances.

Hazards associated with people

The different types include:
- intruders
- handling procedures
- violent and aggressive behaviour
- visitors to the building.

Environmental hazards

These include:

- worn carpets or rugs
- wet or slippery floors
- trailing electrical flexes
- clutter on stairways or in hallways.

Staff in care settings must be trained to be aware of dangers in their environment. If they are unsure how to deal with any hazard, they must seek advice from a senior member of staff. All staff must contribute to a safe care environment.

All employees should be given training when they first start a job. Training could include first aid training, moving and handling, risk assessment and basic food hygiene courses. Any training they receive should help the carer to understand and be able to deal with any hazard or emergency that may arise in the course of their job.

Safety training	Activity 3

1 Interview a care worker and ask them about the training s/he received when s/he first started their job.

2 Explain how training of staff can help to reduce risks in care settings.

Health and safety policies

Staff are required to comply with the health and safety policies at their care setting. Policies and procedures exist to help to protect service users and staff from harm. Health and safety policies will differ from care setting to care setting depending on the size of building, number of staff and number of service users. However, wherever a carer works, the principles will be similar, such as the storage of dangerous chemicals (such as bleach), the safety and security of both indoors and outdoors, and the storage and administration of medicines. Carers must ensure that they read and understand the health and safety policy at their care setting so that in the event of an emergency, e.g. a fire, they will know what to do.

Early warning systems

Early warning systems such as CCTV (closed circuit television) are becoming increasingly necessary in schools, residential homes and hospitals. CCTV consists of a series of cameras placed around the building often covering places of possible access. Monitors are linked to the cameras and staff are able to view any potential problems. CCTVs are proven to cut crime as burglars are likely to think twice if they know they will be caught on camera.

Another early warning system could be an alarm on any door into the building. Again this could prevent a burglar entering the building or at least alert staff that someone had attempted to enter the building.

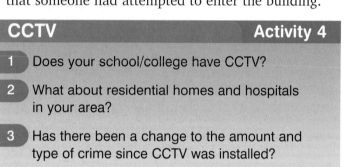

CCTV	Activity 4

1. Does your school/college have CCTV?

2. What about residential homes and hospitals in your area?

3. Has there been a change to the amount and type of crime since CCTV was installed?

4. Explain how CCTV can reduce risks.

Use of safety and warning signs

As explained, in 4.2.1 safety signs are yellow triangular signs with a black border. With a yellow background the hazard type is clearly shown in black.

Safety features

Different care settings have different needs as far as safety features are concerned but all will have certain common features such as fire alarms, smoke alarms and health and safety policies. All premises will have undergone a risk assessment. For example, if a service user has an visual difficulty then it is important to keep the floor clear of any unexpected obstacles or hazards.

Personal protective equipment (PPE)

Employers have a duty to provide personal protective equipment (PPE) at work as a result of the Personal Protective Equipment at Work Regulations 1992. PPE

Strong magnetic field

Obstacles

Drop

Biological risk

Low temperature

Harmful or irritant material

Warning signs

is defined in Regulations as 'all equipment which is intended to be worn or held by a person at work which protects him against one or more risks to his health and safety'. The Regulations require that PPE is:

used correctly by employees

properly assessed before use to ensure suitability

Regulations require PPE to be:

provided with instructions on how to use safely

maintained and stored properly

Regulation requirements of PPE

Area of body	Hazards	PPE options
Eyes	Chemical/metal splash, dust, **projectiles**, gas and vapour, radiation.	Safety spectacles, goggles, visors, face shields.
Head	Impact from falling or flying objects, risk of head bumping, hair entanglement.	Range of helmets and bump caps.
Breathing	Dust, vapour, gas, oxygen-deficient atmosphere.	Disposable filtering face-piece or respirator, half- or full-face respirators, air-fed helmets, breathing apparatus.
Protecting the body	Temperature extremes, adverse weather. Chemical or metal splash, spray from pressure leaks or spray guns, impact or penetration, contaminated dust, excessive wear or entanglement of own clothing.	Conventional or disposable overalls, boiler suits, specialist protective clothing, e.g. chain-mail aprons, high-visibility clothing.
Hands and arms	Abrasion, temperature extremes, cuts and punctures, impact, chemicals, electric shock, skin infection, disease or contamination.	Gloves, gauntlets, mitts, wrist cuffs, armlets.
Feet and legs	Wet, electrostatic build-up, slipping, cuts and punctures, falling objects, metal and chemical splash, abrasion.	Safety boots and shoes with protective toe-caps and penetration-resistant mid-sole, gaiters, leggings, **spats.**

Types of hazards and PPE

PPE   Activity 5

Look at the above list of hazards and the suggested PPE.
Describe the types of hazards likely to be encountered in a hospital situation and which types of PPE would be required.

PPE cannot be charged to the employee; it is the duty of the employer to provide the necessary equipment free of charge. The PPE must be carefully chosen to ensure it is the right type for the different hazards in the workplace. Different types of PPE are suitable for different tasks. The following must be considered when assessing whether the PPE is suitable:

- It must be appropriate for the risks involved and the conditions at the place where exposure may occur.
- It must prevent or adequately control the risks involved without increasing the overall level of risk.
- It must be adjustable to be able to fit the wearer correctly.
- It must take the state of health of those who will be wearing it into account.
- It must take the needs of the job and the demands it places on the wearer into account, e.g. the length of time the PPE needs to be worn, the physical effort required to do the job, and the requirements for visibility and communication.
- It must consider compatibility if more than one item of PPE is being worn.

Anyone using PPE must be aware of why it is needed, when it is used, repaired or replaced and its limitations. Users must be trained to use it properly and must wear it all the time they are exposed to the hazard.

PPE must be properly maintained and any defects must be reported. It must be correctly stored.

How does reducing risks benefit service users and care workers?

Reducing risks benefits both service users and care workers and ensures that their health and safety is not compromised. For example, the PPE would benefit service users by ensuring that any infection is not passed on to them from the care worker, as the care worker would have been dressed in disposable apron and gloves which would be thrown away and replaced after attending to a previous service user. The care worker, too, would be protected by the gloves and apron. Policies benefit everyone in the care setting as there are firm guidelines to follow.

All staff working in care settings are now subject to a police clearance from the Criminal Records Bureau. This is an essential requirement to protect vulnerable service users, and employers must ensure they request and see this certificate. References from previous employers should also be followed up.

Discussion point

The police clearance from the Criminal Records Bureau has a flaw in that if someone has not been prosecuted or cautioned for an offence it will not appear on his/her record. Is this a satisfactory situation where vulnerable service users are concerned?

The Fire Precautions (Workplace) (Amendment) Regulations 1999

These Regulations were introduced by the EC to rationalise fire safety in the workplace. The Workplace Regulations apply to any employer who employs one or more workers. A Fire Officer will come out and give advice on the premises.

The Regulations require the employer to:

- carry out a fire risk assessment of the workplace
- record findings of risk assessment if more than five people are employed
- provide and maintain adequate fire precautions – these include fire-fighting equipment such as extinguishers, blankets, etc.; and safeguard those who use the workplace
- provide information, instruction and training to employees about fire precautions in the workplace
- provide an emergency action plan which should be available to employees
- nominate, inform, instruct and train employees in fire precautions and fire fighting
- identify location of people at significant risk in case of fire
- establish a suitable means of contacting emergency services
- maintain and test fire precautions
- train staff in fire safety
- if measures are inadequate ensure improvements are carried out.

Fire procedures — Activity 6

1. How often does your workplace carry out practice fire drills? Why are these carried out?

2. Explain what happens during a fire procedure.

3. Explain what is required by 'The Fire Precautions (Workplace) (Amendment) Regulations 1999'.

All premises are inspected by the fire brigade to ensure there is a means of escape and that there is maintained fire-fighting equipment. A fire certificate will be issued.

Fire safety
Detectors and alarms

Detection systems are available which, when linked to a warning device, give an early warning of fire. These systems can detect smoke, high temperatures or the gases produced by a fire. Automatic or manual fire alarms then warn of danger by making a lot of noise. Batteries in fire/smoke alarms must be checked regularly to ensure that they are working properly. Employees should be familiar with the sound of the fire alarm and be ready to evacuate the building if necessary. All fire detection and warning systems must be carefully maintained.

Types of fire-fighting equipment

If it is a small fire, e.g. chip pan fire, then sometimes simple fire-fighting techniques can stop the fire before it gets out of control. Sometimes, a fire extinguisher can be used (see next page).

Care homes sometimes have a sprinkler system which can detect and control a fire at an early stage. They must be permanently connected to a water supply and checked regularly. Maintenance is essential.

Hose reels should be easily accessible. These are normally provided for the fire brigade's use.

Portable fire extinguishers

It is essential that any fire extinguisher used should be the correct type for the fire. There are a number of different types of extinguisher.

It can be dangerous to attempt to tackle a fire using an extinguisher if you do not know how to use one. You must also ensure you can get out of the building.

Extinguishers should be fixed in accessible places usually situated by doors along exit routes, and must be clearly indicated by specific safety signs. There should be sufficient for the type of premises and they must be regularly checked and maintained.

Fire-fighting equipment   Activity 7

1   Which fire-fighting equipment would you use for an electrical fire?

2   For which situations would you use the following equipment?
   • black fire extinguisher
   • fire blanket
   • blue standard fire extinguisher.
   Explain why each would be used.

3   List five safety points to be remembered when fighting a fire.

Extinguisher type and colour	Used for	Danger area
Red Water	Paper, cloth, wood, coal, plastics, etc. Fires involving solids.	NOT to be used on burning oil or fat, or on electrical appliances.
Blue Multi-purpose dry powder	Paper, cloth, wood, coal, plastics, etc. Fires involving solids. Liquids such as fats, oils, paint, petrol, grease but NOT on chip or fat pan fires.	Safe on live electrical equipment but fire could re-ignite as this type of extinguisher does not cool fire. Do NOT use on chip or fat pan fires.
Blue Standard dry powder	Liquids such as fats, oils, grease, paint, petrol, etc., but NOT on chip or fat pan fires.	Safe on live electrical equipment but fire could re-ignite as it does not cool fire very well. Do NOT use on chip or fat pan fires.
Cream AFFF (aqueous film forming foam) multi-purpose	Cloth, paper, coal, plastics, wood, etc. Fires involving solids. Liquids such as grease, oils, fats, paints, petrol, etc., but NOT chip or pan fat fires.	Do NOT use on chip or fat pan fires.
Cream Foam	Limited number of liquid fires.	Do NOT use on chip or fat pan fires.
Black Carbon dioxide	Liquids such as grease oils, fats, paint, petrol, etc., but NOT chip or fat pan fires.	Do NOT use on chip or fat pan fires. Follow manufacturer's guidance on suitability for use on fires involving liquids.
Fire blanket	Fires involving both solids and liquids. Especially good for small fires in clothing and for chip and fat pan fires, provided the blanket completely covers the fire.	Blanket must completely cover the fire otherwise it will not be extinguished.

Types of fire extinguishers

Evacuation routes

All buildings must have an exit which can be used safely in the event of a fire. Emergency exits allow people to get out of a building in the opposite direction from a fire. Escape routes must be well planned and if they are in a large building must not be overly complicated.

To protect the escape routes some additional fire safety measures may need to be installed. For example, these could include fire doors, emergency exits and fire resisting staircases. All emergency doors must open outwards and must **never** be blocked by anything. If possible they must not be locked.

Permanent signposting **must** show the way out **clearly** in an emergency. Fire doors must be kept clear at all times as must escape routes. Internal fire doors should be kept closed as they help to prevent smoke and flames from spreading and cut off the oxygen supply to the fire.

Emergency lighting should be checked and maintained regularly. Lifts must **never** be used during a fire as there is the danger of people becoming trapped.

Managers or people in charge need to know who is in the building, so staff, visitors and anyone else should sign in and out. A register should be taken to ensure everyone is accounted for. No one should re-enter the building, once evacuated, unless told to do so by a fire officer. People should remain in the designated assembly area.

Evacuation of premises

When a fire or other emergency necessitates the evacuation of a building, then care workers have a duty to follow the evacuation procedure as laid down by the care setting. In the event of an evacuation it is important for the care worker to remain calm at all times. This will help to reassure service users who may otherwise panic. Service users should be removed from the premises as quickly as possible with minimum panic. In the case of, for example a nursing home, where a large number of service users may be confined to bed, there may be a phased evacuation plan. This is when service users are moved away from the fire zone area to an adjoining safe zone. Fire doors can

be kept shut to contain the fire. If the fire is not brought under control by the fire brigade, service users will be moved into the next adjoining zone always moving away from the fire towards the nearest exit.

The following boxes are examples of fire procedures from residential homes.

FIRE

On Discovering a Fire

Raise the fire alarm by:

1 Breaking the glass at the nearest alarm break glass point, or at the fire alarm control panel, turn the key switch to ARM CONTROL and press EVACUATE.

2 Call the Fire Brigade on 999 and inform them of a 'Fire at Nursing Home' and ensure the operator understands your call.

3 Escort all residents who are within the area of the fire to adjoining safe areas, which are through adjacent passage-way fire doors (reference phased fire evacuation plan).

4 Do not open any doors to gain access within which a fire is suspected.

5 Prepare to evacuate residents to the fire assembly point.

6 Wait for attendance of the Fire Brigade, who will instruct what further action is required.

FIRE

Visitors' Information

1 Please always ensure that you record your presence in the building by signing in and out in the log book provided.

2 In the event of the fire alarm being activated, you are instructed to return to the foyer immediately.

3 This procedure will always help staff and fire brigade to tackle a genuine emergency, by either minimising unnecessary searches or gaining your assistance to evacuate residents to the fire assembly point.

FIRE PROCEDURE

1 In the event of fire it is the first duty of all concerned to try and prevent injury or loss of life. The safety of the residents and staff is of prime importance.

2 In view of the above, you should make sure that you are familiar with all means of escape in case of fire. Additionally, since there may be an opportunity in the event of a fire for you to attack it with the nearest fire appliance, you should ensure that you know the location of each item of fire-fighting equipment and should also ensure that you know how to use each appliance.

3 If you discover a fire, or one is reported to you, you should:

Sound the Alarm

4 The person in charge of the home at that time will be responsible for calling the Fire Brigade, by dialling 999.

5 Evacuate residents to the next safe zone, away from the fire zone (behind fire doors).

Do not use the lift

6 When the evacuation is complete, ensure a roll call of all residents and staff (a list of all staff and residents who are in the building should be available at all times – nominal roll call).

7 The person in charge should give precise details to the Emergency Services when they arrive. In the event of one or more persons being missing, you should give the name(s) and likely location(s) of the missing person(s).

Try to Stay Calm and do not Panic

8 Remember, however small the fire, Dial 999.

Fire Extinguishers

RED Extinguishers may be used on material fires.

BLACK Extinguishers (Carbon Dioxide) to be used on electrical fires.

FIRE

Phased Evacuation Action Plan

Traditionally in the event of a fire occurring within, say, a hotel or office block, the fire alarm is sounded and all occupants make their own way to a designated fire assembly point. For obvious reasons this procedure would not be realistic at our Home.

'Phased Evacuation' is a term applied to the procedure to apply in the event of a fire occurring within the building.

SCENARIO

1 Fire detected

2 Fire alarms activated either automatically or manually

3 All passage-way fire-break doors automatically close

4 Fire confined within particular fire zone by the closure of fire-break doors

5 Fire confined within a particular room area

PHASED EVACUATION

1 Do not attempt to open the door leading into a room in which a fire is suspected, until competent personnel are in attendance.

2 Escort all residents/visitors from the fire zone area through the passage-way fire-break door, to the adjoining safe zone. Ensure fire-break doors stay closed.

3 Within the relatively safe zones, be prepared to escort residents into the next adjoining zone via the fire-break doors, always moving away from the seat of the fire, towards the nearest exit.

4 Some judgement is necessary during this evacuation. The underlying aim is to maximise the effectiveness of staff available and to minimise unnecessary movement of residents, until the Fire Brigade expertise arrives.

5 Fire Brigade arrives and staff follow Fire Officer instructions.

FIRE

Philosophy of Fire Procedure

In the event of a fire within the building, the safety of our residents, visitors and staff is of paramount importance.

Our initial actions and effective use of time, combined with the in-built safety features of the building, will greatly influence the outcome of a real fire, 'relative failure' or 'success'.

From the time of the Fire Brigade being requested, it will take approximately 12 minutes for the services to arrive. It is essential that this time period is not extended by delaying the call for the brigade's assistance.

Once a fire has been confirmed remember:

- Fire alarms activated
- Telephone the Fire Brigade

This procedure should not add more than 3 minutes to the time necessary for the Fire Brigade to arrive.

All doors fitted to residents rooms and passage-ways are fire resistant for a minimum period of 30 minutes; this allows time for the Fire Brigade to arrive, ascertain the situation and instruct action required.

Security in early years settings

Parents must be secure in the knowledge that, when they leave their children at the early years setting, the children are safe. Children should not be able to leave the premises and there should be no unknown visitors on the school premises whether inside or outside.

Care settings should seek the support of parents by explaining their security arrangements. Some of the following measures may be useful in maintaining a safe, secure system within early years settings:

- Visitors should ring a bell/press a buzzer to gain access into the building – this allows the visitor to be screened.
- Official visitors, e.g. from gas board, should have their identification checked before allowing entry to the premises.
- External gates should have a security system so no one can walk into the playground without being screened.
- An adult should always be on duty in the yard during outside playtimes/times of arrival and departure. This helps the members of staff to observe children arriving at school and ensures the child does come into the school building. Parents can be observed collecting their child at the end of the day.
- An adult should ensure any visitors sign in.
- Parents should state who will collect their child from school – the child must not be allowed to leave the school with anyone else.
- Passwords agreed at registration are sometimes required before a child may be collected.
- Any child with stories about someone 'hanging around' outside must be taken seriously and the claim should be investigated.
- If it can be afforded, a CCTV could be useful to monitor the outside of the premises.
- Door handles should be placed too high up for small children to reach.

If there are any unwanted visitors it is good practice not to allow them onto the school premises. However, if they are already on the premises they must be asked to leave and if they are reluctant to go then the police should be called.

Parents will feel reassured if the above measures are adopted, particularly if there is an ongoing custody battle.

Safety measures   Activity 8

1 Visit a local nursery (or ask a manager of a nursery to come into school). Explain **five** measures the nursery has in place to protect children.

2 Explain how the nursery could deal with unwanted callers.

3 What procedures should the nursery have in place for visitors?

Security in residential homes

The security set up in a care home very much depends on the capabilities of the service users. Most care homes operate a locked door system which prevents outsiders accessing the home without ringing a door bell or buzzer, but often service users can open the door from the inside if they wish to go out. However, some care homes, especially if the service users suffer from dementia, have door alarms which operate if a service user tries to open any of the external doors. This system is to prevent a confused service user wandering off out of the building.

It is the duty of the home to provide:

- security which allows service users to retain their privacy and choose their visitors
- security which protects service users from intruders
- security which protects people's property
- security against being abused.

Security which allows service users to choose their visitors and retain their privacy

Service users are entitled to decide who they will or will not see. The care worker must respect the wishes of the service user and not try to persuade them to accept visitors they are clearly unhappy about. If the unwanted visitor is forceful, the care worker has a duty to protect the service user's interests and must not be coerced into passing on messages that the service user does not want to receive.

Security which protects service users from intruders

No one must be allowed on to the premises without being signed in – this will prevent unauthorised people gaining access to the care home. Anyone whom a care worker suspects to be an intruder should be politely challenged.

Security which protects people's property

Service users have the right to expect staff to help to safeguard property brought into the care home.

All possessions will be recorded on admission, with any valuable items being recorded separately. If any property goes missing, a thorough search and investigation must be carried out before finally reporting the missing property to the police.

Security against being abused

All service users have the right to be protected from abuse and a care worker must report any suspected abuse immediately to his or her line manager. Abuse can be:

- physical – any force used against service user
- sexual – when informed consent is not given
- emotional – e.g. putting down, ridiculing
- financial – e.g. withholding or refusing access to money
- institutional – e.g. privacy and dignity not respected.

Security   Activity 9

1   List **three** ways that a residential home could ensure its residents are protected. Explain how each method would benefit both the service users and the residential staff.

Assessment activity 4.2.2

Risk assessment   CASE STUDY

Anika works in a large residential home as a care assistant. There are over seventy residents living in the home. Each member of staff is responsible for five residents. There is a supervisor for every ten care assistants. There are also five trained nurses on duty for each shift.

While she has been on duty, Anika has been required to use her workplace skills to treat three residents who required basic first aid.

1   Name and give the date of the regulations that relate to the provision of work equipment which places a general duty on employers.

2   List three requirements placed on employers as a result of this legislation.

3   Identify the five key stages used in making a risk assessment. Describe the purpose of each.

4.2.3 Safe moving and handling techniques

It must be stressed that you may **not** move or handle service users unless formally trained to do so and only then if you meet the age and training requirements.

The Manual Handling Operations Regulations 1992

The Manual Handling Operations Regulations 1992 were introduced to reduce the numbers of injuries from moving and handling in **all** industries not just the care sector. Key duties to come from these Regulations are:

Key duties from The Manual Handling Regulations

If a care worker has to move and handle then they must consider:

- if the job is necessary
- can the job be mechanised?
- are there different ways of moving the service user?

Care workers can be held personally and legally accountable for their actions or inactions if they are a care worker who normally deals with handling.

Spinal injury

The most common form of injury caused by manual handling is spinal injury. Carers who handle service users as part of their daily tasks are the most at risk group when it comes to back injury – they are more likely to injure themselves than people in any other profession.

Lifting all, or most, of a service user's weight is no longer considered acceptable. Indeed, the Royal College of Nursing states in their guidelines that the manual lifting of people should be eliminated in all but life-threatening or genuinely exceptional situations.

Lifting Operations and Lifting Equipment Regulations 1998

These Regulations aim to reduce risks to people's health and safety from lifting equipment provided for use at work.

The Regulations state that equipment must be:

- strong and stable enough for particular use
- positioned and installed to minimise any risks
- used safely – that is, the move is planned, organised and performed by competent people
- subject to ongoing examination by competent people
- visibly marked by any appropriate information which may be taken into account for its safe use, for example information on weight-lifting limits should be displayed on hoists
- when the equipment is used to lift people, it should be safe for the purpose, for example all necessary precautions need to be taken to eliminate or reduce risks
- where appropriate lifting equipment should be examined thoroughly before it is used for the first time and re-examined at least every six months thereafter, as recommended by the regulations
- the report on the equipment must be submitted to the employer after the examination by the competent person.

How to assess risks when moving and handling people

Risk assessment

A risk assessment must be carried out for all manual handling operations. Every service user who requires manual handling must be assessed for:

- weight
- factors affecting handling, e.g. unpredictability
- methods which will be used
- equipment required to help with move.

This assessment must be recorded and put on the service user's records unless:

- it could be repeated easily and could be explained as it is simple and obvious
- the manual operation is straightforward, low risk and would take longer to record than carry out.

Summing up, when assessing for moving and handling remember:

- task
- load/weight
- working environment
- individual's capabilities.

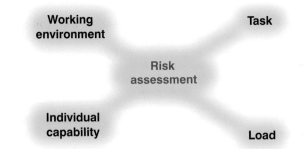

Risk assessment involves

Most injuries in moving and handling are caused by the care worker:

- holding the load at a distance from the body
- bending, twisting, stooping or stretching
- moving the load over long distances
- sustaining physical effort.

Assessing service user handling needs

Service user handling criteria will always take into account several points:

- The service user's condition, e.g. how well they are.
- Any attachments he or she might have, e.g. are they attached to a drip?
- Any special problems, e.g. are they abusive or unpredictable?
- The service user's ability to assist in the procedure.
- Whether the service user can be moved without causing pain – e.g. does the service user have osteoporosis?
- The condition of the service user's skin with contact points needed during the manoeuvre.

When considering ways in which a client may be injured during a transfer, there are four main points:

- friction – particularly between the skin and the transfer surface;
- joint damage – caused by stressing weak joints;

- resistance from service user – perhaps due to lack of communication or understanding;
- falls – due to lack of knowledge of the technique or the carer exceeding his or her capability during the lift.

Service user handling assessment form

This gives comprehensive information with regard to the service user's handling requirements, and criteria which could affect the handling of that service user. See the example at end of this section.

The most useful assessments are set out in a simple format so that it is possible to assimilate quickly what equipment, techniques and numbers of staff are appropriate for a service user's needs. A good plan will cover both daytime and night-time care, focusing on key moves including:

- individual details, including identification, height and weight
- the extent of an individual's ability to support his or her own weight and any relevant factors such as pain, disability, spasm, fatigue or tendency to fall
- problems with comprehension, co-operational behaviour
- recommended methods of movement for the relevant tasks such as going to the toilet, sitting, bathing, transfers and movement in bed;
- details of equipment needed
- the minimum number of staff required to help
- any other relevant risk factors.

Within the caring environment the care worker needs to ask him/herself whether there are basic constraints preventing good posture, for example is there a lack of space especially by beds, chairs or baths? Are there inadequate or insufficient storage facilities? Are floors uneven, slippery or unstable? Do carpets impede the free movement of hoists, etc.? Are there slopes or stairs which change the floor level?

Body Mass Index (BMI)

This provides a method of predicting the service user's body type through the use of a rating system which takes into consideration the service user's height/weight ratio. See BMI chart on next page.

First convert weight to kilograms (1lb = 0.45kg. 2.2lbs = 1kg approx)
Then read across from client's height until you reach the weight which is equal to (or the nearest below) that of the client. Then read up the chart to obtain the client's BMI.

Body Mass Index (BMI)

Height		Weight in kilograms										
Feet	Metres	20	21	22	23	24	25	26	27	28	29	30
4/8	1.42	40	42	44	46	48	50	52	54	56	58	60
4/9	1.45	42	44	46	48	50	53	55	57	59	61	63
4/10	1.47	43	45	48	50	52	54	56	58	61	63	65
4/11	1.50	45	47	50	52	54	56	59	61	63	65	68
5/0	1.52	46	49	51	53	55	58	60	62	65	67	69
5/1	1.56	48	50	53	55	58	60	62	65	67	70	72
5/2	1.58	50	52	55	57	60	62	65	67	70	72	75
5/3	1.60	51	54	56	59	61	64	67	69	72	74	77
5/4	1.63	53	56	58	61	64	68	69	72	74	77	80
5/5	1.65	54	57	60	63	65	68	71	74	76	79	82
5/6	1.68	56	59	62	65	68	71	73	76	79	82	85
5/7	1.70	58	61	64	66	69	72	75	78	81	84	87
5/8	1.73	60	63	66	69	72	75	78	81	84	87	90
5/9	1.75	61	64	67	70	74	77	80	83	86	89	92
5/10	1.78	63	67	70	73	76	79	82	86	89	92	95
5/11	1.80	65	68	71	75	78	81	84	87	91	94	97
6/0	1.83	67	70	74	77	80	84	87	90	94	97	100
6/1	1.85	68	72	75	79	82	86	89	92	96	99	103
6/2	1.88	71	74	78	81	85	88	92	95	99	102	106
6/3	1.90	72	76	79	83	87	90	94	97	101	105	108
6/4	1.93	74	78	82	86	89	93	97	101	104	108	112
6/5	1.96	77	80	84	88	92	96	99	103	107	111	115
6/6	1.98	79	82	86	90	94	98	102	106	110	114	116
Feet	Metres	20	21	22	23	24	25	26	27	28	29	30

Less than **20** – underweight   **20–24.9** – desirable   **25–29.9** – moderately obese   more than **30** – obese.

The traffic light hazard handling system

This system facilitates the allocation of one of three colours – red, yellow or green to the service user. The colour rating is dependent upon an assessment of the service user's condition, based upon the handling hazard he or she represents. Carers can then see, at a glance, the difficulty they will have, with red being the most difficult.

How to work with an individual who needs to be moved

The moving and handling tasks should be designed to suit individuals rather than the individual to fit the task. Effective training has an important part to play in reducing the risks but is not a substitute for improving the task, the load and the working environment.

Training should be appropriate for the job. Staff who are moving and handling people may need to have annual refresher training.

Some service users may become angry or agitated when being moved. Others, whilst willing to help at the beginning of the move, may be unable to sustain the effort needed. It is, therefore, important that staff are trained for such situations and thus are able to avoid injury both to themselves and the service user.

Service users may suffer from inappropriate handling; they may have painful areas which should be avoided. Their needs may change through the course of the day as they may no longer be able to assist with moves as they become increasingly tired. It is good practice to reassess service users frequently and to include their moving and handling assessments in their individual care plans, which should be available to all workers caring for them.

Special techniques may be required for moving and handling service users depending on the situation and the ability of the individual. It is very important to remember their dignity, tell them about the equipment and explain how it will be used. Ask service users how much they can contribute to the move.

Handler's clothing

Clothing, uniforms, footwear and protective equipment are other factors that have direct impact on movement, as does the ability to choose the appropriate posture while moving and handling. Clothing should allow caring staff to perform a full range of movement.

Shoes should be flat and comfortable as high heels can cause a care worker to lose balance which could result in an accident. Both service user and care worker could suffer injury.

Jewellery, too, should be avoided as this could catch the service user who is being moved and cause injury.

Hair should be tied back out of the way of equipment such as hoists as, if it were to be caught, it could be dangerous for both care worker and service user.

Encouraging service users' independence

Service users should always be encouraged to help themselves whenever possible. Sometimes care workers can discourage service users from doing things for themselves as the workers feel it is faster and easier to do it for them. This is an unwise move as the service user can then become a victim of 'learned helplessness'. This is when a service user gives up doing anything for him/herself and waits for the care worker to do it; the service user then becomes dependent on the care worker. So in order to ensure that a service user maintains independence, he or she must always be encouraged to take part in looking after or caring for him/herself. A person who is not allowed to help themselves may become unable to move themselves and could become physically weaker.

A service user who is able to assist in her/his handling and moving will feel better physically or emotionally as his/her self esteem and sense of purpose will be raised. The care worker's job is also made a lot easier if the service user co-operates.

It must be remembered that a service user's respect and dignity must be maintained. If all manoeuvres are explained then this will contribute to the service user's sense of involvement in the process.

Principles of safe manual handling

1 Never manually handle unless you have no other option. Always ask, 'Do I need to handle manually?'

2 Wear appropriate clothing and footwear – clothes that are comfortable and allow for easy movement. Wear flat, comfortable and well fitting shoes.

3 Assess the person or object to be handled before commencing a manoeuvre.

4 Always select the appropriate manoeuvre and handling equipment for the task in hand.

5 Identify a team leader prior to the manoeuvre. All instructions and explanations to both the service user and any assisting carers should come from the team leader.

6 Explain the manoeuvre to the person being transferred and any assisting carer(s).

7 Prepare the handling area.

8 Where appropriate, apply the brakes on equipment. It is so easily forgotten.

9 Make a good stable base with your legs and feet. If working on a bed make a stable base with your foot and knee, and hand and arm if appropriate. Position your feet correctly to reduce spinal rotation.

10 Keep the person or object, to be transferred as close to your body as possible. (Where necessary, use personal protective equipment.)

11 Make sure of a good hand grip.

12 Test your grip and the weight, if necessary, before attempting the manoeuvre.

13 Avoid static stooping. Try to work as close to your natural, erect spinal posture as possible.

14 Know your own handling capacity and do not exceed it.

15 The team leader must give clear, precise instructions (e.g., ready, steady, slide).

16 Where appropriate, use rhythm and timing when transferring.

17 Raise the head on commencing the manoeuvre.

18 Bend the knees when transferring – not the back.

19 Never twist during a manoeuvre.

The acronyms to remember are:

A	Avoid	T	Think
A	Assess	A	Assess
R	Reduce	P	Plan/Prepare
R	Review	E	Execute and Evaluate

Ergonomics

Ergonomics is the science of fitting environments to the people working within them, and tasks to the people performing them.

Education, training and ergonomics are the three key requirements for good load management. All three are interdependent and failure to address any one of these factors can increase error, accidents and ill health.

Service User Details	Weight
Name	Body Mass Index rating
Address	
	Service user's comprehension
Date of Birth	
Key Carer	
	Cultural/Religious considerations
Disability / Weakness / Deformity	
	Behaviour that may affect safe handling
Handling Constraints	Equipment normally used by service user
Pain	
Skin lesions	
Infusions, etc.	
Other	History of falls (circle) Yes No
Rating	

Problems and capabilities	Day	Night
Walking		
Standing		
Toileting		
Transfer to bed		
From bed		
Movement in bed		
Chair to chair		
Bathing		
In/out of car		
Other		

Tasks	Methods to be used	Equipment needed	Date of risk assessment

Completed by: Date: Review date: Grade:

Manual Handling Risk Assessment Form	
Summary of Assessment	**Overall priority for remedial action (circle)**
Operations covered by this assessment:	Nil Low Medium High
	Remedial action to be taken:
	Date by which action is to be taken:
Locations:	Date for re-assessment:
	Assessor's name:
Date of assessment:	Signature:

Section A - Preliminary

Q1   Do the operations involve a significant risk of injury?   Yes/No
If 'Yes' go to Q2. If 'No', the assessment need go no further. If in doubt, answer 'Yes'

Q2   Can the operations be avoided/mechanised/automated at reasonable cost?   Yes/No
If 'No' go to Q3. If 'Yes' proceed and check that the result is satisfactory.

Q3   Are the operations clearly within the guidelines set out by the appropriate manual   Yes/No
handling operations?
If 'No' go to Section B (overleaf). If 'Yes' you may go straight to Section C if you wish.

Section B - More detailed assessment (overleaf)

Section C - Overall assessment of risk:

Q   What is your overall assessment of risk of injury?   Insignificant/
If not 'insignificant' go to section D. If 'insignificant' the assessment need   Low/Med/High
go no further.

Section D - Remedial action

Q   What remedial steps should be taken, in order of priority?

i

ii

iii

iv

v

vi

And finally: Complete the SUMMARY above
Compare it with your other manual handling assessments
Decide your priorities for action
TAKE ACTION – AND CHECK IT HAS THE DESIRED EFFECT

Section B - More detailed assessment, where necessary

Questions to consider (If the answer to a question is 'Yes', place a tick against it and then consider the level of risk)	Level of risk (tick as appropriate)				Possible remedial action (Make rough notes in this column in preparation for completing Section D)
	Yes	Low	Med	High	
The tasks – do they involve:					
• holding loads away from trunk? • twisting? • stooping? • reaching upwards? • large vertical movements? • long carrying distances? • strenuous pushing or pulling? • unpredictable movement of loads? • repetitive handling? • insufficient rest or recovery? • a work rate imposed by a process?					
The loads – are they:					
• heavy? • bulky/unwieldy? • difficult to grasp? • unstable/unpredictable? • intrinsically harmful, e.g. sharp/hot/etc.?					
The working environment – are there:					
• constraints on posture? • poor floors? • variations in levels? • hot/cold/humid conditions? • strong air movements? • poor lighting conditions?					
Individual capability – does the job:					
• require unusual capability? • constitute a hazard to those with health problems? • constitute a hazard to those who are pregnant? • call for special information or training?					
Other factors:					
• is movement or posture hindered by clothing or personal protective equipment?					

How to use equipment for moving and handling

The following aids can be used to assist a service user in sitting to standing or vice versa:

- raised chair
- raised toilet seat
- tip-up chairs/cushions
- grab rails.

The following aids can be used to encourage independent transfers or to reduce stress on the care worker:

- transfer boards
- sliding boards
- turntables
- handling belts
- handling slings
- bed/draw sheets
- towels.

The following aids can be used to move the service user on the bed:

- hand blocks
- transfer netting
- trapeze
- bed ladder
- transfer sheets
- immoturn
- bed lever.

Sliding sheets are an integral part of a minimal/no manual handling policy. They allow friction-free movement of a service user on almost any surface and help to eliminate the need for carers to lift.

The following aids can be used to assist the carer in moving the service user from bed to bed or bed to trolley, etc.:

- large transfer board
- large sliding sheet with integral bridges.

Remember

Equipment or aids selected for a particular task should:

1 reduce the handling effort from carers
2 be easy to operate
3 be capable of moving the service user in safety
4 be capable of being used in its intended location
5 be in sound condition and properly maintained
6 be suitable for the condition and comfort of the service user.

Before using any equipment, remember work assessment procedure and take into account:

- task
- load
- working environment
- individual capability.

Task

1 Improve task layout – is area accessible?
2 Improve work routine – is all equipment nearby and ready?
3 Staff should have training in handling while service user is seated.
4 Leader of team should have training in team handling.
5 Personal protective equipment should be provided.
6 Equipment must be maintained and should be easily accessible for use.

Load

1 Make the service user easier to manage perhaps by explaining what is going to happen. Even if the service user is unconscious the move should be explained in detail.
2 Make service user part of procedure if possible – if s/he can participate, encourage them.
3 Make load more stable by ensuring correct lifting equipment is used and carer is correctly balanced on floor.
4 Make service user less likely to be injured by grasping (e.g., use handling belt).

Working environment

1 Remove any space constraints, after asking service user's permission to move items of furniture that may be in the way.
2 Consider condition and nature of floor. Is it damp or wet, raised or uneven?
3 Reduce work at different levels – ensure you are working on the same level.
4 Control thermal environment – do not have care home too hot.
5 Maximise lighting conditions – being able to see everything clearly reduces the risk of accident.

Individual capability

1 Be aware of your personal capacity – only carry out manoeuvres you feel comfortable with.
2 Ensure the staff chosen for the task are appropriate, i.e. they know what they are doing and are appropriately trained.

Hoists

Hoists can be divided into three categories:

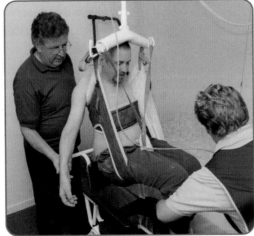
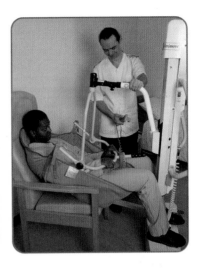

Pictures of different hoists

1 Fixed, floor-mounted hoists which are used mainly when bathing. They can be hydraulically, mechanically or electrically operated and can be useful where space is limited.

2 Overhead hoists are usually electrically operated. They can be fixed permanently overhead (ceiling) or mounted on mobile frames. Ceiling hoists run along permanently fixed tracks so they offer less flexibility in use than a mobile system. However, they do not take up as much floor space as a mobile hoist. Positively for the service user, they can be used independently, which is not possible with a floor standing system. Generally less arduous for a carer to operate than a mobile hoist, they are very suitable for larger distance transfers.

3 Mobile hoists are the largest of the three categories and can be operated hydraulically, electrically or by geared winding mechanism. As mobile hoists are self-contained units they do not need any track installation so therefore offer more flexibility of use. They do, however, demand more of the carer and are limited as they are not designed for moving people over long distances. When selecting a mobile hoist it is important to consider the environment it is to be used in. Is there enough room to manoeuvre it? Will the legs of the hoist fit around beds, chairs, etc.? Is the floor surface suitable for it to move over it easily?

Slings

Hoists are frequently used in conjunction with slings when moving service users. Slings are designed to suspend the service user whilst being transferred mechanically.

The design of the sling depends upon:

- the function
- the type of service user to be lifted
- the reason for the lift
- the condition of the service user.

Selecting the correct sling is as important as choosing the correct hoist. It requires equally careful assessment as the service user needs to be supported properly and also to feel comfortable. The sling must be suitable for the task being undertaken.

There are a range of slings available in different sizes including:

- hammock style
- divided leg
- toileting/access
- dressing
- amputee slings.

It is also possible to have slings made to order to meet service users' individual needs. Slings that can

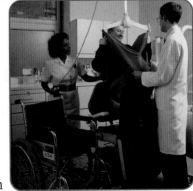

Sling

be easily laundered as well as ones with a protective anti-bacterial coating are useful in multi-user facilities. Some manufacturers supply colour-coded slings to make right type/size selection easier.

Transfer boards/slide boards

These come in a range of designs – straight, curved with or without hand-holes – for use in a variety of different situations. They enable a service user to be transferred by a care worker, if not able to move independently, from one level surface to another, e.g. from bed to chair, chair to wheelchair, wheelchair to car seat. They can also be used by a service user to help transfer him/herself. These are covered with ultra-low friction material.

Slide sheets

For less independently mobile individuals, slide sheets can facilitate movement without the need to lift. These are made from ultra-low friction material which allows a carer to turn a service user or move them off a bed on to a trolley or vice versa without causing pain or any damage to delicate skin.

Turntable

Turntable or transfer disc

This allows for smooth controllable turning without the carer having to twist him/herself. There are no jerky movements which could be uncomfortable for the service user. There is little risk of loss of balance and the likelihood of injury to both service user and carer is much reduced. Most turntables have non-slip surfaces which add to the service user's security.

Leg lifters

Lifting the legs into or out of bed, or moving their position in a chair, can be tiring or difficult for a disabled person. Powered or manual leg lifters could be the solution. Recent research suggests that manual leg lifters may be particularly useful for people with impairments that only affect their legs. Powered leg lifters benefit those service users with more generalised disabilities hindering their ability to balance while sitting.

Leg lifter

Some service users may need assistance to move from lying to sitting – two ways of helping them could be use of a monkey pole or a bed ladder.

Monkey pole

This offers a horizontal bar to help with independent movement between sitting and standing positions and a trapeze handle to enable the service user to pull themselves upright from lying to sitting.

Monkey pole

Bed ladder

This is another solution which is based on a rope ladder. This bed ladder lies on the surface of the bed enabling the service user to pull themselves up to a sitting position, hand over hand.

Remember any handling aid should:

- reduce the handling effort required from carers
- be easy to use
- be capable of moving the service user in safety
- be capable of being used in its intended location
- be in sound condition and properly maintained
- be suitable for the condition and comfort of the service user.

Principles of safe hoist and sling use

1 Wear appropriate clothing and footwear.
2 Assess the service user before hoist lifting. Is the service user suitable for a hoist lift?
3 Always select the appropriate hoist, sling and attachments for the task in hand.
4 Check that the sling and hoist are in good condition.
5 Check your posture whilst hoisting.
6 Explain the lift and manoeuvre to the service user and any assisting carer(s).
7 Prepare the handling area. A great deal of room is often needed to operate a hoist safely. Practise the manoeuvre before lifting the service user, to ensure there is sufficient space.
8 Place the service user in the centre of the sling, ensuring that the sling is correctly applied and free of creases.
9 Attach the sling to the hoist correctly.
10 Explain the procedure to the service user once again prior to lifting. Reassure him/her.
11 Raise and transfer the service user smoothly and efficiently. If necessary, have another carer available to prevent the sling from swinging or moving unduly.
12 Minimise the amount of time that the service user remains suspended in a sling. Once again, comfort is a consideration.
13 Ensure that the service user is correctly positioned in the new location to prevent further manual handling once the sling is removed.
14 Remove the sling carefully to avoid damage to the service user's skin.
15 Pack away all equipment.

Example of checklist for moving and handling assessment of risks

---

CHECKLIST FOR MOVING AND HANDLING

1 Name of person ....

2 Height of person ....

  Weight of person ....

3 Number of staff needed to assist ....

4 Are required number of staff available? ☐ Yes ☐ No

5 Level of mobility of service user ☐ Good ☐ Poor

6 Can service user assist in move? ☐ Yes ☐ No

7 What pieces of lifting equipment are needed?

☐ Hoist ☐ Sling ☐ Transfer board ☐ Trapeze

8 Is necessary equipment available? ☐ Yes ☐ No

9 If the equipment not available is the alternative safe? ☐ Yes ☐ No

10 Special considerations (e.g. attached to drip)

....

Assessment activity 4.2.3

Moving and handling   CASE STUDY

Ada is 86 and suffers from senile dementia which makes her behaviour unpredictable. One day she is pleasant and co-operative, the next day she is not. Ada is 5ft 1in and weighs over 13 stones. She has arthritis and her movement is very restricted.

1. a Explain how a risk assessment should be carried out for Ada.

   b Describe the environmental steps care workers should take before moving Ada.

   c Identify two pieces of equipment that could be used to move Ada. Explain the advantages and disadvantages of each.

   d Give advice to care workers about moving and handling service users like Ada.

2. Kim is the nominated Health and Safety representative who works at Manor Nursing Home. Most of the service users are not mobile and have to be moved from the bed to chairs each morning. When this is carried out, care workers have to ensure that there is minimum risk to service users and carers. Regulations give strict guidelines about how moving and handling should be carried out.

   Care workers at the nursing home use transfer boards and hoists to move service users, therefore keeping hazardous lifting to a minimum.

   a Name and give the date of a Regulation which provides instructions for moving and handling people.

   b Explain how employers and care workers at Manor Nursing Home should prepare before moving and handling service users.

   c Explain how transfer boards would be used when moving and handling service users at Manor Nursing Home, analysing the benefits to service users.

4.2.4 Contribution to infection control

Cross infection

When working in care settings, it is important that precautions are taken to prevent the spread of infection, particularly **cross infection**. Cross infection is the passing of infection from one person to another. It is the biggest killer of NHS patients and occurs when microbes are passed from one person to another. This can happen in many different ways from:

- the clothes of a care worker
- the hands of a care worker, especially when unwashed or when using the same pair of gloves for more than one service user
- droplets of infection in the air (breathing it in)
- inadequately sterilised equipment or instruments
- inadequately washed linen.

Simple precautions such as washing the hands between service users, wearing the care uniform only at work and ensuring all equipment and linen are adequately sterilised will contribute to the control of cross infection. Cleaning, disinfecting and sterilising are essential components of an infection-free environment.

Hand washing procedures

Step 1
Wet hands thoroughly under warm running water. Squirt liquid soap onto the palm of one of the hands.

Step 2
Rub hands together to give a good lather.

Step 3
Rub the palm of one hand along the back of the other and along the fingers. Then repeat with the other hand.

Step 4
Rub in between each of the fingers on both hands and around the thumbs.

Step 5
Rinse off the soap with clean water.

Step 6
Dry hands thoroughly on disposable towel.

The importance of wearing protective clothing and knowing its purpose

Gloves

Gloves act as a protective barrier against infection. Gloves must fit properly and must not have any holes or tears. Hands should be washed before and after using gloves. Any contact with body fluid (e.g., blood, mucus, sputum, vomit or urine) or body waste (e.g., faeces) necessitates that the care worker wears gloves. Contact with service users who have sores, wounds, rashes, bleeding or any broken skin also requires the wearing of gloves. When cleaning up spilt body fluid or blood, or dealing with soiled bedding or dressings, gloves should be worn.

Plastic aprons

A plastic apron or gown should be worn when dealing with any procedure which involves body fluids or waste. This is because the apron can be removed at the end of the procedure and thrown away. The apron will stop the spread of infection by preventing the care worker's clothing coming into contact with the infection and spreading it on to the next person.

Masks

A disposable mask will protect the mouth and nose from any procedures that produce droplets of body fluids or blood. If a service user is coughing for prolonged periods, wearing a mask would be a sensible precaution.

Overshoes

Overshoes should be worn when there is the possibility of feet being splashed by body fluids or blood.

With all of the above disposal personal protective equipment, care should be taken to wash hands both before and after wearing. All equipment should be removed carefully and disposed of safely. **Never** wear the same piece of personal protective equipment for more than one service user.

Personal hygiene

One of the most effective ways of cutting down on cross infection is washing hands using the correct procedure. Hands must be washed as many times as necessary – after using the toilet, after dealing with a service user, after coughing and sneezing, etc. Hair, if hanging on the face, should be tied back, as this could spread infection. Jewellery, which can harbour bacteria, must be kept to a minimum. Ideally, uniforms should be left at work and changed into at the beginning of a shift. It should be changed regularly and washed at 60°C to ensure microbes are destroyed. Footwear should be comfortable and closed as open shoes such as sandals can be dangerous where scissors and needles are in use, and where body fluids or blood spillages are likely.

Special precautions

Special precautions are necessary when dealing with a service user who has a certain type of infection such as **MRSA** or some other highly infectious condition. In these circumstances the workplace will have special measures in place to protect staff and service users. These precautions should be strictly adhered to. Soiled linen should be placed in red bags direct into the laundry and the bags will disintegrate in the wash.

In recent years, rising levels of health care associated infection (HAI) such as MRSA have gained prominence in the media and in politics, leading to great public concern. All NHS organisations are required to put infection control and basic hygiene at the heart of good management and clinical practice and ensure that appropriate resources are allocated.

Standard precautions

Standard precautions, also known as universal precautions, must be used by all health and social care workers to prevent the spread of micro-organisms that may cause infection. Standard precautions should be used at all times, whether an infection is known to be present or not, when dealing with:

- blood
- excretions (e.g., urine, faeces, vomit – not sweat)
- secretions (e.g., saliva, sputum).

Standard precautions are there to protect the carer, the service user, other health and social care workers, visitors, relatives and friends.

There are nine main standard precautions which can help in the prevention and control of infection. Standard precautions were formerly called universal precautions sometimes known as Standard Infection Control Precautions (SICPS)

Summary of standard precautions	
Standard precaution	**Reason**
1 **Perform hand hygiene** • when necessary, e.g. before and after contact with service user or before or after wearing gloves • in most appropriate way – it may be hand washing and drying or using alcohol solutions or gels.	This is the single most important precaution to protect against cross infection.
2 **Use personal protective equipment (PPE)** • gloves • aprons – gowns – footwear • eye and face protection.	To protect skin, face, eyes, mouth and clothing from soiling/splashing/contamination and potentially harmful micro-organisms.
3 **Prevent occupational exposure to infection** • cover all breaks in skin • avoid sharps injuries • avoid splashes with blood or body fluids • report any exposure incidents.	To protect health and social care workers, carers and others from exposure to micro-organisms that cause infection, e.g. MRSA, HIV, etc.
4 **Manage blood and body fluid spillages** • immediately they have occurred as stated in setting policy. Disinfect area.	To protect all of those in surrounding area from exposure to micro-organisms in spillages that could cause harm.
5 **Manage care equipment** • prevent re-use of disposable items • ensure re-usable devices are decontaminated between use • prevent any associated environmental contamination • ensure safe handling of contaminated items.	To ensure equipment is not instrumental in the spread of potentially infectious micro-organisms.
6 **Control of environment** • ensure cleaning and maintenance schedules and responsibilities are clear.	To ensure fitting and fixtures in care setting are adequately decontaminated and maintained to prevent cross infection taking place.
7 **Safely dispose of waste – including sharps** • know procedure for safe disposal of clinical waste.	To prevent avoidable exposure to micro-organisms which could harm health and social care workers, service users and others.
8 **Safely manage linen** • safe storage, handling, transport and processing.	To prevent avoidable exposure to micro-organisms that could harm health and social care workers, service users and others.
9 **Provide care in most appropriate place** • if there is a concern seek advice from Infection Control Team.	To prevent spread of infection through inappropriate placements or transport of service users.

How to maintain personal safety when dealing with, and disposing of, clinical waste and instruments

Clinical waste is anything that is contaminated by body fluids. This is potentially hazardous to the care worker who may have to deal with it on a regular basis. Clinical waste can be divided into five categories – see table below. The category of the waste determines the packaging and labelling requirements. If a risk assessment shows that sanitary towels, tampons, nappies, **stoma bags** or incontinence pads do not present a significant risk of infection, they need not be classed as clinical waste. However, the offensiveness of non-infectious waste needs to be taken into account when packaging waste for disposal.

Waste group	Types of clinical waste
Group A	Identifiable human tissue, blood, soiled surgical dressings, swabs and other similar soiled waste. Other waste materials, e.g. from infectious disease cases, excluding any in Groups B–E.
Group B	Discarded syringe needles, cartridges, broken glass and any other contaminated disposable sharp instruments or items.
Group C	Microbiological cultures and potentially infected waste from pathology departments and other clinical or research laboratories.
Group D	Drugs or other pharmaceutical products.
Group E	Items used to dispose of urine, faeces and other bodily secretions or excretions that do not fall within Group A. This includes the use of disposable bedpans or bedpan liners, incontinence pads, stoma bags and urine containers.

Staff need to be given clear information, instruction and training on what is clinical waste and what constitutes domestic waste. There is a widely used system of colour coding to help with waste segregation:

- YELLOW – Group A clinical waste for incineration or other suitable means of disposal.
- YELLOW with BLACK STRIPES – non-infectious waste, e.g. Group E and sanpro (sanitary towels, tampons, nappies, stoma bags, incontinence pads). Waste suitable for landfill or other means of disposal.
- BLACK – non-clinical or household waste.

These disposable sacks should **never** be filled more than three-quarters full.

Group B must be disposed of in sharps containers which meet the requirements of BS 7320:1990 and are UN type approved. When the sharps bin is three-quarters full the container should be sealed. Sharps must **not** be placed in bags at any time. Sharps containers should not be left lying around where children or vulnerable people could gain access. Needles should **not** be re-sheathed after use but must be placed directly in sharps bin. Used needles must **never** be disposed of in domestic waste.

All chemical waste must be stored in a secure, enclosed space prior to removal from the care setting.

All employees who are required to handle and move clinical waste must be adequately trained in safe procedures and how to deal with spillages. Procedures will need to be drawn up to cover arrangements for suitable medical advice and counselling if a sharps injury occurs. Spillage kits contain disposable aprons, latex-free gloves, clinical waste bag and tag, paper towels and sodium hypochlorite, and instructions help to ensure that staff take the correct action.

Staff in health care settings can be at risk from infections carried in blood and body fluids, e.g. hepatitis B. However, steps can be taken to minimise the risk of contamination from blood/body fluids. Precautions that could be taken include:

- covering cuts/grazes with waterproof dressings before starting work;
- good environmental hygiene – cleaning and disinfecting contaminated equipment (if not disposable) after use and keeping the environment clean;
- wearing latex-free gloves, disposable aprons, etc., for high risk/messy activities.

Staff should have clear instructions on how to clear up and disinfect a spillage of body fluids/blood. This should include how to mop up the spillage, preparing the chemicals, applying the chemicals to the spillage site and the final clearing up. Staff should be aware of the personal protective equipment (PPE) that needs to be worn.

Both clinical waste and risk assessment for infections are covered by Control of Substances Hazardous to Health Regulations 1999 (COSHH).

Accident report

The Reporting of Injuries and Dangerous Occurrences Regulations 1995 (RIDDOR) require employers and others to report certain types of injury, occupational ill health and dangerous occurrences that arise in connection with work.

Reporting an accident does not suggest accepting responsibility for the event or that an offence has been committed; it is merely informing the relevant authority that an accident has occurred. Failure to report a reportable injury, dangerous occurrence or disease within the set time is a criminal offence.

What should be reported?

Under RIDDOR, some work-related accidents, diseases and dangerous occurrences must be reported. If accidents happen at work, whether it is to the carer or the service user being cared for, then the details must be recorded in the accident book. This applies whether there is an injury or not. The accident should also be reported to the manager or person in charge.

The accident report should be completed with name/s of any witness/es. The following must be recorded on the accident report:

- date and time of accident
- place where accident took place
- people involved
- details of what was observed
- help summoned with time of calling
- time help arrived
- names and contact numbers of other witnesses
- condition of person after accident.

It is essential that accident records are completed accurately as this is a legal document. The report provides information for any future legal action. For example, if someone was seriously injured as a result of assistance not being called immediately then legal action for negligence could follow.

The accident reports provide information for the care setting about the types of accidents that occur regularly on their premises – perhaps a risk assessment needs to be carried out. It could highlight improvement that should be made to make the care setting safer.

Records are available for inspection by any Health and Safety Inspector and could provide a wealth of information about the setting's safety record.

As a result of an accident report the injured person will receive the correct medical treatment. It could also provide information if the person needs treatment at a later stage, due to delayed reaction to the incident.

Assessment activity 4.2.4

Contribution to infection control
CASE STUDY

At Manor Nursing Home, two service users have an infection. The staff do not want other service users to be affected by the infection:

1. Explain what is meant by the term 'cross infection'.

2. Describe **three** circumstances where cross infection could occur.

3. Outline how standard or universal precautions help to prevent the spread of infection in care settings.

4. You have been asked to give advice to the manager of the nursing home about the Health and Safety Law poster.

   Give **four** pieces of information which should be included in the poster and the purpose of each piece.

Contents

About this unit

Within this unit you will investigate:

- the causes of additional needs and the effects of additional needs on service users

- the care management process and key roles of service providers who support service users with additional needs

- models or approaches used to support service users, recognising attitudes and values of society towards service users with additional needs

- a service user who has an additional need, including the barriers experienced, support, aids and adaptations used, and evaluate their impact on the service user.

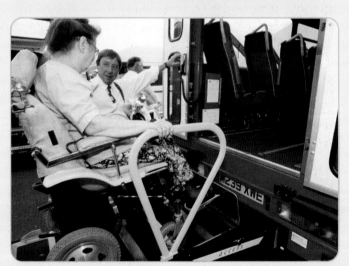

Caring for people with disabilities

Introducing this unit

All care workers have a responsibility to apply the care values when providing care. This is especially so when working with people who have disabilities. Care workers have a legal and moral responsibility to ensure discrimination, on the basis of disability, does not take place in the care setting and in their professional practice. Caring for others as we would like to be cared for ourselves is important. Care workers need to develop their own positive, professional approach to caring, which will empower and support service users in their day-to-day living experience.

Understanding the types and causes of disability and the effects these may have on service users is an important aspect of the professional care worker's role. Although the international symbol for 'disability' is a wheelchair, only a small percentage of disabled people are wheelchair users. Some disabilities can be 'invisible' which causes additional problems for people, for example those who have dyslexia.

The care management process is an important part of a professional care worker's role as all will be contributors to the process. Understanding the different stages of the care management cycle and the different roles that professionals can take during the various stages is also an essential aspect of caring.

Service users with additional needs would prefer to experience the same access, the same considerations, the same positive attitudes as those that are able bodied. This will only be achieved if those who provide care have a real and genuine desire to make this possible.

5.2.1 Common causes of disability

There are many causes of physical, sensory and learning impairment. The problems that can cause disability can be many and varied and may involve the senses as well as body functions and mobility. Service users who are impaired or have a disability do not wish to be treated differently from those who are able bodied.

Hereditary conditions

Many hereditary diseases are passed on within families from one generation to the next. Just as children may inherit normal features such as brown eyes or curly hair from one or both parents, children can also inherit certain disorders. Whether or not a specific trait or disorder is inherited is determined by hereditary material called '**genes**'. Genes are the units of hereditary material. They contain coded instructions that direct the development of every cell and tissue in the human body. Genes can be thought of as blueprints, specifying how the body will develop and function.

Thousands of genes are found on thread-like structures, called **chromosomes**, which are located in the centre or 'nucleus' of each cell. Genes and chromosomes exist in pairs. At the time of conception, each parent contributes one gene and one chromosome from each of his or her genes and chromosome pairs. The genes and chromosomes from each parent combine into new pairs that determine the **characteristics** a child inherits.

Generally genes produce normal traits but sometimes a gene becomes altered from its original form. A gene that is thus changed is called a '**mutant**' gene. Although researchers know that mutations occur, they do not completely understand the reasons. Some mutations are not harmful, but most often a mutant gene causes a disorder, malfunction, or malformation within the body.

Mutations can occur in any family generation. If a **spontaneous** mutation occurs, it is then possible for a child to be the first family member to get a genetic disorder even though both parents are normal. There are many different genetic disorders, some of which are listed below:

- cystic fibrosis
- haemophilia
- sickle cell anaemia
- muscular dystrophy.

Chromosomal abnormalities

A child with Down's syndrome

Down's syndrome is a chromosome disorder – a disease caused by a visible abnormality of the chromosomes, rather than a mutation affecting a single gene. In Down's syndrome, the abnormality is a complete extra copy of chromosome 21. The most severe chromosome disorders involve the loss or gain of whole chromosomes. Such abnormalities change the copy number of hundreds or even thousands of genes causing a gross imbalance of the gene products.

The presence of an extra autosome (extra chromosome) is usually **incompatible** with full-term development and results in spontaneous abortion. However, a few can survive to term because the additional chromosome has relatively few genes (chromosomes 13, 18 and 21, with fewer than 500 genes each). Those with Down's syndrome are the only ones capable of living a normal lifespan and this may be because chromosome 21 contains only about 240 genes. The extra copy of chromosome 21 appears when the paired chromosomes fail to separate as the cell divides, leaving one cell with two copies and the other with none. If the cell with two copies of chromosome 21 becomes an egg or a sperm, fertilisation will produce an embryo with three copies. More rarely, one copy of chromosome 21 can become irreversibly attached to another chromosome (translocation Down's syndrome), and in some cases both copies of chromosome 21 can be fused together and behave as a single chromosome.

The incidence of Down's syndrome is about one in 700 live births, but more are found in spontaneous abortions. This suggests the incidence per conception is much higher. The incidence of Down's syndrome is strongly related to maternal age. Down's has an incidence of one in 1,500 in young mothers (early 20s) but rises sharply to as much as one in 30 by the time the mother is 45. The recurrence risk (risk of having a subsequent Down's child if one has already been born) also rises with maternal age and is higher for translocation Down's syndrome, which runs in families.

Symptoms

The symptoms of Down's syndrome include:

- mild to moderate mental retardation
- limited growth
- characteristic facial features (slanting eyes sometimes with a squint, small ears, open mouth with protruding tongue, small nose)
- and in about 50 per cent of cases, a simian-like crease across the palm, sometimes accompanied by fused fingers (syndactyly).

Two-thirds of Down's conceptions are spontaneously aborted and many individuals with the disease die in childhood. However, life expectancy can be as high as 40–50, and there is no effect on fertility. A small number of children have been born to Down's women, about equal numbers of which have been normal and Down's.

The life expectancy of Down's individuals is lower than normal because the disease symptoms often include heart defects (such as ventricular septal defects) and problems with the duodenum and colon. Older Down's patients are at increased risk of developing Alzheimer's disease.

Environmental factors

More than 120 diseases have been definitively linked to pollution, and in another 33, evidence of a link is judged to be 'good'. For the rest, the evidence is 'limited'. Nine different pollutants have been identified that have the capability to cause asthma – including four from car exhausts. In a study in the *Independent on Sunday* it was shown that:

- Testicular atrophy is caused by oestrogen, increasingly found in British rivers that supply drinking water, the source of which is the contraceptive pill.
- Mercury poisoning can cause cerebral palsy.
- More than 50 pollutants – ranging from dioxins to PCBs – have been shown to cause cancer.

Other effects of pollution on the body can include:

- kidney disease
- heart disease
- hypertension (high blood pressure)
- diabetes
- dermatitis (skin disease)
- bronchitis
- hyperactivity
- deafness
- sperm damage
- Alzheimer's
- Parkinson's disease.

Air pollution

Air pollution can cause disease

Research suggests air pollution is responsible for 310,000 premature deaths in Europe each year. A study by the European Commission calculated that air pollution reduces life expectancy by an average of almost nine months across the European Union. The figures show that workers take on average half a day off sick a year due to illnesses linked to air pollution – costing the European economy more than £55 billion.

The main threat to health is posed by tiny particles known as particulate matter, which can enter the respiratory tissue and also the bloodstream. Particulates are emitted by traffic, particularly diesel engines, industry and domestic heating. Ozone, produced when sunlight reacts with pollutants emitted by vehicle exhausts, is also a major cause of respiratory disease. Poor air quality is thought to result in more than 32,000 premature deaths in the UK each year from problems such as heart and lung disease.

In some EU countries premature deaths due to particulate matter are even higher:

Country	Number of deaths per year caused by particulate matter
Germany	65,088
Italy	39,436
France	36,868
UK	32,652
Poland	27,934
Spain	13,939
Netherlands	13,123
Hungary	11,067
Belgium	10,669
Czech Republic	7,996
Austria	4,634

Central Office of Information

The levels of air pollution that are usually experienced in the UK are unlikely to have any serious short-term effects on people who are in good health. On the rare occasions when air pollution levels are high, some people may feel eye irritation, others may start to cough, and some may have breathing difficulties.

Pollution can be a factor in the development of lung diseases or heart conditions and can put greater risk on older adults. Daily changes in air pollution can trigger increased admissions to hospital. It can also contribute to the premature death of those who are seriously ill.

The following table describes the health effects that individuals might experience at very high levels of pollutants.

Pollutant	Health effects at very high levels
Nitrogen dioxide Sulphur dioxide Ozone	Irritation of the airways, increasing the symptoms in those suffering from lung diseases.
Particulates	Fine particles can be carried deep into the lungs where they can cause inflammation and a worsening of heart and lung diseases.
Carbon monoxide	This gas prevents the normal transport of oxygen by the blood. This can lead to a significant reduction in the supply of oxygen to the heart, particularly in people suffering from heart disease.

Julian   Activity 1

Julian suffers from Down's syndrome and asthma and is, therefore, affected by the levels of pollution in the air. Because of his condition, his parents are always cautious with any activity that could affect his health.

1. Do you think that Julian's asthma is hereditary? Explain the genetic process that has caused Julian to have Down's syndrome.

2. Describe the environmental conditions that could have a negative effect on Julian's asthma.

3. What other medical problems could Julian develop?

4. Explain how environmental factors could cause disability.

Water pollution

It is estimated that 60 to 80 per cent of all cancers are environmental in origin. There is a growing concern that the majority of cancers are preventable because chemical carcinogens in the environment cause them. Several studies have demonstrated the presence of chemical carcinogens in surface, ground water and treated drinking water. Chemicals known as **trihalomethanes** can actually be produced during the chlorination of our drinking water.

Where water remains untreated, people run the risk of catching disease from bacteria and viruses. Diseases from untreated water can include:

- typhoid
- dysentery
- Weil's disease.

Discussion point

How much health benefit would society gain from replacing existing vehicle engines with electrically powered alternatives?

Accidents

Accidents can be avoided

Accidents are common throughout life. Most of them are not serious, but a significant number each year cause disability.

Every year 10,000 people die from accidental injury and it is the leading cause of death among children aged 0–14 years. There are many millions of non-fatal accidents each year and 2.8 million of them occur in the home. Many are caused by falls and others by fires. Over 300,000 people are hurt in road traffic accidents and 95 per cent of them are adults. In these ways accidental injury takes a heavy toll of society, particularly children and older people. And it strikes hardest at the most disadvantaged. Over half a million accidents result in admission to hospital for treatment and this costs the NHS a staggering £2 billion a year. The consequences simply of injuries received at home cost society a further £25 billion a year.

The list of possible causes of accidents is endless. Road traffic accidents are a major cause of fatal accidents, especially when the pedestrian is a child, followed by fire, drowning, suffocation, falls, inhalation of a foreign body, and poisoning. Head injury leading to brain damage is the main cause of disability from accidents, while accidents that cause

disfigurement or cosmetic damage, such as burns and scars, can lead to profound psychological problems.

Accidents can lead to traumatic injuries, for example damage to normally functioning tissues such as broken bones, cuts and wounds, bruises and haemorrhages, burns and scalds, which are clearly related to the event. But sometimes the lack of any obvious harm can be falsely reassuring.

In particular, trauma to the abdomen can lead to internal injuries, such as a ruptured spleen. This may not be apparent at first but can cause the sudden onset of severe symptoms, such as collapse, some time later. The effects of accidental poisoning and of smoke inhalation are two other examples. The effects of accidents are many and varied. The dysfunctions that occur can be sensory, physical and, in the young, can affect learning.

Disease-related causes

Acute and chronic diseases are prolonged conditions that often do not improve and are rarely cured completely. Diabetes, depression, congestive heart failure, hepatitis and asthma are examples of chronic diseases.

Acute and chronic illness has a profound effect on the physical, emotional and mental well being of individuals, often making it difficult to carry on with daily routines and relationships. However, in many cases, deterioration in health can be minimised by good care. This often depends upon individual choices made on a daily basis.

Health concerns are usually classified as either acute or chronic. Acute illnesses usually begin abruptly and last only a short time. Most people with an acute illness can expect to return to normal health. A throat infection is an example of an acute illness: it is easy to diagnose and is cured with antibiotics.

Chronic diseases are different. They usually develop slowly, last long periods of time, and are often never cured. In most cases, there is no cure and the long-term effects may be difficult to predict. Some conditions cause few problems whilst others cause only **episodic** problems or symptoms that can be controlled with medication.

However, in some cases, a chronic disease may severely limit a person's ability to work, go to school or take care of routine needs. Examples of chronic diseases include:

- diabetes
- congestive heart failure
- asthma
- hypertension
- chronic kidney disease
- depression
- irritable bowel syndrome
- arthritis
- emphysema
- multiple sclerosis.

Despite the wide variety of diseases, there are many similar concerns for those who live with them. Such concerns may include:

- knowing how to recognise and respond to changes in a disease
- dealing with problems and emergencies
- using medicines and treatments effectively
- finding and using community resources
- getting enough exercise
- coping with fatigue, pain and sleep problems
- maintaining good nutrition
- making decisions about when to seek medical help
- working with doctor(s) and other care providers
- talking about illness with family and friends
- managing work, family and social activities.

Chronic conditions impose challenges for those affected, their families and care providers. A patient's ability to follow medical advice, accommodate lifestyle changes, and access resources such as education are all factors that influence successful management of an ongoing illness.

The management of the disease or illness involves many people from all sectors of the health system sharing a common vision and working together. They not only support health service delivery but assist them with developing self-management strategies.

Discussion point

How should we support disease-related disability, impairment and learning difficulty in society today?

Birth injury

Although most women give birth in a hospital, a birth injury can happen at almost any point during the labour and delivery. A baby with a birth injury may recover fully and quickly, or may suffer life-long damage as a result of the birth injury. If the baby does not receive enough oxygen during delivery then there is the possibility that brain damage can occur due to the lack of oxygen. This may lead to both physical and cognitive development problems. Many types of birth injuries can occur during a prolonged or difficult labour. Premature birth, large newborn size, abnormal birth presentation, and other complications can all increase the risk of birth injuries. The most common types of birth injuries include:

Caput succedaneum – is a birth injury that affects a newborn's head. Caput succedaneum is a severe swelling and/or bruising of a baby's scalp that usually disappears within one to two weeks. Traumatic vacuum extraction during delivery is most likely to cause this type of birth injury.

Cephalohaematoma – is another birth injury that affects a newborn's head and is usually temporary. Bleeding occurs in an area beneath one of the cranial bones in the head. If the bleeding is extensive it can cause jaundice.

Subconjunctival haemorrhage – is a birth injury that causes small blood vessels in a baby's eye to break but does not do any permanent damage to the child's eyes. This birth injury usually resolves itself after one to two weeks.

Forceps laceration and bruising – causes damage to the newborn's head.

Facial paralysis – can occasionally occur in a newborn's face. This happens when there is excessive pressure on the face during delivery and may require surgery to correct it.

Brachial plexus palsy – is another type of birth injury that may require surgery. This injury occurs during shoulder dystocia (difficult birth due to the position of the baby) and can result in paralysis in the upper arms. This often resolves itself but can require surgical correction.

Fractures – the most common fractures that can occur during childbirth are fractures of the clavicle or collarbone. Immediate treatment is required for these types of birth injuries.

Cerebral palsy – is one of the most serious types of birth injuries that a child can develop.

There are many factors that can contribute to these types of birth injuries. Cerebral palsy is the general term applied to brain injury that results in impaired **motor** functioning and other chronic physical and cognitive impairments.

Development disorders

Learning disabilities can be caused by damage to the brain or central nervous system both before and after birth. In a third of all cases of learning disabilities there is no known cause. The remaining have genetic or environmental origins. Genetic causes result from inheritance or abnormal development of genes or chromosomes when a child is conceived. About 60 per cent of known causes are genetic with the two commonest causes being Down's syndrome and Fragile X.

Environmental factors account for about 40 per cent of all known causes and are related to infections during pregnancy. These can be:

- toxoplasmosis
- rubella
- substance abuse
- damage during birth
- damage through early childhood illness, e.g. encephalitis and meningitis
- damage through accidents or abuse.

Learning disability may not be obvious at birth and may show itself in the first two years of life as a delayed milestone (sitting, talking late). Often the mother is aware that something is wrong before the professionals. Diagnosis is helped by a thorough developmental history, supported by antenatal and birth history. Particular attention is paid to social and language development as being the most sensitive indicator amongst the developmental milestones. Autism can occur in up to half of all children with severe learning disability and 1–2 per cent of mild learning disability.

Discussion point

Surely learning disability is not a big problem in this day and age!

People with learning disabilities are likely to experience a much greater range and intensity of health problems than the rest of the population. People with learning disabilities have a greater number or variety of health care needs compared to those of the same age and sex in the general population. Improved life expectancy is significantly increasing the number of people with learning disabilities who are elderly and, therefore, the number with the physical and mental illnesses and disabilities associated with old age. Over 60 per cent of people with learning disabilities have one or more chronic physical or mental health problems sufficient to warrant ongoing medical intervention.

Very often GPs will have no information on the intellectual ability of the person. There is an unwillingness to recognise mild learning disability as a distinct developmental disorder. Instead it is seen as a socio-cultural problem. Yet people with learning disabilities are particularly vulnerable and need special help. Their social clumsiness and misreading of social situations can often be misread and misinterpreted. This means that health care professionals do not always recognise the true problem.

The mental health of adults with learning disabilities has become an important issue over the past 20 years. This is because their vulnerability to emotional distress has been increasingly recognised. There are real difficulties in accurate diagnosis and assessment, particularly in people with severe learning disabilities. This is why a comprehensive multi-disciplinary approach is very important. At present there are a variety of drug treatments and psychological treatments available to those with learning difficulties.

Many services routinely fail to recognise the difficult emotional life of people with learning disabilities. Depression can go undiagnosed because the symptoms are not usually disruptive. The manifestation of mood disorders in people with mild learning disability is normally no different from that of the general population.

The age of onset of schizophrenia can be earlier in the learning disabled population but the reasons are unclear. It is generally accepted that the presentation of schizophrenia in people with mild learning disabilities is similar to that of the general public.

Epilepsy and its treatment can worsen cognitive function by impairing attention and the capacity to process incoming information.

Sensory impairment

Sensory impairment covers:

- sight
- hearing
- touch
- taste
- smell.

It is impairment of sight and hearing which are more common but hidden impairments, such as lack of taste, can cause as much distress to service users. The sensory organs provide information about the environment outside the body, for example if it is cold the body will respond by shivering.

A receptor in the sense organs responds to a particular stimulus by producing nerve impulses. Different receptors monitor conditions outside the body, the external environment; and the conditions inside the body, the internal environment.

Those that are responsive to the external environment are:

- rods and cones in the eyes, which are sensitive to light
- organs of Corti in the ears that are sensitive to sound

- taste buds on the tongue that are sensitive to stimuli
- olfactory cells in the nose that are sensitive to chemical stimuli
- receptors in the skin that are sensitive to touch, pressure, pain, heat and cold.

The sense organs convert stimuli into nerve impulses and the brain interprets these impulses as particular sensations depending on which sense organ sends them.

The needs of service users will vary according to which type of impairment they experience, but it is likely that service users will have more than one need, for example a person who is blind may have physical, intellectual, emotional and social needs (P.I.E.S.).

Discussion point

A child is born blind. What will be its physical, intellectual, emotional and social needs?

An adult has loss of smell. Discuss the impact on the person and their needs.

Examples of sensory impairments are:

Organ	Impairment	Effect/needs of service user
Nose	Sinusitis	Mucous membrane becomes inflamed and can swell producing abundant mucus which causes headaches.
	Anosmia	Loss of smell which takes away the quality of life as the individual is not motivated by the smells of food cooking or alerted to the danger of gas or chemicals in the environment.
Eyes	Short sight (myopia)	Individuals can only see things that are close at hand. Glasses or contact lens can help with the problem.
	Long sight (hypermetropia)	Distant things can be seen clearly but items close can seem blurred.
	Blindness	Very little can be seen by the individual. Total blindness is rare. Braille may help a person to read, while guide dogs are often used to help with mobility.
	Colour blindness	This affects men more than women and means that the individual does not have the ability to distinguish colours. Red-green colour blindness is the most common form.
Ear	Deafness	This can be partial or total. Hearing aids can help those who have partial hearing. Sign language and Makaton could be useful when communicating for those who are totally deaf.
Skin	Anaesthesia	Loss of the sense of touch in all parts of the body.

Assessment activity (AO1)

Disability awareness   CASE STUDY

You must use a **range** of sources to provide information for a disability awareness day that is to take place at the health promotion unit. You will be required to carry out research and to provide detailed information to give a comprehensive account of:

- **Three** causes of additional needs for service users, showing a thorough explanation of the:
  - short-term effects on service users
  - long-term effects on service users

Make sure you cover all aspects of P.I.E.S.

Case studies could be used to convey the information to others.

Remember: to keep a bibliography and to reference within the text the sources of information used.

5.2.2 The care management process

Accurate assessment is important

Tailoring services to meet the individual needs of service users who have a disability or impairment is an important part of the care management process. The care management process is a system for assessing and organising the provision of care for an individual. Even when a service user appears to have the same condition as another, their needs will be different because of their circumstances.

The main focus of care management is to find the best way of achieving the objectives that have been agreed during the assessment process in order to meet the needs of the service user. Decisions have to be made about who could be the best provider of the services required from the possible resources available. It is important that within the care programme the resources are the best fit for the service user and not which resources best fit the client!

Discussion point

Why is it important not to fit the resources to the client?

If resources are wasted, or if they are duplicated, it is possible that the service user will not be receiving the best possible care and that money will be wasted.

The stages involved in care management

The care management process is a **cyclical** process. There are seven main stages in the process. These include:

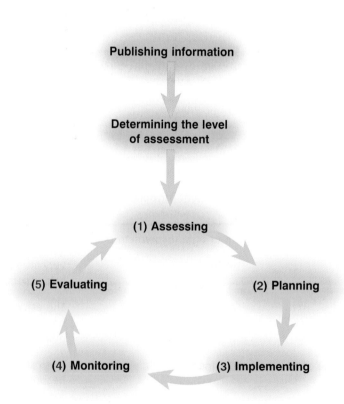

Publishing information

At this stage of the process care agencies provide information about the type of care they can offer, when they can offer it and a broad indication of costs. The care agencies clearly indicate, to both service user and to Social Services, the areas of care for which they are prepared to take responsibility. This is usually published as an information leaflet or in the form of a booklet or guide. Both service user and Social Services are then fully aware of what services are available for their use. Such services, if used, will have to be purchased, either by Social Services, if they are to be provided free to the service user, or by the service user themselves. The latter is usual if the service user has an income which is above that determined by the government for receiving free care.

Service Available in the Broadmead Area

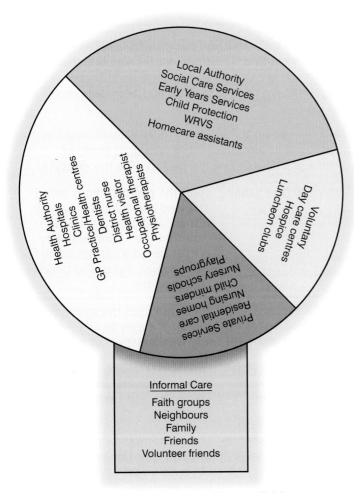

Published information about services available

Determining the level of assessment

A decision has to be made as to whether an assessment of need is of a simple or complex nature. The service user making an enquiry will indicate whether, for example, they need an assessment for one particular need or whether there are multiple needs that require assessment.

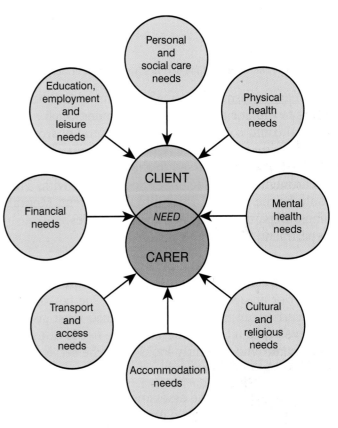

Determination of need

Stage 1: The assessment

Let's see if you can work out what to do with this piece of equipment

People with a disability should be provided services according to the level of risk to their independence that may occur if their needs are not met (Fair Access to Care Service Guidance, FACS). Four different types of assessment considered by FACS are:

- Initial assessment

- Assessments which considers wider needs

- Specialist assessments

- Comprehensive assessments.

Source: Fair Access to Care Services (Department of Health, 2002)

When an assessment is sought, a referral will be made to the Social Services Department. Such a referral could come from a GP, a hospital or from another care professional. Once the enquiry is received, it will be passed to the most appropriate department within Social Services to deal with. This could be the Physical Disability Department, Mental Illness Department, or Learning Difficulties Department, for example.

Within the department a person will be allocated to assess the service user's needs, for example a social worker or an occupational therapist. The person who carries out the assessment of need must also, however, take into consideration the needs of the main carer who currently looks after the service user who is being assessed.

The order in which the assessment is carried out always follows the same pattern. That is:

- establishing the **scope** of the assessment
- deciding which location will be best for the assessment to take place
- making sure the service user is aware of the expectations
- ensuring the service user will participate in the assessment process
- making sure that a trusting relationship is established between the service user and the person undertaking the assessment
- assessing the needs of the service user
- making an agreement with the service user about the objectives
- recording the findings of the assessment
- forming a report about the results of the assessment.

When undertaking an assessment it will be important to find out what is the least that it is necessary to know. The assessor (social worker) must, therefore,

know how to target the relevant areas of need. If a complex assessment is to be carried out, a high level of skills will be needed to determine the scope of the assessment.

For example, in a complex situation it may be necessary to involve more than the assessor and the service user. An occupational therapist or a physiotherapist may also need to be involved. Assessment is between the assessor and the service user, being a two-way process that involves a great deal of trust. If other professionals are involved in the assessment, consent will need to be obtained from the service user for this to occur.

Discussion point

What other situation would be 'complex' involving the attendance of another person during assessment? Why would this be so?

An assessment, when it is carried out, will:

Principle	What will this mean?
Be person centred	Consider the whole person not just the parts that are not functioning according to the norm
View the person to be assessed in the context of their family	Look at the needs of others in the family as well as those of the person with the disability
Apply the care values	Treat the person who is being assessed and their family with respect and dignity, making sure that their confidentiality is maintained and that equal opportunity, rights and beliefs are respected
Identify the service user's weaknesses as well as their strengths	Try to build on the strengths of the service user to assist with any weaknesses that exist
Take a multi-disciplinary approach to service provision	Linking health and social care services together to provide continuity and seamlessness of service
Be based on evidence-based knowledge	Using information gained through questioning and observation on which to base decisions
Be clear	Will set out exactly what is to be assessed

Assessment is often carried out in the service user's home, if this is deemed the most suitable place. On other occasions, however, assessment may take place in an office or in a health or care setting. If a service user is considering moving into a residential home, for example, the assessment would need to take into consideration:

- whether the residential home was able to meet the needs of the service user
- whether the service user's experience of the setting is satisfactory, to make sure that he/she feels that this is a place in which they would like to live.

An assessment in the service user's home

The assessor will need to make sure that the service user is quite clear about the depth and breadth of the assessment. For example:

- what is the likely timescale for completion of the assessment?
- what will the service user be expected to do during the assessment? e.g. answer questions, do practical tasks
- the service user will need to be informed that they have the right to withdraw from the assessment at any time
- the service user has the right to know the outcome of the assessment.

During the assessment it will be important for the assessor to make sure that the service user does not confuse 'wants' with 'needs'. The service user may have made a request to move to a different type of accommodation, because they feel isolated, but the assessment may prove that only adaptations and aids will be necessary in order to meet the service user's needs.

The outcome of the assessment should be that the service user's strengths and weaknesses have been identified. It will then be possible to balance the two in order to achieve an holistic approach.

Records of the assessment will be kept by the assessor. This could involve:

- a record of questions answered
- a tick box showing which tasks were accomplished successfully and which the service user was unable to complete
- an observation sheet indicating the skills demonstrated.

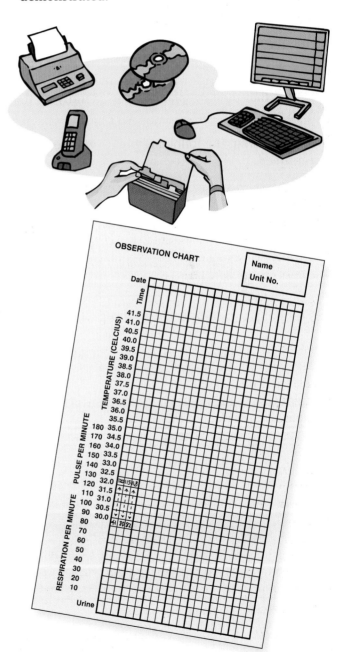

Different records used to record the assessment process

Stage 2: Care planning

Care planning is identifying the most appropriate ways of achieving the objectives set during the assessment process. This will mean that the assessor (probably a social worker), will have identified the needs of the service user and will then have to link these to the best type of resources available. They will also have to set priorities.

During the assessment, the service user's needs will be **prioritised**. The assessor will need to find out which services will best suit those needs and whether they are available. The main aim of the care plan will be to promote the independence of the service user. Any options being considered must be discussed with the service user and any relevant carers to ensure that all agree that what is being proposed is the best for that particular service user. It is vital that the care plan is clear, identifying the targets to be achieved.

When planning, the following points will need to be determined:

Needs	How needs are met	Action Taken by
Personal Hygiene	Washing morning and evening	Care Assistant
	Bathing once every 2 days	Health Care Assistant
Domestic Tasks	Cleaning kitchen and sitting room each day	Care Assistant
	Cleaning bathroom/ bedroom twice each week	Care Assistant
	Shopping twice a week	Care Assistant
Nursing Needs	Dressing on leg to be changed daily	District Nurse
	Medication to be renewed	District Nurse
Personal Needs	Putting to bed – each day	Health Care Assistant
	Getting up – each day	Health Care Assistant
Social Needs	Visit to day care centre twice each week	Social Worker

Clearly recording the care plan

Explore the resources
What is available? Will they cost the service user or social services? Are they the best to meet the service user's needs?

Consider alternatives
What alternative services are on offer? Will they cost more or less than those first considered? Will they better meet the needs of the service user?

Establish preferences
Set the proposals with the alternatives to the service user and the main professional care workers. Discuss whether these are the most suitable.

Cost the care plan
How much will the individual services cost? Can the budget meet this need? What will the service user have to contribute from a financial perspective?

Agree with the provider the objectives that will be met
Finalise the arrangements with the service user and the providers, making sure the objectives are being met.

Co-ordinate the plan
Look at the whole plan to ensure that it makes sense to all concerned.

Set the review date
The service user should be given the name of the 'key worker' and a date set for the first review.

Identify any needs which have not been met
For what reason has a need not been met?

Record the agreements made
Clearly set out the actions that have been agreed.

Stage 3: Implementing the care plan

The key worker will be responsible for ensuring that the care plan is implemented at the correct pace. Implementing means carrying out the plan, that is putting the theory into practice. The service user and the main carer(s) should be encouraged to contribute their ideas as much as possible, as the intention of any plan is to improve the quality of life for the service user and to ease the burden of caring on the main carer.

The services supplying the care will need to be carefully monitored by the key worker to ensure that:

- the expected quality of care is being provided
- the care being provided meets the objectives that were agreed
- the care being provided meets the cost agreed
- the timing of the service provision is suitable to the service user and the main carer
- any changes from the agreed plan and the reasons for such changes are recorded
- a check is made of whether there are any deficiencies within the plan.

While the plan is being implemented, it is important to set out the arrangements for monitoring it. This is essential to make sure that the plan is still on course.

Providing a service

Stage 4: Monitoring the care plan

When a care plan has been put in place for a service user, it should be remembered that the service user does have rights and that these rights must be maintained while the care plan is being implemented. Rights are discussed fully in Unit 1 but these same rights apply throughout the implementation period. Clients with disabilities have exactly the same rights as everyone else. These are:

Making sure service users' choices are maintained

Supporting service users by using effective communication

Treating service users with respect and dignity, for example calling service users by their preferred name

Avoiding discrimination and promoting anti-discrimination

Service users' rights

Maintaining service users' independence

Being aware of the codes of practice and policies that must be followed

Allowing service users to say 'no'. Not forcing them to participate in a proposed action

Understanding how to maintain confidentiality

Monitoring a care plan is important because it ensures that the service users' needs are continuing to be met. Monitoring involves:

Monitoring the objectives of the care plan
Is each agency delivering the service that was agreed and delivering their specific objectives?

Monitoring the co-ordination of services
Do the services complement one another? Is all information being shared? Are they being managed? Is there continuity of care?

Monitoring service delivery
Are all contributors fulfilling their commitment to the standards that were agreed?

Monitoring the quality of care
The quality of care that is delivered will be specified in the contracts agreed. Is the detail being met? Are personal likes and dislikes of the service user being met?

Monitoring the budget
Is the amount of money being spent as agreed by each provider? Does this amount fall within the budget allocated by the care manager?

Supporting service users
Finding out if the service user is satisfied with the care received.

Supporting informal carers
Is the care meeting expectations? Is it providing the desired help required?

Monitoring professional care workers
Resolving conflicts, checking on progress and chasing where there is a deficit.

Monitoring if needs are being met
Is fine tuning and change necessary to reflect the needs of the service user?

Where possible, the person who is responsible for managing the care plan should also be responsible for monitoring as this will ensure continuity of care. A variety of people will be involved in the monitoring process, for example:

- service users
- main informal carers
- service providers
- purchasing agencies
- inspection personnel
- managers/key workers.

Discussion point

Why is monitoring such an important part of the care management cycle?

Monitoring takes place to ensure that the objectives are being met and to ensure that care plans are adapted to meet the changing needs of service users. Exactly how the monitoring will take place will depend on the simplicity or complexity of the care plan. Monitoring could involve, for example:

- telephone calls
- questionnaires
- observation
- home visits
- interviews.

Whichever way is used it will be essential to establish exactly what has happened, what is happening and to check that this matches the needs of the service user and the intended outcome of the care plan.

Monitoring the care plan

Stage 5: Reviewing/evaluating the care plan

A review of a care plan must be made within the first six weeks of the starting date, according to 'The Department of Health Practice Guidance'. Following this, an evaluation or review must take place every year, or more frequently if it is considered necessary. Evaluation involves:

- looking at the objectives
- considering the nature of the interventions
- assessing the effectiveness of what has taken place
- considering if there is a need for improvement.

It is essential that a balanced view is taken when reviewing/evaluating. Those involved will need to reflect and to make informed judgements about what has taken place. They will need to analyse and to make critical judgements about whether aspects of the care plan could have been improved and whether the outcomes actually match with the objectives set.

Juanita — Activity 2

Juanita is 73 years of age. She has recently had several falls, one of which caused her to be in hospital for several weeks with a broken hip. She is now ready to return to her own home, where it is hoped that she will be able to manage with some support. An assessment of her need is to be done in her own home before she finally leaves hospital.

1. Identify who is likely to attend the assessment of Juanita. Explain each of their roles.

2. Explain what is likely to occur during the assessment, explaining the types of recording documents that may be used.

3. Prepare a table. Within the table:
   - identify the stage of assessment
   - describe two activities that are likely to take place at each stage.

4. Explain the difference between 'monitoring' and 'evaluating' the care plan.

Professionals involved in the care management process

Examples of professionals who could be involved in the care management process

A wide variety of professionals can be involved in providing care for service users. It very much depends on the type of service that the service user requires or agrees may take part in their care. For example:

Vic — CASE STUDY

Vic, aged 80, has an ulcer on his leg that needs attention twice each week. He finds mobility difficult and cannot carry out daily living tasks.

In this situation Vic could be assisted by:
- a district nurse – who would dress the wound and take care of his medical needs
- a General Practitioner – who would provide medication, diagnose illness and give health advice
- a social worker – taking responsibility for assessment and liaising with other professional staff to provide care
- a care assistant – who would help Vic with domestic care responsibilities.

Kara — CASE STUDY

Kara is 23 years of age. She was involved in a car accident when the taxi she was travelling in was hit head on by a car speeding at 80 miles per hour, driven by a man who was drunk.

Kara has spent 12 weeks in hospital, suffering from broken legs, broken pelvis and broken arms. She is returning home to see if she can manage.

Kara will be assisted by:
- a General Practitioner – who will prescribe medication and diagnose any other medical needs
- a social worker – who will assess her and act as a key worker to liaise with other agencies
- an occupational therapist – who will assess Kara's home to see what aids and adaptations would improve the quality of Kara's life
- a physiotherapist – who would provide exercise and massage to help improve Kara's mobility
- a health care worker – who could help Kara with bathing and who would monitor her health by taking temperature and pulse
- a home care assistant – who could help with daily living tasks
- a dietician – who could advise Kara on her dietary needs.

In both situations there are other professionals who could assist with the care of both clients, but these are the main professionals selected after joint consideration between the service user and the social worker.

Other professionals who could be involved in the care management cycle are:

Speech therapist
Helps people who have had a stroke who may not be able to speak properly or those with a speech impairment.

Health visitor
Gives health advice to all and can cover a range of health issues.

Psychiatric nurse
Is qualified to deal with mental health conditions.

Specialist social worker
A social worker who specialises in disability or sensory impairment, for example.

Nurse
Providing medical care, for example stoma nurse or district nurse.

Counsellor
Drawing out issues that worry people by talking and listening to their responses.

Benefits advisor
Giving advice on benefits available.

Audiologist
Provides help for those with hearing impairment or who may be deaf.

Child psychologist
Specialises in diagnosing educational and behavioural problems in children.

Caring for the informal carer

Informal carers often need support as caring for others can be a very physically and emotionally exhausting role. The Carers (Recognition and Services) Act 1995 amending the Community Care Act 1990 places a duty on the local authority Social Services department to assess the ability of a carer to provide and continue providing care. The Social Services department has a duty to take this into consideration when deciding what services a service user might need. Once assessed the informal carer, for example a partner, husband or wife, does not have to be offered any further help. They are made aware of the type of help that would be supportive but decisions about whether the help is actually provided depend very much on the informal carer's state of health.

Are you asking for an assessment of your needs Vera?

A multi-disciplinary approach

A **multi-disciplinary approach** means that professionals from health and Social Services work together as a team rather than in isolation. Sometimes the voluntary sector will also be involved, depending on the type of care that is needed. There are advantages to this type of approach. For example:

- all will know what the targets are and will be working together to achieve these
- notes will be shared
- there will be discussion and agreement as to who will be responsible for each task

- timings will be co-ordinated to prevent overlap during visits
- discussion will take place with the whole team in order to achieve monitoring and evaluation
- costs will be shared.

What are the advantages of a multi-disciplinary approach?

- Observation – to see what is needed.
- Have regular meetings of the team – to check on what each is doing, to prevent duplication of activities.
- All to be involved in drawing up the care plan so that each knows what the other's role is.
- Each to meet together to review the care plan so that they can evaluate the contribution each has made, to have an holistic approach, so that together future planning is meaningful.
- Leave notes to say what the previous professional has done to keep each member of the team informed, to prevent duplication.
- Keep a log – to see what has been done, to avoid duplication, to provide a record.
- Work out shared cost of care, to keep within the budget, to save money, to save human resources, to save on material resources.
- Shared responsibility so decision making is not dependent on one person.

Geoff	**Activity 3**

Geoff is 35 years old and has had an accident while riding his motorbike. He has been in hospital having suffered a broken leg, broken arm and he also had to have his spleen removed.

Geoff is ready to return home but is being assessed to see what help he is most likely to need.

1. List the **five** main stages of the assessment process. For each stage give a different professional care worker who would be involved, explaining what each would do.

2. Explain how **three** of the professionals who are caring for Geoff could work together as a multi-disciplinary team. State the advantages of such an approach.

3. Which piece of legislation would help Ada, Geoff's wife? How would it help her?

The staged approach to assessment and intervention for service users with learning difficulties

People with learning difficulties often need help to make decisions and to understand what is happening. The actual stages within the care management process are exactly the same. The government's initiative 'Valuing People' (2001) was followed by the setting up of a department called 'Valuing People Support Team'. The aim of the team is to improve the planning of services for people with learning difficulties. This system involves more direct planning, involving the service user and their family in a person-centred approach.

There are five main principles of Patient-Centred Planning (PCP). These are:

- the service user is at the centre of consideration
- the service user's family and friends are full partners in the process
- the service user's abilities are taken into consideration and his/her values and wishes must also be taken into consideration
- there is a shared commitment that will provoke action, that takes into consideration the person's rights
- the intention is for the PCP to work towards continual improvement in the quality of life for the person so that they can achieve the type of life they want.

The service user is not just fitted into existing services, but instead is encouraged to find solutions that could involve alternatives or different approaches. The main aim of the PCP is to encourage service users with learning difficulties to make a contribution to the community. In having this approach it is hoped that service users with learning difficulties will be able to make their own decisions and that care workers will not avoid asking them what they want to do. So many care workers at present ask the family members what they would like done rather than asking the service user.

Lucy is 12 years old and suffers from Down's syndrome. It has been decided that she has reached the point where residential education would be of benefit. Her parents, therefore, have decided that Lucy will be going away to boarding school.

Lucy's parents, Gill and Colin, have a number of problems that they need to solve because Lucy is not entirely happy with this arrangement. The first problem is that because she will be sharing a room with another student she must have identifying marks on all of her possessions. This is proving difficult as Lucy does not want this done. It appears that despite the fact that her name is being put on almost everything she feels that she is losing ownership of her possessions.

Lucy is also aware that she will not be seeing her parents on a daily basis and this is beginning to scare her into having nightmares. Lucy is not a very gregarious person and having to share a room has an impact on her personal privacy, which her parents think might be an initial problem. Their concern is that they think that her personal hygiene might suffer if she feels that she is being watched.

Gill and Colin are having to rethink their plans for Lucy's education. They have been made aware that PCP will allow them to be more selective about the choice of Lucy's school. This will allow them to involve Lucy totally in the choice of residential school. They will also be able to build up slowly the time that she spends there as a resident, until she becomes totally familiar with the environment.

The flexible arrangement for the provision of the services allows Gill and Colin to design a much more suitable situation for Lucy. The PCP funding will still be available as it is being spent for the same purpose. Gill and Colin can now become more relaxed in knowing that they have been involved in providing the best possible educational environment.

Individual learning plans

Individual learning plans will vary according to the needs of the person that is being given support. Any action for service users will consider:

- what are the service user's needs?
- what is the situation that requires a solution?
- what are the possible strategies that could be applied?

- how much time is available?
- what are the targets?
- what is the overall goal?

When forming an individual learning plan it is important to have a clear goal. Such a goal will be supported by targets. These targets must be:

- **Specific** – a clear description of what needs to be done
- **Measurable** – it must be possible to measure whether they have been achieved
- **Appropriate** – not impossible to meet
- **Realistic** – it should be something that is sensible to the situation
- **Timed** – a time limit should be placed on the task to ensure that it is completed within a reasonable timescale.

Individual learning plans are recorded so that it is clear to the service user and to the person who is assisting the service user what is expected, when it is expected and how it is to be achieved. Below is an example of an individual action plan format:

Individual Action Plan for Matt		
Task		
What are the options?		
Goal to be achieved		
Targets	**By whom**	**By when**
Date, time and place of review		
Signed **Signed**		
Date		
Professional **Date**		

Drawing up an individual learning plan for Matt — Activity 4

Matt is a child of 5 years of age who has learning difficulties. He is very withdrawn and hardly speaks to any of the other children in his group in the reception class. His teacher is quite worried about this situation and draws up an individual action plan that could help with this situation. The plan is going to be carried out by the learning support teacher who helps Matt each day.

1. Draw up an individual action plan that could help Matt.

2. Explain how it will be put into action.

3. If this plan is successful how will Matt benefit?

Some people with learning difficulties will need help to express their ideas and opinions. *The People First movement* tries to provide help for service users who have this problem. They set up groups to help individuals to express themselves. Such groups have **self advocacy** as the focus for action. This is achieved by listening to what people with learning difficulties actually have to say rather than what others think they are saying. *Mencap* sponsors the activities of the groups, called *In Control*, trying to promote self directed support for people with learning difficulties.

Discussion point

Why do you think that the views and opinions of people with learning difficulties are often ignored?

Assessment activity (AO2)

Care management   CASE STUDY

Case Study 1: Emily

Emily has recently broken her arm and has had to have a knee replacement operation. She has now returned home and is having support from different professional care workers.

Choose **one** that meets Emily's physical needs. Explain the role of the care professional, how they would provide support for Emily and meet her needs. Choose from:

- a physiotherapist
- a social worker
- a home care assistant.

Case Study 2: Elziz

Recently Elziz has been bereaved. His wife and his daughter were both killed in a car accident. Elziz is finding it very hard to cope. He is being cared for by different professional care workers. Choose **one** that meets his social or emotional needs. Explain the role of the care professional, how they would provide support for Elziz and how they would meet his needs. Choose from:

- GP
- a counsellor
- a psychiatric nurse.

1   Analyse and illustrate, by using the case studies, how the five main stages of the care management process would be carried out, showing how in each stage both individual P.I.E.S. would be met.

2   Explain the evaluation procedure used when care planning, showing how evaluation can lead to modification of individual plans to ensure the changing needs of service users are met.

3   State which care professionals would be involved at each stage of the care management cycle, accurately discussing their roles and showing how they would provide support for each service user. Make sure you include information to show how the P.I.E.S. for each individual would be met.

4   Explain the skills and qualities required by each of the professionals involved in caring for Emily and Elziz.

5   Explain how a multi-disciplinary approach could be used when working with each service user giving examples to show exactly how this could be achieved.

5.2.3 Models and approaches

The way additional needs are defined will dictate the way in which help and support will be provided. This applies not only to the health and care services that may become involved but also to societal and individual responses. There are two main approaches or models that are commonly used:

- the medical model
- the social model.

The medical model

The traditional approach is the medical model. This is demonstrated in the definition of impairment, disability and handicap as produced by the World Health Organisation (WHO).

- *Impairment is any loss or abnormality of psychological, physiological or anatomical structure or function.*
- *Disability is any restriction or lack (resulting from the impairment) of ability to perform an activity, in the manner or within the range considered to be normal for a human being.*
- *Handicap is a disadvantage, resulting from an impairment or disability, which limits or prevents the fulfilment of a role (depending on age, sex, social and cultural factors).*

(WHO 1980)

Discussion point

Consider the definition and put it into simpler language, using examples to show understanding.

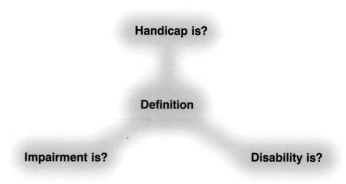

Explanations and examples from your discussion might have been:

- Impairment – part of the body that is missing or not working properly – a condition, e.g. a broken arm or dyslexia.

- Disability – being prevented by an impairment from taking part in normal activities – a condition which limits activity, e.g. a broken arm that prevents a person from cooking for themselves, or having difficulty understanding written instructions on a medicine bottle because of dyslexia.

- Handicap – being disadvantaged by the impairment or disability, e.g. not being able to lead an independent life because of the broken arm or not being able to work as a secretary because of having dyslexia.

Impairments and disabilities may be either:

- acute – likely to last for a relatively short period of time, e.g. a broken leg, or
- chronic – could develop over a long period or last for a long time, if not permanently, e.g. Down's syndrome.

Using the medical model, the person with an impairment or disability tends to be seen as having a medical problem because part of the body is not working properly. The response is to try and cure or manage the problem using medical means. This then becomes the responsibility of the medical and associated experts, e.g. doctors, physiotherapists, support workers, social workers and care staff, all of whom tend to be non-disabled.

> **Discussion point**
>
> What might be the advantages and disadvantages of this approach? What part would the disabled individual play in this? How might they feel?

Social model

Whilst acknowledging that impairments and disabilities exist and have medical causes that require treatment and/or management, this model identifies many of the problems facing disabled people as being based in society. It sees disability, as defined by the WHO, relating more to the attitudes within, and design of, society that prevent impaired people from 'performing normally' rather than the impairment itself. People who have had a leg amputated are likely to experience mobility problems. This is more likely to be due to a transport system that is not impaired-user friendly rather than having a leg amputated.

Factors in society are seen as barriers that help keep the individual in the **restrictive** medical model rather than enabling them to move to the empowering social model. Under the social model, the main solution lies with taking advantage of modern technology to enable people to overcome their impairments, changing negative attitudes and creating a more equal society. This will also affect the style and type of support services available to help and support individuals.

I think you could be sorted out by using an artificial limb

	Medical model	Social model
Who favours this model?	Medical and social care 'experts'	Impaired/disabled people and advocacy groups
Where is the problem located?	The disability is an individual medical problem which prevents or restricts activity	Whilst a medical restriction is acknowledged, external factors tend to disable
How should disability be tackled?	By providing services to meet people's additional needs and care for them	By making society more user friendly, which would benefit a wide range of people (e.g., parents with push-chairs)
Types of services favoured	Caring services that take charge and protect disabled people	Advocacy services which argue for the full integration of impaired people into society

Different approaches to impairment and disability

Discussion point

Identify some of the barriers that might face impaired people in society today. What types of services would the social model promote?

The social model encourages an empowering approach and looks at ways of enabling rather than disabling people. The aim is to enable impaired people to fully participate, on an equal basis, in everyday life. A simple example is the garage with a self-opening door, controlled by a remote control. This enables drivers, regardless of ability, to drive in and out of a garage without getting out of the car. It is beneficial to people who are small, frail, concerned about personal security, or have children in the car. It enables a range of different people, including impaired people, who would struggle or not be able to carry out the task.

The services this model promotes would be those that assist impaired people, in practical terms, but also empower them. A home care service may assist an individual in getting up, washing and dressing, because they couldn't do it for themselves, but would support them (rather than do it for them) in preparing their own breakfast as they had the ability to do so. The service would focus on encouraging independence but not dependence. Assessments would also be carried out to identify the individual's skills shortages with a view to developing their skills base further, e.g. if they do not know how to use a microwave to heat food then they would be shown how to do it.

This contrasts with a medical model service that would want to do it all for the impaired person, as they were not seen as being able, and therefore not able to 'do for themselves'. Various voluntary and self help disability organisations focus on bringing about a change in attitude in society so that impaired people are not seen as being unable to take a full and active part in everyday life.

Discussion point

Discuss and mind map the words that come to mind when you hear the word 'disability'.

Wheelchair

?   Cripple

Disability

?   Sickness

Old people

Fill in the gaps

Most words that spring to mind tend to be negative. This is because society and its values usually visualise disability in this way. In the past, people with additional needs were kept out of sight, either at home or sent away to an institution where they were contained and maintained but not developed. This process has become known as 'warehousing' where people are 'stored' for their own safety and that of others. Their impairment is seen as a disability about which nothing can be done. Their personal development needs are not considered and they live their lives in a vacuum, away from mainstream society. People were officially called idiots, cripples, and sub-normal and, with such negative attitudes being expressed, were treated as second-class citizens with fewer rights, if any, than others.

Discussion point

Discuss, with a small group of people, what words they associate with disability and their views as to the place of disabled people in today's society.

Consider your own use of language. Have you called someone a 'mong' or a 'spaz' recently? 'Mong' comes from the term 'mongol' or 'mongoloid'. This was a medical classification that referred to children who had facial characteristics similar to people from Mongolia. People with this condition are now known as having Down's syndrome. Similarly, 'spaz' refers to 'spastic', which was the term used for people who had cerebral palsy. How far have we come if we are still using 'disability' words as insults?

Society's attitudes have tended to follow the medical model. Service users with impairment have been seen as 'not able' and needing to be looked after.

This has had a **stereotyping** effect in that people who are seen as having a disability are lumped together under an assumed common identity. This encourages the use of negative words to describe 'the disabled'.

Once a group becomes stereotyped and seen as having a common identity, prejudice or pre-judgement can develop. A dictionary definition offers the following as an explanation of prejudice – 'a judgement or opinion formed prematurely or without due consideration of relevant issues' (*The Chambers Dictionary* 1999: 1295). Based on the stereotype, certain assumptions and judgements are made, usually without contact with the group in question. Once these prejudices are acted upon, they become forms of discrimination. Discrimination exists when some individuals are treated differently to others because of the way they are perceived or seen. This is usually, but not always, in a negative way.

Disabled people tend to be stereotyped as a group of people who are not able to fully contribute to society because of their disabilities. They need to be looked after and decisions made on their behalf, and in their best interest. Society tends to focus on their disabilities rather than their individuality and abilities. The negative comes first. This leads to individuals having low self confidence. What they cannot do is focused on before attention is given to what they can do. A person will be described as a disabled employee rather than an employee who has a disability. People will see the wheelchair before they see the person who is using it. Assumptions, prejudice and discrimination start at that point.

A self-fulfilling prophecy can emerge where, if a person is told often enough that they are not able to do something, they will come to believe it is true. In 1944, The Disabled Persons (Employment) Act required all businesses that employed over twenty people to ensure that three per cent of their workforce was made up of people who were registered as 'disabled' with the Department of Employment. The Act also required certain jobs to be reserved for disabled people but only two were specified and they were car park attendants and lift operators. What message would this send out?

Discussion point

What are the advantages and disadvantages of such a quota system? If you were disabled, would you welcome such legislation?

Service users, in the past, had their lives organised for them. In hospitals, along with other patients, they were woken between 5.30am and 6am so that medication, toileting and breakfast could be completed by the end of the nightshift. Decisions about treatment were often made without the patient's knowledge because it was done in their best interest. It was felt they might not understand the procedure.

In the community, well-meaning home helps might take over the cleaning of the house and organise things in the way they thought would best suit the individual, without first asking them about their preferences. Disabled people might be moved into a residential home so they could, in the view of the professionals, be safe. This was often achieved without any real discussion or informed agreement. Such actions were designed to protect the service user but could build up a dependency on the services provided. Independency was not encouraged. Whilst, with hindsight, much of this can be seen as negative, it was usually done with the disabled person's welfare as the main concern, even though it seems they were wrapped up in cotton wool.

In more recent times, there has been a societal and professional shift towards the social model. Disabled people are consulted and are involved in the decision-making process about their needs and preferred services. The 1995 and 2005 Disability Discrimination Acts outlawed disability discrimination by employers and providers of goods and services. Public bodies are required to promote positive attitudes and a date of 2020 has been set by when improved access to trains and buses should be completed. Service users are becoming equal partners in the treatment and management of their disability. The care management process should now fully involve them in the assessment, planning and delivery of services. All of these are positive moves that are aimed at bringing about change in society so that it becomes more user friendly. However, there still remain environmental, economic and attitudinal barriers that need to be tackled before disabled people feel there is full equality of opportunity available to them.

Impairment   Activity 5

Imagine you have an impairment. You may need to use a wheelchair when you go shopping or you have poor sight so that you can only see things in detail when they are within 10cm of your eyes, the rest is a blur. You might be deaf or frail and have little strength so that you need regular rests (sit down) and have difficulty opening doors.

1   Visit your local shopping area in small groups (each group to focus on a range of impairments) and survey the environment to find out how accessible it is for impaired people.

2   How might the design disable people? How could it be made more user friendly?

3   Feedback to the whole group and identify how the design of the shops and facilities might 'disable' other groups. Parents with buggies often have similar problems to wheelchair users in using lifts, opening and closing doors, etc.

Environmental barriers

Access to sport/leisure

Access to work

Transport

Environmental barriers

Access to information

Access to buildings

Access to social life

Transport

The ability to move freely from place to place is important for the majority of people. Many journeys are made by public transport. People with impairments find the design of the transport disables them. The gap between station platform and carriage step may to be too wide or the step up into the train too high. If you are in a wheelchair, you will need to depend on portable ramps being available, as well as someone to put them in place and assist. Similar problems may exist with getting on and off busses that have too high a platform,

or the pavement is too low. People with poor or no sight can have problems finding where to cross the road or knowing which bus is about to arrive. Street furniture (litter bins, shop advertising boards, seats, flower tubs, etc.) can create an obstacle course for this group of people.

Access to buildings and services

Buildings that have steps, but no ramp, at their entrance present many a person with mobility restrictions with an access problem. Even where a ramp is available, some of the older ones are too steep to be used. Doors that open outwards or are heavy or difficult to open can present a barrier depending on the needs of the individual. Lifts that do not have operating buttons accessible to wheelchair users discriminate against them, as do 'non-speaking' lifts against blind people.

Access   Activity 6

1   Investigate and explain how the following may restrict access:

- stairs
- heavy doors
- unrestricted parking
- lifts
- poor lighting.

Access to social life

Many social activities take place in locations that are not service user friendly. Social clubs may be in pubs or church halls that have poor access. The design of many flats and houses could preclude access by people in electric wheelchairs because of the width of doorways. To visit a friend might first involve the question 'How wide are your doors?'

Wheelchairs   Activity 7

1   Measure the width of an ordinary wheelchair and that of an electric (battery operated) wheelchair. Record your findings.

2   Measure the width of an average doorway and corridor. Record your findings.

3   Explain the differences.

Access to information

Physically gaining access to information, which would inform the individual of the help and services available, could be difficult if that information is not in a form that they can understand. More and more information is available on the Internet but if the person cannot gain access to an adapted computer, e.g. voice activated, information is restricted. Being unable to read because of impairment, e.g. learning disability or difficulty, can make many day-to-day activities difficult. If you have been to a country where you do not understand the language being spoken, you may have some insight into how difficult it can be to read signs and instructions. Imagine trying to find your way around a hospital if you cannot understand the directions.

Discussion point

Mind map and discuss how you get your information about what's happening. Would you still be able to do it that way if you were impaired?

Access to sport and leisure

Access to sporting and leisure venues may be restricted for people with mobility restrictions. Football grounds restrict the number of wheelchair users who can attend a match because of a limited 'disabled' watching area. Health and safety reasons are also quoted. This applies to night clubs and cinemas that restrict numbers of wheelchair users in case of a fire and a speedy exit is needed. Concerns have, in the past, been raised about the users being a 'fire hazard' as people could trip or fall over them in the rush to get out.

Discussion point

How would you feel if you were prevented from going into a night club, with a group of non-impaired friends, because you were a 'fire hazard'?

Access to work

Employers, in the past, often discriminated against people with additional needs because they focused on their disability rather than their ability. Many workplaces did not have suitable access or equipment that could support the individual.

The working environment was not user friendly. The 1995 Disability Discrimination Act required employers to make 'reasonable adjustment' to employment practice and premises to enable current and **prospective** employees who have disabilities or long-term health conditions. This might take the form of installing a voice-activated computer, providing a reader or sign language interpreter or altering working hours. Whilst things are moving in the right direction, change is slow and frustrating for many people with additional needs.

Provision for disabled children — Activity 8

1. Investigate what provision has been made for disabled children in an early years setting.

2. What special equipment has been made available to them?

3. What types of disability are these designed to overcome?

Attitudes

Historically, society's attitudes and values towards people with additional needs were negative. They were 'contained' and hidden from view because of the perceived shame they brought to the family. They were seen to embody a family weakness. This negative approach contained positive elements in that the aim was also to protect those who could not look after themselves.

Attitudes have mellowed in recent years. This could be traced back to the end of the World War II, which created many new disabled people who were seen as deserving of help. The establishment of the National Health Service in 1948 provided free medical care for all, including disabled people. This and the great improvements in medical technology increased health education awareness. Higher standards of living and health care have enabled impaired people to live longer and become more integrated into mainstream society.

This has not prevented stereotyping from continuing and employment opportunities being limited. The 1995 Disability Discrimination Act and others are tackling discrimination, together with the Disability Rights Commission. The Commission aims to educate, challenge and test society's views of disability. They promote the social model.

Economic barriers

These continue to exist. The degree to which an individual is disabled can depend on their financial situation. If the person can afford to take a taxi everywhere or has someone available to drive them whenever they wish, then their degree of mobility restriction is reduced. If the person has limited funds then their choice of transport will be reduced.

In everyday life, the ability to buy the various aids and adaptations can determine the degree of disability. An electrical powered scooter will give more freedom and ability to do things than a manually operated wheelchair.

Finding out   Activity 9

1 Research, using the Internet, equipment catalogues and visits to specialist shops or Disability Living Centres, the range and cost of help available through modern technology and invention.

2 Find out how much a disabled person is likely to receive in benefits if not working. Could they afford these aids?

The cost of transport to and from services and facilities can act as a barrier. Taxis are expensive, when on a limited income, but public transport can be also. If the local advice service is two bus rides away, with a half hour wait for the second bus, this can be expensive and physically demanding in the winter. A similar situation could occur when going to work or the local swimming baths.

With leisure activities, there is also the cost of using them to be taken into account. Some people will earn less in wages than they could on benefits but will do this for their own self esteem and to fight the label of 'disabled'. Some impairments can cause excessive wear and tear on clothes, e.g. the rubbing of a sleeve against the side of a wheelchair and the dragging of a shoe along the ground, because of paralysis from a stroke. Specialist clothing may be needed or ordinary clothing will have to be replaced more often. All involve extra cost to someone who could be on a limited income.

Overcoming barriers

Environmental, attitudinal and economic barriers are being tackled through legislation, advocacy, technology and education. The Disability Discrimination Act 1995 and subsequent Acts have given people the power of the courts through which to challenge discrimination. The setting up of the Disability Rights Commission has created a body that will take forward test cases and advocate on behalf of disabled people. The Act also sends out a very powerful societal message that people with disabilities should not be discriminated against.

The number of charities and voluntary bodies that provide services and speak out on behalf of disabled people are many and are working towards changing societal attitudes. These include those that focus on disability in general, like RADAR, and those representing specific conditions like SCOPE, for people with cerebral palsy. There are also various self help groups run by disabled people, e.g. People First, a group of people with learning disabilities. Legislation and technology is being used to improve the environment. The Disability Discrimination Act has set a date of 2020 by when public transport must be accessible to impaired people through having lower loading platforms and easier access trains, etc.

I can't afford the fare to outpatients

As society disables less, then people with additional needs should find they are able to participate fully in day-to-day life with the financial benefits that others enjoy. With full inclusion in society will come increased self esteem and self worth as all people are seen as being unique individuals who have different needs.

Assessment activity (AO3)

CASE STUDY

You have been asked to produce information for a group of trainee care workers. You need to carry out research, using a variety of sources to show:

- a comparison of the medical and social models, giving examples to illustrate how they meet the service users' needs.
- both positive and negative effects of the attitude and values of society towards service users.

Remember:

Produce a bibliography to show the variety of types of resources used.

Your analysis should be detailed and should show the ability to reflect on your findings and to make reasoned judgements.

There should be no errors or omissions.

5.2.4 Production of a profile of a service user with additional needs

Profile: James and Todd

James was born in 1999 with Down's syndrome. He was born to an older mother who already had three children. She did not consider an amniocentesis test or chorionic villus sampling as her strong religious beliefs would not have allowed her to even consider an abortion.

Discussion point

Gianna Jessen has been in the news recently. She has cerebral palsy as a result of her teenage mother going into a Los Angeles clinic for an abortion 28 years ago. Gianna's mother was seven-and-a-half months pregnant. The mother was given a saline injection but against all the odds Gianna was born alive weighing just over 2lb. Her cerebral palsy was diagnosed when Gianna was seven months old. Doctors believe it was caused by oxygen starvation during the attempted termination. Gianna is campaigning to have the 24-week time limit on abortions reduced.

As a group discuss the time limit you would put on abortions.

When James was born his mother recognised that he looked and seemed different to her other babies. A blood test confirmed that James had Down's syndrome. Whilst waiting for the results of the blood test both parents started to bond with James. When his Down's syndrome was confirmed both parents were shocked and distressed. James' parents felt it was their fault and were concerned about telling their other children and also their friends.

James   Activity 10

Telling any parent that their new born baby is disabled is always very difficult for any doctor.

1   Explain how a doctor could try to reassure James' parents.

2   Are there any organisations that could help?

When James came home at ten days old he was an easy baby to care for as he spent a lot of time sleeping. He was a happy baby and he made slow but steady progress throughout his toddler years. James did not have problems with either his hearing or his eyesight but he did suffer from colds and coughs and after this had upper **respiratory infections**. James had regular health assessments and was kept up-to-date with his immunisation schedule.

From the moment James came home and left the care of the **paediatrician** he was to receive his health care from the primary health care team. The family was appointed a special needs health visitor who visited them and was the 'named person' as recommended by The Warnock Report 1978.

Warnock Report   Activity 11

Research the Warnock Report 1978.

What were the main recommendations to come out of the report?

The health visitor would be James' point of contact for advice and support. She would link James' parents with the family doctor and specialist health services as well as social services, voluntary support groups and education services when he was old enough to go to nursery school.

James started to walk at two-and-a-half years old and it was decided that he should have a Portage Home Visitor. Portage is a scheme which is

'a home-visiting educational service for pre-school children, with additional support needs and their families. Portage supports the development of young children's play, communication and relationships and encourages full participation in day-to-day life within the family and beyond the home. Portage services are committed to securing inclusion to the wider community for all children and their families.'

(National Portage Association)

Portage recognises that parents are very important in the care and development of their children. James' parents were helped to do their best for him, with practical advice offered. Their assigned Portage Home Visitor was going to assist James to go to the local nursery one day each week as this would help his social and educational development.

Portage   **Activity 12**

Visit www.portage.org.uk. Read the list of support that the National Portage Association offers parents/carers of children with a disability.

1 Discuss each characteristic of the support offered and say how this will help both the parent/carer and the child.

2 Use the comments from parents to back your answer.

The weekly visit from the Portage Visitor helped James' development as he was usually set a particular task to accomplish between visits. His parents pushed him to meet the challenge. His parents often felt guilty as they seemed to spend a lot of time concentrating on James as he needed a lot of care and attention. Sometimes, they felt they looked after James at the expense of the rest of their children. They spent a lot of time trying to stimulate James – trying to develop his fine motor skills and improve the strength in his limbs. By the age of five James could dress himself if he had help, especially with buttons. Laces he could not manage. His appetite was good and he could feed himself using a spoon. He liked a variety of food and had no problems eating, although he was very slow. James had a vocabulary of about fifty words although he could use Makaton to make himself understood – he could use about one hundred signs.

Makaton   **Activity 13**

Log on to www.makaton.org.uk

1 What is Makaton?

2 Try to learn some simple signs and present them to your group.

James' parents were very keen for him to attend the mainstream junior school as his older siblings attended that school. However, he was assessed and at the age of five it was recommended that he attend a special school. Unhappy at the decision, his parents prepared to appeal against it. Unfortunately, before they could do so, James contracted bacterial meningitis. After a fierce battle to survive, during which he had septicaemia, he had to spend six months in hospital where his recovery was very slow. He now has very reduced mobility which makes the use of a wheelchair essential.

Before James came home from hospital his special needs health visitor contacted the local Social Services and asked for a needs assessment. A social worker came to the family home to talk about James' needs as well as the needs of the other family members, including his mother as carer. The types of services which would meet the family's needs were discussed. The assessment was multi-agency – that is it included consideration of health, social care and educational needs. It was carried out according to the Framework for the Assessment for Children in Need and their Families (Department of Health, 2000). What methods of support could James and his family expect?

Assistance with daily living routines

Under the Children Act there are a range of services available to children with disabilities and their families, if they are assessed as needing them. The services vary from council to council. James could be **eligible** for services which include:

- **respite care** – short or long break services
- holiday play schemes
- care at home
- some aids and adaptations
- financial help (for example, to pay for fares for hospital visits).

During the assessment process both health and social services put together a package of support which would help James and his family. James and his family could benefit from:

- respite care – this is where children can be looked after for either short or long breaks. This can be organised and funded by the Social Services department but could also be arranged by the health service and some voluntary organisations. The idea is to remove some of the stress and strain and physical hard work of caring for a child with disabilities. It is often a twenty-four hour process for the carer but with short or long breaks to look forward to, it can make the difference between the parents being able to cope or having to place the child in permanent residential care. Respite care is meant to be a positive experience for the child and not just a break for the family. When respite care is being planned, the needs of the child are considered. Respite care can take the form of:

Children's holiday schemes   Own home care

Respite Care

Family link care   Approved residential accomodation

Types of respite care

- Children's holiday schemes – often arranged by voluntary agencies but paid for by the family. These schemes often provide one-to-one care for the child. Sometimes family holidays are organised allowing all the family to have fun together.
- Own home care – often cared for in the child's home by a carer. The child feels relaxed and comfortable in their own home while the family goes on holiday.
- Family link care – this is where the child will go to stay with an approved carer. This would be in the carer's own home. The child would get to know the carer before s/he went to stay with them.
- Approved residential accommodation – this could be in a hospital unit or ward or in a children's home. If proper medical nursing is required then a hospital ward would be the ideal place for the child to stay.

- Holiday play schemes – as the name suggests, these are play schemes which are run during holidays from school especially during the long summer break. These schemes offer the child with a disability the same opportunities of socialising and playing as an able-bodied child.
- Care at home – this is where a carer comes to the child's home to allow the parent or full-time carer the opportunity of leaving the house for the agreed session. This could be to go shopping, go out with friends for a coffee or just get out of the house.
- Some aids and adaptations – while James was in hospital his home was adapted for his use as it was unsuitable for use by anyone in a wheelchair. His family home was assessed by an occupational therapist to find out what adaptations were necessary and appropriate to meet James' needs. Grants can be used on any adaptation that would make it easier for the person with a disability to get into and move around his/her home. In James' case it was decided to add a downstairs extension which consisted of a bathroom/toilet and a bedroom. This would mean that his parents did not have to carry James upstairs to use the bathroom/toilet. Ramps were added at the front and back doors so that James would be able to leave the house by either exit. He would also have access to the garden in summer. After James' family had been awarded the grant, their local council arranged for the work to be carried out. They also supervised the work. Even if James had been older or indeed already an adult, these adaptations, if deemed necessary, would still have gone ahead.

Sometimes local councils may provide low cost loans as well as grants to private homeowners and others to help renovate or adapt their home. They also provide other types of assistance such as helping someone move to more suitable living accommodation, if it would benefit the person with a disability. James' parents also had home help care to assist with the cleaning and shopping even though James was at special school throughout the day. This was because James often could not sleep at night. Once a week, a carer spent a night in James' house so that his parents could get a decent night's sleep.

Supporting People is a government programme that provides housing-related support to help vulnerable people live as independently as possible in the community whether in their own homes, sheltered housing or other specialised supported housing or in hostels.

James' cousin Todd uses the above programme to help him stay independent in his own home. Ten years ago, on his eighteenth birthday, after celebrating in the local pub he decided to go for a swim in the river. Rather than just go into the river he decided to jump from the pedestrian bridge. Unfortunately, the river was not deep at this point and he hit the bottom. He was taken to hospital where x-rays showed that he had broken his neck. He had lost the use of his legs. He spent over a year in a spinal injuries unit. After eighteen months in a residential home he now lives in his own home funded by the local authority. Two carers care for Todd – one gets him up in the morning and the other one puts him to bed.

Having the right equipment is **crucial** to independent living. Some equipment may be related to a particular health need while some equipment may be needed to give practical help on a daily basis. Todd and James' doctor referred their families to the National Health Service specialist service for some of the health equipment they needed.

Equipment that makes life easier to manage at home is provided by Social Services following James' and Todd's assessment by an occupational therapist. Equipment could help with the preparation of food or managing personal hygiene. If someone has a hearing impairment a vibrating alarm clock could be useful.

Disabled Living Centres (DLCs) offer a range of services to help people with disabilities they:

- offer disabled people the chance to see and try out a wide range of products to find those that suit their needs
- aim to increase opportunities for people to live independently
- offer free and independent advice about what products are available, how much they cost and where to get them
- arrange training on a variety of topics of interest to disabled people, carers and professionals, for which there is generally a fee.

Assessing your home — Activity 14

Look around your home and decide if you could invite a person who uses a wheelchair for tea.

1. Would they be able to come to your front door?
2. If they did, could they get into the house?
3. Once inside could they move around?

The NHS and Community Care Act 1990 promoted the idea that domiciliary, day and respite services should be available to support people and enable them to live in their own homes, wherever possible. It also stated that service providers should make practical support for carers a high priority. Assessment of needs should always take into account the needs of family, friends and neighbours. Packages of care should then be designed in line with individual needs and preferences.

Todd's package has been designed with his best interests at heart.

Daily routine for Todd (except on college days)

8.00   Home care assistant comes to get Todd up. He is helped to shower, wash and shave. Breakfast is prepared for him. He is made comfortable in his chair and he starts to watch television or sometimes he will go out in his wheelchair to meet friends. His carer leaves about 9.30 am after tidying up and loading washing into the machine.

- Elastic stockings
- Appliances for colostomies
- Communication aids
- Artificial limbs and surgical appliances
- Wheelchairs and walking aids
- Continence pads
- Pressure-relieving cushions and mattresses
- Urinary catheters
- Hearing/vision aids
- Wound dressings

Examples of equipment supplied by NHS

Examples of equipment supplied by the NHS

11.00 Next door neighbour calls in to check everything is alright, makes coffee and spends time chatting.

12.30 Meals on wheels arrives.

1.00 After lunch Todd might go out to visit friends or stay in and watch sport. Sometimes he goes to the sports centre to take part in wheelchair basketball.

5.00 Auntie or mother arrives for chat. Makes tea for Todd and herself and they have snack. Mother irons anything needed and puts washing into dryer.

7.00 Todd might go down to pub with friends.

11.30 Health care assistant arrives and helps Todd to get ready for bed.

Other days include:

Monday — Goes to college to follow Sports Science course 9.30–2.30

Wednesday — Goes to college to follow Sports Science course 9.30–12.00

Thursday — Goes to college to follow Sports Science course 9.30–12.00

On college days the home care assistant comes in one hour earlier and helps Todd get ready for college. Meals on wheels does not arrive on Monday and Thursday as Todd eats lunch at college.

One of the best aids and resources Todd has is the human one – his carers. Without them he could not manage to live independently.

Education and training

As already stated, James attends a special school. His local education authority (LEA) prepared a statement of special educational needs – this is usually called a 'statement'. The statement described all James' special educational needs and the special help he should receive. A statement contains:

- part 1 – gives general information about the child

- part 2 – gives the description of the child's needs following the assessment

- part 3 – describes all the special help to be given for the child's needs

- part 4 – gives the type and name of school the child should go to

- part 5 – describes any non-educational needs the child has

- part 6 – describes how the child will get help to meet any non-educational needs.

Parents (such as James') have the right to disagree with the statement and have 15 days to respond and say which is their preferred school. They can appeal to the Special Educational Needs Tribunal against the contents of parts 2, 3 and 4. The statement must be reviewed at least once each year.

Todd is attending college and studying on a Sports Science course. There were several options open to Todd to allow him to continue his education. Most further education colleges and universities offer access to disabled students. If the local college could not have offered Todd a course to suit his disability-related needs then the Learning and Skills Council (LSC) would consider funding a place at another more suitable college. Most of these colleges are independent and are specifically for students with disabilities or learning difficulties. These are called specialist colleges and are often residential. If the LSC decided that someone's needs could only be met by going to a specialist residential college, they have a duty to find them a place there.

All 16 and 17 year olds who are not in full-time education or employment are guaranteed a suitable work-based training place. This applies to those over 18 if entry has been delayed due to disability or a health problem. Most work-based training is delivered through the Modern Apprenticeship (MA) programme.

Career advice for disabled people aged 16–25 comes from a Job Centre Plus adviser. Connexions bring together a full range of support services so that young people can overcome barriers to their employment, training and education.

There is also a New Deal for Disabled People (NDDP). This helps people move from disability and health-related benefits into paid work. Many people who have joined this scheme have benefited from the support to develop new skills and improved confidence plus the financial benefit of being in work.

Day care provision

Day care centres provide the opportunity for people to meet socially. Sometimes day care takes place in purpose-built day care centres or sometimes in residential homes. If in a residential home, a service user can arrive at the home in the morning, have a bath, relax and socialise with people of a similar age, have a meal and maybe have personal grooming attended to. This could happen once or twice each week.

Day care centres can be owned by Social Services, NHS or voluntary organisations such as Help the Aged or Age Concern. Usually the centres are open every weekend from about 9.00 am to 4 pm. Sometimes service users are picked up by social service transport or the centre's transport but sometimes service users make their own way there. As well as social activities, medical and personal services are provided. The service users mainly live at home and in the community and for some carers the centres offer day **respite** care.

Service users can use the centre every day; others come once or twice each week. The old image of a day centre filled with older service users playing bingo is no longer applicable in most day care centres. There is a wide range of activities in day care centres. Activities such as dancing, cookery, aromatherapy, music, reflexology, gardening and relaxation take place, thereby stretching the service users' intellectual capacity and improving their existing skills or developing new ones.

Examples of day care activities

Day care centres enhance the lives of their service users, as they provide the opportunity for social interaction. They also allow service users to develop new interests and maximise possibilities of a

different lifestyle (especially if the person is disabled). The centres often have a coffee bar or snack bar which helps to give an informal, relaxed atmosphere. Day care provides the opportunity for people to gain and grow in confidence. They are allowed choices and often diversify into unexpected interests. They feel part of the community and self esteem grows as a result.

Assistance with health problems

Disabled people share the same general rights of access to health and social care as other people but there are also some special provisions under the Disability Discrimination Act 1995 (DDA). This Act gives disabled people important rights of access to health services such as doctors' surgeries, dental surgeries, hospitals and mobile screening units. The anti-discrimination of the Disability Discrimination Act means that a GP should not refuse to register, or refuse to continue to treat someone because of their disability.

The DDA means that someone has the right to information about health care and social services in a format that is accessible to them, where it is reasonable for the service provider to provide it in that format. For example, for someone with a visual impairment, a hospital may provide forms and explanatory literature in large print or Braille.

The Disability Rights Commission (DRC) can provide advice and support to help secure a person's civil rights, if they feel they are being discriminated against because of their disability.

The role of a physiotherapist is to improve a person's mobility and independence. This could be through helping them recover from a chest infection, controlling their pain or helping them to mobilise after a stroke or accident. This approach can save a disabled person from being admitted to hospital, speed up their recovery if in hospital and promote an early discharge.

Occupational therapists work with people who have a physical disability, a mental health problem or a learning disability. They help people who have difficulties with practical everyday tasks. Todd's occupational therapist helped him to regain his confidence and taught him to manage on his own. The aim of occupational therapy is to enable people to live as independently as possible – at home, in employment or in education. An occupational therapist can help a person to adapt to changes in their everyday life by:

- providing advice
- looking at ways an everyday task can be done differently
- recommending alterations or changes to a person's home
- referring people to other services, e.g. speech therapy
- helping someone to address work-related issues.

Occupational therapists often give children a series of daily activities to do at home or at school or both. For some children, it is vital that problems with balance and posture are addressed as early as possible, as this can have a major impact on their co-ordination and ability to walk in later life.

If someone is unable to visit a dentist due to a disability, it is possible for the dentist to treat the person at their home. Alternatively, the NHS community dental service, provided by the Primary Care Trust, may be able to treat the person at home.

Social opportunities

Normalisation or social role valorisation is a term coined by W Wolfenberger (1972). By this Wolfenberger meant that people with disabilities need to have a valued role in society and that they must be helped to develop their skills and capabilities to the full. The implication for professionals was that they need to:

- encourage people with learning difficulties to make their own choices
- ensure people with learning disabilities should not be hidden away but should be present in the community
- enhance respect for people with learning difficulties
- develop competences of individuals so they are confident about their ability to function in normal situations
- ensure individuals play a full role in society by participating and having a wide network of relationships.

A person with a disability also has to face social problems:

- social exclusion – can occur if physical barriers prevent someone accessing normal leisure/ social pursuits

- housing – there is a shortage of suitable housing
- poverty – depending on benefits leads to poverty
- employment – much higher rate of unemployed and much reduced number of management positions
- social welfare – patronising towards people who are disabled
- education – have to fight to get into mainstream education – not always successfully
- stigma – negative reaction from other people.

Everyone has social needs, and relationships with other people are important. Opportunities to meet and talk to others are beneficial to everyone whether young or old, able-bodied or disabled, male or female. According to Maslow, social needs have to be met before anyone can reach self actualisation.

One problem that people with disabilities can have is that although they may become independent from their parents, they are often dependent on carers. Because of this dependence, it is essential that people with disabilities have a separate social life. As long as there is suitable access to the building then it is possible for people with disabilities to go to clubs and bars, the same as anyone else. They are also able to attend evening classes, e.g. art, drama, etc. as long as the access is achievable. There are clubs which are run with people with disabilities in mind.

Sporting activities are a good way of meeting and socialising with other people and also learning to be part of a team. Physical energy, too, is used in sport. There are lots of 'disability sports organisations', e.g.

- BBC Disability Sport
- British Blind Sport
- Cerebral Palsy Sport
- Disability Sport England
- English Federation of Disability Sport
- Wheel power – British Wheelchair Sport, etc.

Todd has plenty of opportunity to socialise with his friends from college. He regularly goes out to the pub with them and enjoys taking part in the pub quiz.

Assistance with mobility

The NHS Wheelchair Service helped both Todd and James to choose the right wheelchair to meet their specific needs. Wheelchair accessories such as cushions, armrests and trays are also available. NHS wheelchairs are provided for as long as they are needed. The NHS will pay for any servicing or repairs as long as they are not caused by misuse or neglect. A therapist may agree that a service user needs a more expensive chair than the local service can offer. The individual may be able to get a voucher to pay the difference.

The NHS Wheelchair Service may be able to provide a powered indoor/outdoor wheelchair but only if their professional assessment recommends it. Usually outdoor electric wheelchairs, electric scooters or specialist sports wheelchairs must be bought by the individual him/herself. Todd's assessment stated that he needed an electric wheelchair for his busy lifestyle whereas James did not.

The Motability Scheme can help the person with disabilities with leasing or buying a car, if the person is on the higher rate of mobility component of the Disabled Living Allowance (DLA). Adaptations can also be made to make a vehicle safer to drive and more comfortable. Getting in and out can also be made easier. There are motoring accessories available for people with upper or lower body disabilities or both.

Adapted mirrors

Cushions, covers and support

Steering wheel knobs

Accessories to help getting in and out of the car

Car accessories

Hand control to operate brake and accelerator

Rotating seats

Lighting

Safety belts, seat belts and harnesses

Examples of car accessories to assist a disabled driver

There is also the Disabled Persons Railcard which allows the person to buy railcards at a discount of up to a third for a 12-month period. If accompanied by another adult, they can travel at the same discounted fare. To qualify (as Todd did) the person must receive the Disability Living Allowance at the higher rate for getting around, or in the higher or middle rate for help with personal care. James, too, has a Disabled Persons Railcard (for 5–15 year olds) and although he has to pay the normal child's fare,

an adult can travel with him at the discounted rate of one third of the adult fare.

Some areas of the country operate a dial-a-bus system whereby a person with a disability (usually a wheelchair user) can phone for a bus to pick them up at a recognised bus stop. As long as the person gives a minimum of one hour's notice and wishes to go on an established route, then the bus will pick them up and leave them at their destination. This service usually operates weekdays only and within a restricted timetable.

Economic

Todd lives in his own home so he is entitled to cash from the Independent Living (1993) Fund (ILF). This fund can give cash to help pay for personal and domestic care in order to keep the disabled person in their own home.
To qualify for the Independent Living (1993) Fund the person must:

- be over 16 but under 66 when first payment is made by the fund
- be receiving the care component of the Disability Living Allowance at the highest rate
- live alone or with people who cannot fully meet the needs of the person with the disability
- be at risk of going into residential care (or be currently in care and wish to leave and live independently)
- receive at least £200 of services/cash from the council each week and be capable of independent living in the community for at least six months
- have savings of no more than £18,500.

Todd is also entitled to Disability Living Allowance. This benefit is available because he needs help to get around and to look after himself. James' parents can also claim this because James has a severe disability. Todd has been assessed as needing care and support services and he has his help paid for by social services. However, he could buy in and arrange help himself instead. James' parents claim the Carer's Allowance. This is a benefit which can be claimed by a person who spends at least 35 hours a week caring for the same relative, friend or neighbour who should be claiming Disability Living Allowance.

Todd also claims Disabled Students' Allowances (DSAs) which provide help for students who have extra costs while studying, because of their disability. The type and level of DSA support is decided after an assessment of the course-related needs by an experienced assessor. Todd was awarded money for travel to and from college. When Todd has finished his course Disability Employment Advisers will help him find a job.

Aids and adaptations

Aids and adaptations can be obtained through the Health Service and Social Services through recommendations of the occupational therapist. Increasingly there are lots of suppliers who sell these items. Both Todd and James have had their homes adapted with ramps, widened doorways and lowered door handles. Todd lives in a purpose-built house so all his kitchen worktops are low enough for a wheelchair user to access.

In the kitchen Todd has:

- a kettle tripper for his electric kettle helping him to pour water
- an electric can opener which needs no pressure from Todd
- specially adapted benches which have been lowered to the correct height
- lowered sink which allows him to fill kettle
- benches and sink which allows wheelchair to fit under it.

In the bedroom Todd has:

- a lowered bed to make it easier to get in and out
- adjustable bed rests and tables
- bed raisers to adjust height of bed
- helping hands/easy reachers which would help Todd to reach things as he cannot bend down or stretch to pick things up
- lifting equipment over the bed to help him move himself.

In the bathroom Todd has:

- tap turners so he has to use less effort to turn on his water
- mobile shower seat – resembles a lightweight waterproof wheelchair so he can access the shower
- toilet support rails and frame.

Other service users who have different disabilities can access other aids and adaptations. Equipment needed to assist service users falls into the following categories:

Examples of assistive equipment

A service user's quality of life depends on their ability to move without pain. Mobility is often taken for granted but if mobility is reduced, a person's life may become very restricted.

Disability aids — Activity 15

Log on to www.blvd.com/disability.aids.htm. There are many types of assistive aids or devices displayed.

1. Find out which aids would be suitable for someone:
   a who has a hearing impairment;
   b who has a sight impairment.

Assistive devices do improve the quality of life for service users with a disability; however, people can become too reliant on the devices and stop making an effort to do things for themselves. For example, a service user who is recovering from an accident might make little effort to become mobile if a wheelchair is used. Or they may not try to raise themselves from their bed if a hoist can do the job. This also means that they take little physical exercise which can cause them to gain extra unnecessary weight. Over reliance, too, can lead to over dependency. The service user's self esteem can fall because they feel they can do nothing for themselves and feel reliant on the assistive devices. The positive effect can be that they feel that they are gaining independence when they use them, which can remove extra work from their family and their carers.

Discussion point

Shiva is 55 and has had a stroke. She feels very depressed because she has lost the use of her left side.

Do you think Shiva would benefit from assistive aids?

Assessment activity (AO4)

CASE STUDY

Choose a service user who has additional needs due to a physical disability, sensory impairment, or learning difficulty, or for any combination of these.

1. When introducing the chosen service user, give detailed information about the additional needs that the service user may have. Include a thorough description of the causes and effects that the additional needs have on the service user.

2. Describe thoroughly three barriers that the chosen service user may face. Show synthesis and understanding of how the barriers restrict the service user, with detailed analysis of the limitations of opportunities to participate fully in the social and economic life of their community.

3. Give a detailed description of a range of methods of support, aids and equipment used by the chosen service user. Evaluate their impact on the service user making reasoned judgements and showing an excellent level of understanding of both positive and negative factors.

Ensure your work contains no inaccuracies or omissions.

Contents

About this unit

Within this unit you will investigate:

- care and education provision for early years in the local area
- job roles and responsibilities available within early years care and education
- values and principles of the early years sector
- the ways children learn and factors that affect performance
- how to plan and implement activities for children in care and education settings.

Working in early years settings can be very fulfilling

Introducing this unit

Children attend many different types of early years care and education settings. Some may go to a nursery which can be privately run or may be attached to a school as part of the statutory provision. Others may attend a parent and toddler group in their local area which may be voluntary provision as they are usually run on a 'not for profit' basis. Reception classes are an integral part of the statutory education system and have to be provided by law. After-school clubs and play schemes provide children with the opportunity to be supervised and participate in various fun activities on an informal basis.

Working in early years care and education is fun and very rewarding. In this unit you will investigate some of the many job roles available in early years care and education. You will find out about the duties and responsibilities, qualifications, skills and qualities required. The daily routine or schedule is important to ensure that children feel secure and are not upset by too many differences occurring from day to day.

When working in the early years sector, there are minimum standards which all service providers are expected to maintain. These values and principles ensure that children receive care and education which will enable them to develop in a safe, secure learning environment. The activities provided will be designed to ensure the needs of all children are met fully. It is essential for all early years care and education workers to understand and apply the values and principles at all times.

All children are individuals who have unique needs. Early years care and education workers must apply a variety of learning styles to meet these needs. If only one style of learning was utilised some children may struggle with the activities and certainly would not benefit from them. The factors which affect a child's performance can vary for each child. Some may have social difficulties linked to family relationships, siblings, play or education which could affect their ability to concentrate. Environmental factors can have an impact on some children particularly the location where they live, the learning environments they experience and the resources they have available to help their development. Others may have limited income in the family which has an impact on where they live and the consumable goods and 'wants', for example toys, computer and television, they have available to use at home.

The activities planned and carried out in early years care and education settings aim to help children learn and develop in a various ways. You will find out how different activities can be used to challenge children whilst helping them to develop skills, knowledge and understanding.

6.2.1 Care and education provision for early years in the local area

Within the early years care and education sector you will find a wide range of services, each with a slightly different purpose but all caring for the **needs** of the young child and promoting their **development**. Parents have the challenge of choosing which service they want their child to attend before they reach the age for attending primary school. They need to consider the type of provision, **facilities**, cost, care and activities that would meet their personal requirements and the needs of their child before making a decision.

What is meant by 'educare'?

Care and education for early years children are linked very closely together and it is impossible to separate them. Early years care and education settings all provide activities which promote learning and encourage children to develop a range of skills. However, they cannot do this without providing care for a child's personal needs and having responsibility for the welfare of the child when they are there. The term **'educare'** is used, in early years services which provide care for children from birth to eight years, to refer to the provision of both **educational** activities and personal care. The proposed Childcare Bill includes plans to introduce the Early Years Foundation Stage which will support the delivery of quality integrated care and education, and care for children from the age of birth to five years.

Discussion point

Why do you think it is important for early years services to provide 'educare'?

Private services

Private services are run as a business with the intention of making profit.

Childminders

Childminders work in their own home providing care for children. The number of children a childminder might care for will vary depending on the layout of the house and the ages of the children.

Childminders need to register with Ofsted and comply with the National Standards. They will need to attend a pre-registration course, first aid training, undergo a screening check through the Criminal Records Bureau and have their premises inspected to ensure it is safe for use by children. A childminder is checked every year to ensure s/he is continuing to provide suitable care and activities.

A childminder can look after any age of child, from a baby to a teenager. The registration applies to the care of children under the age of eight. The government regulations state that a childminder is allowed to look after a maximum of six children under the age of eight. Of the six children, no more than three should be under the age of five and no more than one under the age of one. If the childminder cares for children over the age of eight this should not be allowed to have a negative **impact** on the care provided for the children under eight.

A contract is usually agreed between the parents and the childminder prior to work commencing. The contract should cover the hours care will be provided, holidays and overtime. The costs are usually calculated per hour and may vary from one area to another.

Childminders involve children in their daily routine

Advantages	Disadvantages
Registered and inspected regularly	Childminders like to organise their routine to suit their own lifestyle
Likely to be experienced in childcare and may also be a parent	There is likely to be a range of ages being looked after at the same time
Usually live locally	May not be flexible about hours
May provide flexible hours of care	May not be prepared to drop off and/or collect from nursery/school
May be prepared to drop off and/or collect children from nursery/school	Unlikely to be able to look after children if s/he is ill
Children have others to play with	Beliefs and values may not match those of the parents.
Care provided in a small group	
Care provided in a home environment	
Children have continuity of care, including after-school care	
Childminders often become life-long friends.	

Summary of childminding

Pre-schools

Pre-schools provide structured day care for young children during term time. Pre-schools charge fees for children to attend, usually on a term, week or session basis. Many are attached to private schools and offer three to five-year-old children the opportunity to learn through a varied curriculum to provide for learning and the development of skills to meet the **Early Learning Goals.**

Some pre-schools (previously known as playgroups) are linked to a church or community centre in the local community and may be run by a parent management committee. These provide care for children between two and four years, although some now cater for younger children. The majority run for short sessions from two-and-a-half to four hours and open during term time only. Many now offer extended day care places for children who require longer periods of care. Fees are usually kept to a minimum and some children may be entitled to a free part-time place in accordance with government regulations. If free places are offered the Early Learning Goals must be met.

Pre-schools have to be registered with Ofsted and are regularly inspected. At least half of the staff must have a recognised childcare qualification at least at Level 2 and the person in charge must be qualified to Level 3. The activities provided offer children the ability to develop and learn through play. Many include the **Foundation Stage Curriculum** in their planning and provision. Parents are encouraged to become involved in the work of the playgroup on a voluntary basis either as a helper or a member of the management committee.

Children develop skills such as speaking, listening, concentration, learning to work together and co-operation with other children. They may also learn reading, writing and numbers which provides an excellent foundation and preparation for Key Stage 1 when they start primary school. Pre-schools provide a comfortable, safe and sociable meeting place for children and parents.

Nurseries

The increase in working parents has led to more private day nurseries, which cater for infants and pre-school children during the normal working week. Day nurseries in the private sector will charge a fee and may offer part- or full-time care. Most will accept nursery vouchers to pay for free places for 12-and-a-half hours care a week for four year olds. Ofsted have been responsible for the inspection of day nurseries since 2001, whereas previously this was a responsibility of the local authority. Under the Care Standards Act 2000 all childcare providers must be registered by Ofsted and must meet the National Standards. The organisation for carrying out this is the Office for Standards in Education and in particular, the Early Years Directorate is the part of Ofsted responsible for inspection of early years provision.

Nurseries vary in size and cater for between 25 and 40 children. The children are usually grouped according to age to enable staff to plan and provide activities which cater for their developmental needs. For children under three the **Framework of Birth to Three Matters** must be applied, pre-school children must follow the Foundation Stage Curriculum.

Some nurseries offer overnight care in exceptional circumstances, for example single parents who work night shifts. These have to meet additional government regulations.

Nurseries cater for children from 0 to 4 years

Statutory provision

Organisations which have to be available to provide a service by law are those which form the Statutory provision.

Primary school reception classes

In England most children begin attending school in the academic year in which they have their fifth birthday. Children in reception classes will be working on the Foundation Stage of the National Curriculum, as they will not start with the National Curriculum until the following year (Year 1 of the National Curriculum). They will have a varied and broad programme of activities designed to promote development in all areas. The reception class is typically staffed by early years teachers and by early years practitioners who will plan short-, medium- and long-term goals for the individual child. The

curriculum will concentrate on the physical, intellectual, language, emotional and social development of all children and will promote equality and diversity in all aspects of education.

Reception class prepares children for the National Curriculum

Family centres

Social Services are responsible for some family centres and day nurseries. These care and education settings cater for families with particular needs and in some areas they will offer **subsidised** places in the day nursery, to enable the parent to work or to return to study. They may offer full-time or part-time provision and might work closely with Health Services and other agencies. Parents or main carers of children who attend family centres and day nurseries are actively encouraged to be involved in all aspects of childcare for their children. Most Social Service nurseries operate a **Key Worker** system where one of the early years practitioners works closely with the individual child. In this way the child always has a familiar person at hand and develops a close relationship with that person. In addition, the Key Worker gets to know the child and the family and can become a valuable link in all aspects of the child's care. The funding is primarily from Social Services and the staffing ratios are usually very high.

Voluntary groups

Voluntary groups are those which are run by charitable organisations on a 'not for profit' basis.

In many areas they provide the extras which the local authorities cannot afford. Sometimes local authorities buy services from voluntary organisations as they recognise the quality provided and expertise available. The existence of voluntary groups is not determined by government legislation although they have encouraged the development of provision.

The voluntary groups working with young children are wide ranging in variety and expertise. They include groups that are part of larger organisations such as Cubs and Brownies (part of the Scout and Guide Movement) as well as informal groups catering for dance, sport, music and bands. Often parents become involved with these groups especially where fund-raising is involved. There are a number of play schemes organised by churches and voluntary groups which provide activities for children during school holiday breaks, and some organisations are developing summer schools for children who might attend on a daily basis.

Voluntary groups help children develop a range of skills

Parent and toddler groups

The purpose of the parent and toddler group is to provide opportunity for parents and toddlers to meet together and access resources which might not be available to the individual. Parents, carers and children will have the opportunity to develop socially and the children will have the added benefit of planned activities linked to the main developmental areas.

Parent and toddler groups are often held in:

- community centres
- church halls.

Toddlers and parents have fun

They are usually run on a non-profit-making basis with donations and or fees used for refreshments and **consumables**. Parents stay with their child all the time, and as the child is not being left in someone else's care, there is no specific requirement for the organisers to be qualified. Such sessions are usually held once or twice a week and children have the advantage of free play, mixing with other children and developing **social skills**. The parents can develop informal support groups and gain encouragement from being with other parents of toddlers. Often parents will arrange to meet at times when the group is not running, perhaps for a chat and refreshments or they may exchange telephone numbers so that they can call each other for mutual support.

Discussion point

Voluntary groups are often supported by charities. Which charities support early years provision in your area?

Informal groups

Informal groups are those which meet on an informal basis and do not necessarily follow a specific structured 'curriculum'.

After-school clubs

These care for school-aged children after lessons have finished, and usually stay open until around 6pm. Some take place in schools or venues close by. For others, the children are transported elsewhere. The best ones offer help with homework for older children and plenty of activities to keep younger children busy. An after-school club which provides care for longer than two hours a day must be registered and regularly inspected.

Many different organisations run these clubs, including local authorities and parents' groups. They are usually staffed by qualified personnel ideally at Level 3 for the supervisors. Some areas run Out of School clubs which include breakfast clubs and total wrap-around provision for school-aged children.

After-school clubs are useful to bridge the gap between when school closes and parents finish work. Fees may be charged according to the length of the session. Children mix with others in different age groups, make new friends and spend time in a secure environment until their parents can collect them.

Baby-sitters provide an invaluable service

Shariff	Activity 1

Shariff is eight years old. His mum and dad both work full time and cannot collect him from school. Shariff's primary school has an after-school club attached to it which provides care for children until 6pm.

1 Explain the benefits to Shariff of attending an after-school club.

2 What would the benefits be to Shariff's parents?

3 What problems might arise as Shariff attends the after-school club?

Baby-sitters

A baby-sitter provides care in the child's own home whenever the parents want to go out. The arrangement is usually an informal one and the hours are variable according to the needs of the parents. Baby-sitters are not registered with government regulatory bodies and may not have any childcare qualifications. The fees paid for baby-sitting are negotiated between the baby-sitter and the parents.

National policies

National Standards

The National Standards were introduced by the Government to ensure that all childcare services provide a safe, secure environment for children and provide peace of mind for parents knowing that their children will receive high quality provision. The National Standards set minimum standards which providers must not fall below. They aim to provide a baseline which will encourage continuous improvement and development.

There are 14 National Standards. Each standard describes a quality outcome and has supporting criteria which state how the outcome is expected to be achieved. The Children Act 1989 includes regulations which legally require childcare providers to meet the 14 standards. The standards work in conjunction with other legislation which covers health and safety, food hygiene, fire or planning requirements.

The National Standards may differ slightly between countries in the UK. You should refer to the standards which apply in your local area. Those responsible are:

England: Ofsted – www.ofsted.gov.uk.
Scotland: the Care Commission – www.scotland.gov.uk
Wales: the Care Standards Inspectorate for Wales (CSIW) – www.wales.gov

Northern Ireland: care standards for the child care sector are being agreed by the Department of Health, Social Services and Public Safety – www.dhsspsni.gov.uk

National Standards for under 8s day care and childminding

Standard	Requirements
1. Suitable person	Adults providing day care, looking after children, or having unsupervised access to them, are suitable to do so.
2. Organisation	The registered person meets required adult/child ratios, ensures that training and qualification requirements are met and organises space and resources to meet the children's needs effectively.
3. Care, learning and play	The registered person meets children's individual needs and promotes their welfare. They plan and provide activities and play opportunities to develop children's emotional, physical, social and intellectual capabilities.
4. Physical environment	The premises are safe, secure and suitable for their purpose. They provide adequate space in an appropriate location, are welcoming to children and offer access to the necessary facilities for a range of activities which promote their development.
5. Equipment	Furniture, equipment and toys are provided which are appropriate for their purpose and help to create an accessible and stimulating environment. They are of suitable design and condition, well maintained and conform to safety standards.
6. Safety	The registered person takes positive steps to promote safety within the setting and on outings and ensures proper precautions are taken to prevent accidents.
7. Health	The registered person promotes the good health of children and takes positive steps to prevent the spread of infection and takes appropriate measures when they are ill.
8. Food and drink	Children are provided with regular drinks and food in adequate quantities for their needs. Food and drink is properly prepared, nutritious and complies with dietary and religious requirements.
9. Equal opportunities	The registered person and staff actively promote equality of opportunity and anti-discriminatory practice for all children.
10. Special needs (including special educational needs and disabilities)	The registered person is aware that some children may have special needs and is proactive in ensuring that appropriate action can be taken when such a child is identified or admitted to the provision. Steps are taken to promote the welfare and development of the child within the setting in partnership with the parents and other relevant parties.
11. Behaviour	Adults caring for children in the provision are able to manage a wide range of children's behaviour in a way that promotes their welfare and development.
12. Working in partnership with parents and carers	The registered person and staff work in partnership with parents and carers to meet the needs of the children, both individually and as a group. Information is shared.
13. Child protection	The registered person complies with local child protection procedures approved by the Area Child Protection Committee and ensures that all adults working and looking after children in the provision are able to put the procedures into practice.
14. Documentation	Records, policies and procedures, which are required for the efficient and safe management of the provision, and to promote the welfare, care and learning of children, are maintained. Records about individual children are shared with the child's parents.

Source: Adapted from The Ofsted Early Years Framework www.ofsted.gov.uk

The criteria for the application of the standards may vary slightly between the five different categories of day care and childminding provision. These are:

- full day care
- session day care
- crèches
- out of school care
- childminding.

If the proposed Childcare Bill becomes statute the National Standards will be replaced by new Ofsted Childcare Register Standards.

Discussion point

Look carefully at the 14 National Standards. How do the standards ensure children receive high quality care and education?

Ofsted

In 2001 Ofsted became the regulatory body for childcare provision for children under eight years. Before a person or organisation can provide care for children under eight, they must register with Ofsted, who check their suitability to look after young children. Ofsted also check that they can meet the National Standards for 'Under Eights' care which were established by the Department for Education and Skills. When registration has been completed, Ofsted inspect the premises within seven months and then at least once every three years. Ofsted have to assess both care and education (educare), when they carry out an inspection and write a formal report. The inspections carried out are used to provide a report to the Secretary of State for Education and Skills on the quality of childcare and education in England.

Ofsted has four main functions:

1. **Registration** of childminders and day care providers who care for children under eight. Registration includes checking the suitability of the person providing the care and, where relevant, others living in the premises. It also checks the safety and suitability of the premises.

2. **Inspection** – within seven months of registration Ofsted inspects childcare providers and then at least once every three years to ascertain that the quality and standards of provision meet the requirements.

3. **Investigation** of any complaints or concerns about a childcare provider in relation to the National Standards to make sure the provider can continue to be registered.

4. **Enforcement** of standards according to information gathered during an inspection. Ofsted may take action to ensure the National Standards are met according to the risk to the children. In serious cases this may result in the registration of the childminder or day care provider being taken away.

SureStart

The SureStart initiative was developed to bring together the health and education and social services to provide an improved level of care and education for children under four and their families. SureStart areas have been targeted due to the levels of social deprivation and poverty. Across the whole country there is a range of programmes in operation designed to improve children's opportunities and widen participation.

SureStart programmes aim to:

- Improve children's life opportunities by working with parents in **deprived** areas.
- Provide better access to family support and advice on nurturing, health services and early learning.
- Identify babies and toddlers at risk of failure and help families to make sure that their children are ready to learn before they start school.
- Be responsive to local needs and preferences.
- Work closely with other local provision to offer a wide range of innovative services, including family learning.

Did you know?

It is planned that SureStart centres will provide services for about a third of children (400,000) under four years old who are living in poverty in England.

Children's centres
which provide integrated health care and
education based on previous good practice

Early excellence centres
offer a one-stop shop for integrated
education and day care and services for
parents, carers, families and the wider
community

Neighbourhood nurseries
which provide care and education for
pre-school age children through a
range of activities

SureStart
services

Childcare Link
which is a national helpline and website
www.childcarelink.gov.uk

Children's information services
which provide free information on SureStart
services for parents in every local authority

Extended schools
that offer a range of services for children, young people, their families
and communities, including childcare, family and life-long learning,
parenting support, some health and social care services, access to IT
facilities as well as sports and arts facilities

SureStart provision   Activity 2

1 Visit a SureStart centre or invite a speaker from SureStart to your Centre. Gather information about the services they offer.

2 Give a presentation to the rest of your group about your findings.

Birth to Three Matters

Birth to Three Matters is a framework set up by SureStart. The framework is intended to provide support, guidance and challenges for providers of care and education of babies and children up to the age of three years. The framework should not be applied in isolation; it is intended to be used in conjunction with the National Standards for Under Eights Day Care and Childminding and Curriculum Guidance for the Foundation Stage. The framework should be used in a flexible manner to encourage the development of children whilst providing high quality care.

The framework of Birth to Three Matters recognises the individuality of babies and children. It acknowledges that they have a need to develop and learn through interaction with people, and

exploration of the world around them. The **holistic** nature of learning and development are recognised and the support provided by adults who work with children is valued and supported. The complex, challenging and demanding nature of working with young children is also taken into consideration.

The main focus of the framework is 'the child' and their personal care and development. It does not include specific subjects, areas of experience or curriculum areas. Four aspects of skill and competence of babies and young children are celebrated. The interrelationship between growth, learning, development and the environment in which they are cared for and educated is highlighted.

A Skilful
Communicator

A Strong
Child

Aspects of
Birth to
Three Matters

A Competent
Learner

A Healthy Child

Each aspect is divided into four components as indicated in the chart below:

Aspects	Components			
A Strong Child	Me, Myself and I	Being Acknowledged and Affirmed	Developing Self-assurance	A Sense of Belonging
A Skilful Communicator	Being Together	Finding a Voice	Listening and Responding	Making Meaning
A Competent Learner	Making Connections	Being Imaginative	Being Creative	Representing
A Healthy Child	Emotional Well Being	Growing and Developing	Keeping Safe	Healthy Children

Source: Adapted from SureStart Birth to Three Matters – An Introduction to the Framework

Each of the components is then subdivided to provide guidance to early years care and education workers under the following headings:

- **Development Matters** – uses symbols to indicate four development stages, Heads Up, Lookers and Communicators (0–8 Months), Sitters, Standers and Explorers (8–18 months), Movers, Shakers and Players (18–24 months), Walkers, Talkers and Pretenders (24–36 months) and recognises that development can be uneven.
- **Look, Listen, Note** – highlights the things that should be observed and noted to support the planning of activities.
- **Effective Practice** – gives tips about interactions that might be useful.
- **Play and Practical Support** – gives examples of relevant activities.
- **Planning and Resourcing** – includes hints for planning of activities and the resources needed.
- **Meeting Diverse Needs** – helps practitioners to consider ideas for providing for the individual needs of children. Particular needs are identified which may need expert advice if the carers have concerns about the development of a child.
- **Challenges and Dilemmas** – explores some of the situations which may have to be dealt with in a setting. They provide a focus for thinking about situations and discussion of issues which may arise.

Foundation Stage Curriculum

The Foundation Stage was introduced in 2000 to provide a distinct phase of education for children from three to five years. The Education Act 2002 extended the National Curriculum to include the Foundation Stage within a variety of early years settings including pre-school groups, early years settings, accredited childminders in networks approved to deliver early education, nursery and reception classes in primary schools, nursery schools and private nurseries. Under the Act children in pre-school settings are entitled to 12-and-a-half hours of free education a week. The Foundation Stage continues into the first year of primary school. Settings delivering the Foundation Stage are inspected by Ofsted to ensure standards are maintained.

The Foundation Stage is based on learning through play and has six learning areas:

1. personal, social and emotional development
2. communication, language and literacy
3. mathematical development
4. knowledge and understanding of the world
5. physical development
6. creative development.

Each area has 'early learning goals' which set out the skills, understanding, knowledge and attitudes which children are expected to achieve or exceed by the end of the Foundation Stage. Stepping Stones are used to describe children's typical progress towards the learning goals from three years to completion of the Foundation Stage. The Stepping Stones are not intended to be age-related goals. Children develop at different rates and providers are expected to take account of their achievements of the Stepping Stones when planning activities for the children in their care.

The early learning goals are linked to the National Literacy Strategy and National Numeracy Strategy. There is guidance provided to ensure that through the 'communication, language and literacy' and 'mathematical development' children are able to have a smooth transition from the Foundation Stage to Key Stage 1 of the National Curriculum. Children should be able to adapt to the literacy hour and daily mathematics lesson as reception class teachers are encouraged to cover elements of this across the whole day rather than in one time slot.

By the end of the Foundation Stage each child who has received government funded education should have a profile completed. The Foundation Stage profile was introduced in 2002–2003 and has 13 summary scales which cover the six areas of learning. Profiling should be completed throughout the year and can be transferred from one setting to another if the child changes setting. The data collected from profiling is made available to others, for example reception class teachers.

Assessment helps plan the provision to meet children's individual needs

Discussion point

Do you feel children should follow a curriculum framework before they start school? Why do you think this?

National Curriculum

From five to seven years children follow the National Curriculum. Ten subjects are set out in the National Curriculum, four of which are considered to be 'core subjects'.

- English
- mathematics
- science
- design and technology
- information and communication technology
- history
- geography
- art and design
- music
- physical education.

A more formal education is provided for children in Key Stage 1 of the National Curriculum. They are assessed at the end of the Key Stage to determine their level of achievement. From September 2005, it has been agreed that the assessments will be less formal and involve the support of the teacher to a greater degree. This is intended to make the assessment process less stressful and enable the children to demonstrate their achievements fully.

Assessment activity (AO1)

Early years care and education provision

CASE STUDY

You have been asked to provide information for local parents about the early years care and education services available in your local area.

1. Research the different types of provision available in the local area.

2. You must give a comprehensive description of the different types of early years provision in your local area.

3. Mark the provision on a map of the local area – include a key which shows in some depth the sectors they belong to.

4. Explain the different types of early years provision available in the local area. You must include **two** services from each of:
   - private
   - statutory
   - voluntary
   - informal.

5. Include detailed information about the main purposes of each service.

6. Explain the influences of **one** national policy on **one** of your chosen examples.

You must show that you have the ability to recall knowledge accurately.
There should be no omissions or inaccuracies within your evidence.

6.2.2 Job roles and responsibilities available within early years care and education

Working in early years settings carries with it a high level of responsibility as infants and children are at a stage when they are learning about the world around them and when their **characters** are developing. If you are considering a career in early years you will need to develop knowledge and skills that will help you progress in your career plan.

Jobs in the early years sector
- Classroom assistant
- Care assistant
- Reception teacher
- Nursery nurse
- Activities leader
- Leader for parent and toddler groups
- Pre-school leader
- Childminder
- Baby-sitter

Early years workers develop a partnership with parents

All early years care and education workers need to have particular **skills** and **qualities** which make them the special people who assist children to learn and develop during a very important phase of their education. Without these qualities the children in their care may not receive the care and attention they require to meet their individual needs.

Anyone working with children also has a responsibility to the parents and primary carers of the children in their care. They must, therefore, develop a close relationship which enables them to share the encouragement, learning and responsibility of each individual child. The parents and carers can then relax in the knowledge that their child will be cared for properly, and have confidence that their child will have an excellent start to their education.

The qualities of any early years care and education worker make them special. Qualities reflect the personality of the care worker and cannot be learnt. They are the **temperament** and features which can make a child feel special, relax and raise their confidence. The qualities enable the parents to leave their child without feeling anxious.

Qualities of early years workers
- Approachable
- Sense of humour
- Enthusiastic
- Respectful
- Patient
- Trustworthy
- Reassuring
- Caring and understanding
- Understanding
- Flexible
- Self aware
- Physically and emotionally fit

Skills are the practical abilities which enable early years care and education workers to plan, prepare and carry out activities with children which help them to learn and develop. Having a range of skills will help early years workers to provide a variety of activities for the children they care for. An individual care worker may not necessarily be good at everything; however, when working in a team, the strengths of one care worker can easily complement the weaknesses of another.

Qualities make early years workers special people

201

Musical
to develop and inspire children through the medium of musical activities

Creative ability
to inspire children to learn through creative activities and provide a stimulating environment

Write reports
to keep accurate records of progress of the children

Work well under pressure
to meet the needs of the children and encourage them to develop to their full potential

Scientific
to provide care and attention in the event of an accident or illness

Team work
working with others in the setting to maintain high standards and share the responsibilities

Well organised
to deal with the wide variety of activities and individual needs of the children

Communication and interpersonal skills
to build a good relationship with parents and children, also interaction with other professionals as the need arises

Early years workers have a range of skills to help them throughout the day

Job roles within the private sector
What does a childminder do?

A **childminder** normally works in their own home and must provide a warm, caring environment where children can take part in stimulating **play** and **learning activities**. Childminders provide a **routine** which is appropriate for the ages and needs of the children they look after and will encourage their development and learning. Childminders often work long hours to meet the needs of working parents. The service offered by a childminder is usually flexible and can be organised around the hours the parents work. The day will be planned according to the hours they look after the children; this will depend on when the child is dropped off and collected.

The routine may include indoor play like painting and drawing, reading, creative activities including music and **construction**. They will provide time for exercise and **outdoor play**. A quiet time when children can have a nap would also be included, where appropriate for the children. The childminder has a responsibility to plan, prepare and serve nutritious meals to the children. For babies, bottles will be prepared, feeding carried out and nappies changed. The childminder is likely to involve the children in daily activities like washing and shopping. Childminders may also take older children to and from playgroup, nursery and primary school, so an ability to drive is an advantage. The daily routine is usually organised so that the children being cared for know what to expect and can receive individual attention during the day.

Childminders provide care in their own homes

If a person is paid to look after a child or children for longer than two hours a day they are classified as a childminder and must meet the regulations of the **National Standards** for Childminding. Every childminder must be registered. **Ofsted** is responsible for registering and inspecting childminders to make sure the standards are met. The process includes the home being assessed for safety and suitability. The childminder must also take a first aid course and complete an introductory training course in childminding. They are **vetted** for their personal suitability to look after children through an enhanced Criminal Records Bureau disclosure. Their insurance is checked to ensure there is the correct cover for their business. The amount of space in the childminder's home will restrict the number of children a childminder can look after. Ofsted can register a childminder for up to six children under 8 years old, no more than three of them can be under the age of 5, this includes the childminder's own children. After **registration**, a childminder is checked every year to ensure a safe and suitable service continues to be provided.

Parents usually visit a childminder before deciding whether or not to send their child there. Parents would want to know that the childminder has similar **values** to their own and that the child will receive the level of care and attention to meet their needs. Childminders often become close friends with the families of the children they look after.

The Introduction to Childminding Practice course, which a childminder completes as part of their registration, is the first unit of a nationally accredited Certificate of Childminding Practice which many go on to complete once registered. The local Early Years Development and Childcare Partnership (EYDCP) distribute funding in the form of a small grant to help new childminders set up their childminding business. Many childminders also gain Level 3 NVQ in Early Years Care and Education. Some childminders may already have a childcare background, having worked in a nursery or playgroup and then decided to start their own business when they have children of their own. They may hold various **qualifications** including **CACHE** or **BTEC** diplomas.

Childminders often belong to **networks** and meet together to share ideas, go on trips and develop their skills. Some childminders are involved in special projects:

- working with teenage parents so that they can complete their education or training

- providing a safe place for children to go if they are in danger
- giving respite to mothers suffering from post-natal depression.

What is the role of a pre-school leader?

Pre-school leaders are responsible for the management of a range of early years settings including playgroups, crèches and pre-schools. They are responsible for the planning and organisation of activities which meet the government requirements for **early years curriculum**. The activities will emphasise learning through play and meet the needs of each individual child. They have to ensure that all legal requirements are met in relation to staffing, **insurance** and the organisation's policies. They supervise the staff and volunteers who work in the pre-school or playgroup and can offer guidance and training where appropriate. The pre-school leader may have to report to the **management committee** and keep them informed of the progress of the group, especially if it is a **voluntary organisation**. They may have to give a presentation during a committee meeting or write a detailed report.

Pre-school leaders have to manage the **income** and **expenditure** of the group. This will involve fundraising and keeping the accounts accurately. They may have to write bids to request grants, and collect money from parents. They also have to keep **records** of the children's progress, which will be inspected regularly by Ofsted inspectors and reported to parents. It is essential for them to be organised and enjoy paperwork. **Interaction** with parents will be a daily duty as the parents may want to discuss the development of their child or even personal problems.

A pre-school leader needs to have a qualification in childcare at Level 3 or above as they will be supervising the other staff in the setting. This may be NVQ3 in Early Years Care and Education, BTEC National Diploma in Early Years Care, CACHE Diploma in Childcare and Education or an equivalent qualification.

The role of a nursery nurse

A nursery nurse is qualified to work with babies and young children in day nurseries, family centres, crèches, and nursery schools or in the family home. They often work with a team of others, sharing responsibility for the care and education of the children. The hours of work will depend on the opening times of the setting; these can often mean an early start or a late finish to match the working hours of parents or carers.

The **duties** of a nursery nurse can vary according to the ages of the children they are looking after. For babies, they spend most of their time meeting their physical needs by preparing bottles, feeding, changing nappies, giving baths and dressing. Toddlers, pre-school children and older children require a programme of activities which support their language development and develop understanding of the world around them through play and exploration. Promoting intellectual learning and **concepts** is important through the learning of colours, shapes, letters, numbers and writing.

Informing parents of the **achievements** of their child is an essential part of the role of a nursery nurse. To perform this effectively they need to be able to observe children when they are playing and carrying out activities, and accurately record their progress. There may be occasions when a nursery nurse has to interact with other professionals, for example health visitors and teachers, if a child is experiencing problems or difficulties.

Nursery nurses need to be qualified at Level 2 to work with children under supervision. To work unsupervised they need to have a Level 3 qualification, Council for Awards in Children's Care and Education (CACHE) Diploma in Child Care and Education or NVQ Level 3 in Early Years Care and Education or an equivalent qualification. A Level 3 qualification can be accessed by achieving a Level 2 qualification first or having GCSE grades A–C or equivalent qualifications.

Discussion point

A nursery nurse working in a large nursery may be working with children in age groups 0 to 18 months, 18 months to 3 years or 3 to 4 years. How might their daily duties differ according to the ages of the children?

Job roles within the statutory sector

The role of a reception class teacher

A reception class teacher has responsibility for children aged 4 and 5 years during their first year in primary school. They focus on developing children's social, communication and numeracy skills through a variety of play and creative activities. They need to develop a **rapport** with the children in their class and know each of them well as an individual so that the child's individual needs are met fully. The reception class teacher should have a lively personality and be dedicated to ensuring the child's first year of formal education provides a sound basis on which to build in the future. Their classroom will be a happy, caring and stimulating environment where children feel respected and motivated.

Assessment and recording of children's achievement and progress in a **profile** is an important element of their role. Teachers in England have to work for 1,265 teaching hours in any school year. They also have to carefully plan a programme of activities which meet the Foundation Stage of the **National Curriculum** and enable children to achieve their full potential whilst meeting the **learning goals**. Reception teachers also have to attend meetings at school and may meet with other professionals both formally and informally. **Discipline**, in accordance with the school policy, is an essential part of their role, as it is important for the children to learn acceptable behaviour when they start school. Good discipline contributes to the quality of the learning environment and has a direct impact on the children's progress in the class.

A partnership with other professionals is important for early years workers

The reception class teacher will develop a close partnership with the parents of the children in his/her class. It is essential for parents and the teacher to work together to ensure the child achieves their full potential. Parents take an active interest in their child's progress and will want to have regular information and ask questions when they collect their child from school. The teacher may have to talk to parents if a child has behaved badly and develop joint **strategies** to overcome the difficulties.

To qualify a reception class teacher must have GCSEs grades A–C in English, maths and science, a Bachelor of Education Degree (BEd) or Bachelor of Arts (BA)/Bachelor of Science (BSc) with qualified teacher status. To qualify for a degree course, the requirements may differ according to the university or higher education institution, usually they are at least 2 'A' levels or equivalent qualifications (AVCE, BTEC/OCR National Diploma) plus five additional GCSEs (A–C). The CACHE Diploma may also be accepted. A Postgraduate Certificate of Education, taken for an additional year following successful completion of a first degree, is also acceptable.

What do classroom assistants do?

A classroom assistant, also known as a learning support or teaching assistant, provides help for teachers by helping to get things ready for activities, helping children to complete their work, displaying children's work in the classroom and organising and playing games with young children. They may work with groups of children or be allocated to support a particular child. Classroom assistants work closely with reception teachers to enable them to concentrate on their teaching without the pressures of the additional tasks that need completing. They also work with parents and other professionals within the school for the normal school hours. They may accompany the children on school trips and visits which helps their development or assist with before- and after-school clubs.

A classroom assistant must be 18 before they start training and there is no upper age limit. Formal qualifications are not always required, although a sound education is useful and they may be qualified at Level 2, 3 or 4. It is expected that all classroom/teaching assistants have literacy and numeracy skills to at least Level 2, as they will be assisting with

Literacy and Numeracy hours and it is important that these are at a functional level. IT ability would also be an advantage as computers are essential in the education of children in the classroom. NVQs and Higher Level Teaching Assistant qualifications are being developed for teaching assistants as their role is increasing with the workforce remodelling in schools. Teaching assistants will need to be qualified to at least Level 3 which includes A levels, NVQ Level 3 Early Years Care and Education or BTEC/OCR National Diploma.

Primary education	**Activity 3**

1. Visit a primary school and observe a classroom assistant working with the children.

2. How many different jobs do they carry out during a day?

Care assistant (children)

Care assistants provide practical help with daily care needs to children with a range of **personal needs**. They usually work with children with physical or learning disabilities and their families. They may provide support in their own homes or in **residential** settings such as children's homes or residential schools. Some care assistants work as part of an **outreach team**, helping families and parents experiencing difficulties adjusting to new **responsibilities** or temporary difficulties. Their working hours could involve shift work and working weekends.

The care assistant's role involves providing personal care to help children to get up in the morning, wash and dress and they may assist with feeding. Their duties will vary according to the needs of the child/children they are looking after. They could also be required to provide activities for the child such as going on trips or playing with them. Whatever the care assistant does for the child, they need to be friendly and supportive at all times. The child may want to talk about particular difficulties or problems, which means the care assistant has to be a good listener and respond accordingly.

A care assistant does not necessarily need **formal qualifications**. However, employers are increasingly looking for some form of relevant experience, and care or early years qualifications would be an asset. A care assistant could have NVQ Level 2 in Care or Early Years Care and Education; a vocational qualification or GCSE in Health and Social Care; BTEC or OCR certificate or a CACHE qualification would be appropriate. A care assistant who does not hold qualifications would be encouraged to take on-the-job training and be working towards an NVQ Level 2 or 3.

Discussion point

What special qualities would a care assistant who works with children with physical disabilities need to have? Why is this so?

Job roles within the voluntary sector

Leader for parent and toddler groups

When a parent and toddler group meets, a responsible person needs to lead the group. The leader would plan activities and ensure the needs of the parents and children are met. The activities are usually informal with play being a central feature. The leader also arranges refreshments and the collection of fees. They do not need to have any specific qualifications as children are the responsibility of their parents during the meeting. Interaction with the parents who belong to the group is essential to ensure their needs are met and a range of activities are agreed upon.

Discussion point

There is a huge commitment to leading a parent and toddler group. What are the benefits for a mother who gives up her time to carry this out?

Job roles within informal groups

Activities leader

Activities leaders usually give up their time voluntarily and can work in different settings. After-school clubs, holiday play schemes, brownies, cubs and gymnastics clubs are only a few examples of the wide variety of groups which children can attend. They could work in the evenings or weekends depending on when the group runs.

Activities leaders need to have a thorough understanding of health and safety requirements and plan their sessions according to the ages and needs of the children. The **aims** of the group will provide a clear focus for the activities, which often focus on learning through having fun. They need to have a desire to support children in their development and be able to handle any situation. Discipline is a key to the success of any activities group and needs to be maintained throughout each session. Communication skills are essential to interact with the children, their parents and other people working with the group.

Activities leaders may have qualifications depending on the group they are representing. These could include Community Sports Leaders Award (CSLA), British Amateur Gymnastics Association, early years care certificates or certification from the organisation, for example Guiding/Scouting. All people who work with children have to have an enhanced Criminal Records Bureau disclosure whether they are getting paid or not.

Baby-sitter

A baby-sitter looks after children on an **informal** basis whenever required by the parents. They offer a service which enables parents to go out, often in the evening, knowing that their child is being looked after in the security of their own home. Baby-sitters are often teenagers who want to earn some extra pocket money.

A baby-sitter's role may vary according to the ages of the children they are looking after. They have the responsibility to follow the parents' instructions while they are out. This may include what activities the children can do, for example watching television, the time they have to go to bed, what they can have to eat and drink. It is important for the child's normal routine to be followed and safety to be maintained at all times. A baby-sitter may need to provide personal care for the child, washing, bathing and getting them ready for bed. Feeding and changing nappies could be a requirement if they are babies. A baby-sitter could provide activities for the child, play with them and read stories. A contact number for the parents should be obtained so that they can call them in an emergency.

Working in Early Years Care and Education
6.2.2 Job roles and responsibilities available within early years care and education /
6.2.3 Values and principles of the early years sector

Baby-sitters often have no formal qualifications. They must be at least 13 years old to have sole charge of a child. Parents usually expect their baby-sitter to be mature, sensible, friendly, confident and able to get on well with their children. Baby-sitters may have experience of looking after younger **siblings** or be following a qualification in health and social care or child care. The British Red Cross offer a certificate in baby-sitting which gives a sound understanding of all aspects of the baby-sitter's role. A group of parents sometimes form a baby-sitting circle where they look after each other's children which gives reassurance knowing that the baby-sitter has experience of looking after their own children.

Gemma	Activity 4

Gemma is 14 years old. She has a younger brother who is 8 years old and a sister who is 4. Gemma wants to earn some extra pocket money and has placed an advert in the local shop window.

1. What information should Gemma give in her advertisement which would promote her to prospective parents?

2. What information should Gemma obtain from the parents before she agrees to baby-sit?

3. How could Gemma make sure her experiences as a baby-sitter are successful?

Schedule of daily activities

The schedule of activities for an early years worker should include the following information:

- the time they start work
- what they do to prepare for the arrival of the children
- start and finish times of all activities
- snack times and lunchtime
- any meetings they have to attend
- the time the children leave
- any clearing up they have to do
- the time they go home.

Note: The assessment activities for 6.2.2 are combined with those for 6.2.3 (see page 210).

6.2.3 Values and principles of the early years sector

In early years settings there are ten care values which incorporate those applied in health and social care settings. These care values are often known as **'principles'** in early years and combine the knowledge and skills required to be an effective practitioner. The values and principles ensure that children receive the care and activities which help them to develop and achieve their **potential**.

Valuing diversity

Keeping children safe

The welfare of the child is paramount

Maintaining confidentiality

Fostering anti-discrimination

Values in early years settings

Working in partnership with parents and families

Providing equal opportunities

Being a reflective practitioner

Working with other professionals

Encouraging children's learning and development

The welfare of the child is paramount

Everything which occurs within an early years setting should be linked to meeting the physical, intellectual, emotional and social needs of the children – this is the main aim that has to be achieved. Whenever a decision is made in an early years setting the impact on the children must be considered; anything which could have an adverse effect on the children must not be allowed as their welfare is of **paramount** importance.

Keeping children safe and maintaining a healthy environment

Every working environment must be safe and secure. However, where there are children this is particularly important as they do not see danger or recognise hazards for themselves. Their **inquisitive** nature means that they will seek out and investigate everything available and they do not understand the difference between safe and unsafe. Children are **vulnerable** to accidents and the early years worker has a responsibility to protect them. **Risk assessments** should be carried out regularly and for every visit/trip to ensure the children are safe and secure.

Early years workers should be trained in first aid and know exactly what to do in an emergency. They should be able to recognise signs of abuse and know what to do if they suspect a child is being abused. **Evacuation** procedures must be planned in detail, known and practised regularly to ensure the children do not panic.

Working in partnership with parents and families

When their children are being cared for, their parents and families need to be actively involved in the process, they do not want to be excluded and therefore it is essential for a partnership to be developed fully. Parents are the most important people in the lives of children and they know their own child best. Parents and families can carry on the work of the early years workers when the child goes home and vice-versa. The learning is more effective when it is reinforced and the benefits to the child's development are extensive.

The experiences a child has at home can have a direct impact on their learning in an early years setting. The development of a positive relationship enhances the transfer of information between them. If a child is experiencing difficulties at home and these are communicated to the setting, appropriate support can be given to help the child deal with the problems and reduce the impact on their learning. The setting should inform parents of the progress of their child, difficulties can be discussed and additional activities, carried out at home, may assist their development. Information about the child's daily routine is often provided so that parents are aware of their diet and sleep patterns. A relationship based on mutual respect enhances the sharing of information which will benefit all concerned.

Children's learning and development

Children need to be offered a range of experiences and activities to support all aspects of development The activities provided by any early years setting should be planned carefully to meet the children's needs according to their stage of development.

Children are unique individuals and their level of understanding may differ greatly within the same age group as they develop at different paces. There should be **differentiation** to enable the requirements of all children in the setting to be met. It is important for the early years workers to know the children well and understand their individual needs so that they can adapt activities accordingly.

A range of activities help children to develop their potential

The planning of the curriculum must meet the government requirements for the Foundation Stage and enhance the physical, intellectual, emotional and social development of the children. Children can easily become bored if they repeat the same activity too often, therefore planning should be carried out over longer periods to include different themes, which will encourage the acquisition of knowledge and skills, according to their developmental stage.

Valuing diversity, equal opportunities and anti-discriminatory practice

The provision within an early years setting must provide equal opportunities for all children whatever their age, religion, **culture**, gender, race or intellectual/physical ability. No child should be made to feel excluded and they must be actively encouraged to join in all activities. The curriculum offered should be unbiased, for example celebrating all occasions and religious festivals not just Christian ones. **Stereotyping** should be avoided by allowing children the freedom to choose for themselves rather than directing what they should do, for example boys playing with cars and girls with dolls. Early years workers must show respect for each family's beliefs, traditions and requests for their child's care and education.

Equal opportunities and **anti-discriminatory** policies are incorporated into the ethos of an early years setting. This enables staff to recognise and deal with their own **prejudices** and ensure they do not have an impact on the learning and development of the children in their care. All children should have equal access to the setting and all of the opportunities provided. Early years workers should never make **assumptions** about a child because of their background, siblings or where they live.

All children are unique and have individual needs

Maintaining confidentiality

All information that is collected about a child and their families should be kept private. The information should be shared on a 'need to know' basis only. This means not discussing a child's progress where other parents or children could overhear the conversation, using a password to access information held on a computer, not leaving written records lying around where anyone could read them and passing information on to others only when there is a professional need to do so, for example where there is evidence of a child being abused.

Breaking confidentiality without good reason could have a serious effect on the relationship between the early years worker and the child or their parents. The relationship is based on trust and this must be maintained at all times.

Working with others

Early years workers need to work closely with parents as already mentioned. They also need to work closely as a team within an early years setting by supporting each other and complementing skills, for example one may be strong at music where another is good at creative activities. This promotes high quality and consistency in all activities carried out. The team of workers share the same aims and **objectives** which ultimately means the needs of each individual child are fully met.

Early years workers may need to work with other professionals as part of a '**multi-disciplinary team**' where individuals combine their skills and expertise to meet the needs of an individual child. Where a child has **special needs** or is experiencing difficulties, they will need to work with **external agencies** including social workers, health visitors, education welfare officers, police and others through a case conference.

Team meetings are essential for all early years workers

The reflective practitioner

A reflective practitioner is one who regularly assesses their working practice and considers where improvements could be made. For an early years worker this is a constant process which ensures the provisions made for the children in their care are constantly being reviewed and improved appropriately. They also become involved in continuing professional development which updates their knowledge and understanding and develops new ideas and methods. As a reflective practitioner, an early years worker will ensure they participate in further development of their role to ensure the needs of the children in their care are met.

Assessment activity (AO2)

Understanding job roles in the early years sector
CASE STUDY

A group of students want to find out more about job roles before making decisions about their future career pathways.

You have been asked to produce an information pack about **two** different job roles in the early years sector. The pack must be detailed and include the following information:

1. **Three** main features of each job role explaining what these involve.

2. A detailed account of the tasks that are carried out on a day-to-day basis.

3. A plan or timescale of each care worker's day with an explanation of the daily routine.

4. Accurately state the minimum qualifications required, including alternatives which would be accepted.

5. Explain in detail **three** skills that are required to carry out the role, giving examples of how they are used.

6. Describe in detail the early years care values, including examples of how both care workers apply them.

You must make sure your information is accurate and interesting to read. You should use the correct specialist vocabulary.

6.2.4 The ways children learn and factors that affect performace

Direct experience

Learning through play

Children spend most of their time playing because they enjoy it; having fun is **instinctive** to children. All children should be encouraged to play frequently and **spontaneously**. They change activities often and their motivation, enthusiasm, concentration and **determination** can differ accordingly. Play has a huge impact on a child's physical, intellectual, emotional and social development. It is important for toys and play activities to be appropriate to a child's stage of development otherwise they may lose their motivation to play. If the toy is too simple, the child will become bored and lose interest, if it is too complicated, the child may not have the skills to play with it and become frustrated. Play is recognised as being **fundamental** to the growth and development of children.

Demonstrating ability
Imagination
Developing empathy
Sharing
Experimenting
Reducing stress
Creativity
Role play
Preventing boredom
Concepts
How play helps development
Discovery
Concentration
Developmental skills
Co-operation
Happiness/ Pleasure
Expression
Social skills
Finding out about the world
Muscular development
Invention
Language development

Discussion point

As a group discuss your favourite toys or play activities from the past. How did these activities help your development? What other benefits did you experience?

Physical skills are learnt and developed through play. Children gain **fine motor skills** by playing with small equipment and intricate toys. **Gross motor skills** are developed through vigorous activities. Children develop balance and co-ordination through playing on large equipment and using toys like push along toys and bicycles. They exercise their body and limbs. Active play increases the heart rate and improves **circulation**, bones are strengthened, lung capacity is developed, a child's appetite is improved which encourages them to eat a balanced diet and also improves their digestion. The senses, sight, hearing, taste and touch, all benefit from play.

Play helps children to develop physical skills

Solitary play

Play has a direct impact on a child's **intellectual development**, their ability to understand concepts and their use of **language skills**. Children learn certain concepts by seeing and experiencing them, but others need adult support by providing a range of opportunities to explore, investigate and discover. Children need adults to support them by playing with them, answering their questions and giving praise and encouragement. **Cognitive development** depends on a child developing the ability to classify, store and remember information. Playing with toys and games and experiencing other activities helps children to concentrate and memorise information whilst developing ideas and an understanding of the world around them.

Children develop social skills through play. They learn to share and take turns when participating in **competitive** activities. Children interact naturally when playing together and this enhances their ability to **co-operate** and function within a group without causing disagreements. The social aspects of play develop gradually as children progress through the different stages:

1. Solitary play

Children are happy to play on their own up to the age of two years. They are not interested in interacting with others because they are **egocentric**. Children enjoy exploring their environment and trying things out. They are happy to do this on their own as the social and language skills required to interact have not yet been developed.

2. Parallel play

Children are more aware of each other and like to play alongside other children from the age of two years old. They often engage in **parallel play** near to others and there is little, if any, interaction between them. Children know that others are playing close to them but are not able to co-operate as they only think of themselves. They may be involved in the same activity but are concentrating fully on their own individual actions and not those of others who may be playing close by, for example in a sand pit.

Parallel play

3. Looking-on play

At around three years, children participate in **looking-on play**. They watch carefully what other children do and may try to copy them. Children at this stage may stand on the edge of older children's games. They do not have the confidence to join in. Observing other children can give a child the confidence to try and do the same activity for themselves.

Looking-on play

4. Joining-in play

From around three years, children will join in games organised by adults but do not usually take the responsibility for themselves. Through **joining-in play** children learn how play can be more interesting when others are involved. They develop social skills of interaction and like to join in with their 'friends' and play the same games. They do not co-operate fully as they prefer to be responsible for the play themselves and take control of their own actions.

Joining-in play

5. Co-operative play

Children will play actively together happily, taking turns and sharing from three-and-a-half years onwards. They co-operate with each other, sharing ideas about games to play and taking on different

roles. Sharing may only last for short periods of time and there are often arguments as children of this age like to take control. **Co-operative play** helps children to learn the importance of being honest, they quickly learn that cheating and anti-social behaviour like kicking will not be tolerated and leads to them being excluded. By the age of seven, co-operative play includes games with rules. Children understand that rules have to be followed, to play fairly and be accepted by others. When asked what they are doing, children of this age will be able to clearly explain what the game is about.

Co-operative play

Play also contributes to the emotional development of children. A child who enjoys playing and is having fun will, inevitably, be a happy child. The sense of satisfaction gained through play activities raises a child's **self esteem** and consequently gives them pleasure. Playing with other children and developing friendships through play will also contribute to a child's emotional state as they are able to share their experiences and have fun. When a child receives praise and encouragement while they are playing, they will feel a sense of pride and satisfaction, which raises their self esteem. Play can improve the emotional well being of a child and is often used as a means of helping them to cope with difficult situations, life events and emotional problems, which they may be unable to express clearly either because they have not developed the necessary language skills or they are too traumatised to speak. Play enables children to explore their feelings, to express themselves and to make sense of their life experiences.

Play   Activity 5

1 Visit an early years setting and observe children playing.

2 Record the stages of play observed and the activities the children were doing.

3 How did the activities you observed help the children's learning and development?

Indirect methods

Learning from other people and children

Adults have a responsibility to provide support for learning at the correct level for their child's age and stage of development. Adults must be careful that they do not 'take over' from the child and restrict the learning that takes place. Early years workers and parents should carefully plan, organise and **facilitate** activities which extend the experiences of the children in their care. The equipment and environment are also the responsibility of adults. These should be safe and stimulating for the children to ensure that they are motivated to explore and extend their learning and development.

Children are fascinated with the actions of others. They see adults as **role models** and like to copy whatever they do. At home children copy their parents. They may follow mum around the house with a duster and **mimic** the cleaning. They see adults eating with a knife and fork and wonder why they are using a spoon. In an early years setting children look up to their carers. They copy the socially acceptable behaviours from their observations. They watch the way adults interact, and incorporate this into their own play activities, for example in the home corner playing mums and dads, using a toy kitchen to 'cook' a meal. Through dressing up, children often role play different jobs, for example policeman or teacher.

Children are naturally egocentric and tend to think only of themselves. Until the age of two years children happily play on their own or alongside others. From three years they develop an inquisitive nature, watching other children and observing what they are doing. When they see another child doing something they have not tried they copy them and find out for themselves the pleasure or displeasure

the action can give. If they are happy doing the activity and enjoy it, they are likely to repeat the same activity in the future. At this age children are more co-operative and willing to share; this helps them learn from each other as they play together. If a child has struggled to complete an activity and they see another child complete the activity quickly and easily they observe and remember what needs to be done, therefore success is achieved in future.

Bandura's social learning theory (Tassoni et al, 2005; Bandura, 1976) is based on the fact that children learn from observing others. Children learn naturally by imitating others, especially other children. Observational learning does not depend on **reinforcement**; however, if one child sees another being rewarded for a particular action, they are likely to copy them in order to receive the same.

Children observe the actions of others

213

Children may copy poor behaviour as well as positive actions. At a young age they cannot differentiate between them, so when they hear a child using bad language or carrying out an action which is not acceptable, they may copy the same. If a child hears swearing at home, they are likely to copy this when they are with others. When children first attend an early years setting they often learn anti-social behaviour from others which they have not seen at home. Parents and early years workers should be **vigilant** and maintain discipline in a consistent manner to prevent poor behaviour learnt from others becoming a problem.

Discussion point

Discuss the positive and negative actions children copy from others. How could parents help children to cope with their observations of negative behaviour?

Learning from books

Books can bring a great sense of pleasure. Children can start learning from books as early as eight months. They become interested in the colours and pictures and enjoy the social aspect of sharing books with parents or carers. Books help children to develop many different skills. They help to develop language and increase their **vocabulary** which then aids progression with word recognition and reading. Fine motor skills can be developed through turning pages. Intellectually, books help children to learn colours, shapes, and facts about different cultures and the world around them.

Books suitable for children should be the correct level according to:

- their age
- their stage of development
- what interests them
- the cost
- the learning purpose.

Encouraging children to develop an interest in books and reading will enhance their learning and development throughout their lives. This can be established early by sitting with them and looking at pictures, reading books to them or encouraging them to read themselves. Different types of books can be used in different ways; sharing with adults, reading aloud and independently.

Factual books

Picture books

Story books

Tactile books

Types of books

Pop-up books

Activity books

Language books

Counting books

Poetry books

Talking books

Bath books

Reading is relaxing

It is important for book areas in early years settings to be arranged so that children can relax and enjoy the books available. There should be a range of different types of books in a space which has enough room for children to sit and enjoy story time or read for themselves. Comfort is important. The area should be bright, attractive and quiet so that children can concentrate and absorb the information they are reading.

Age range	Learning activities with books
1–2 years	Looking at simple picture books Naming objects they see in their daily lives Naming colours Enjoy looking at a favourite book repeatedly Activity books with buttons to push or music playing
3–4 years	Enjoy listening to stories and following stories through pictures Like to hear the same story repeatedly Start to read books independently even though they may not understand any words Near the end of this stage they will recognise simple words Counting and nursery rhyme books are enjoyed Like to choose books for themselves Can recite short stories from memory Stories help children deal with problems, e.g. going into hospital Nursery rhyme books and counting books are popular Colouring books are useful to enhance fine motor skills
5–8 years	Learning to read stories for themselves or to others Continue enjoying stories being read to them Enjoy factual books and learning about topics that interest them Older children in this age group enjoy joke books and activity books

Impact of television on children's development	
Positive	Negative
• stimulates inquisitiveness • promotes curiosity • provides topics for discussion in the family • increases vocabulary • develops concepts • enhances knowledge of the world around them • provides entertainment	• may impair development of social skills if it is watched for too long • can impair conversation as it is difficult to talk over it • children may get frightened by inappropriate programmes • they may not want to go outside and exercise • lack of fresh air • reduces opportunities for playing and interacting with other children • reduces desire for reading, writing, colouring • TV programmes can encourage anti-social behaviour

When children watch television and then discuss what they have seen with an adult, their understanding is enhanced because they are able to reinforce their learning. Continuous watching of television is not a suitable substitute for parents and carers spending quality time with children.

Television programmes   Activity 6

1 Observe a children's television programme.

2 Explain how the television programme supports children's development.

Learning from television

Most homes now have a television and they are an integral part of children's lives. From a young age babies like to watch the changing colours and patterns of the screen even though they do not understand the content of a particular programme. Children quickly learn how to operate the television and are fascinated by the variety of programmes available. As they develop language skills they understand the programmes, especially those which are designed for children. Many programmes use music and fun activities to stimulate a child's attraction. Programmes can be educational or focus purely on entertainment. Television can have both positive and negative impact on a child's development.

Strategies used to aid learning

Research into different **learning styles** has revealed that children learn in different ways. They may have a preference for one particular style or a combination of styles.

Visual

Visual learning occurs when children are given pictures, objects or words to look at. They learn through observation which can be enhanced with the use of colours, diagrams and photographs. Some children are visual learners and retain more information and remember finer details if they actually see it for themselves. A child will be able to name an object when they see it or a picture of it before they are able to read the word. Mathematical concepts are more easily understood when a child uses visual aids to help them solve the problem. For example, when adding together two numbers, if they have bricks representing each number, they can then put these together and count them to give the total.

Listening

Some children learn better through **auditory** methods, by listening to information. They prefer to have someone explain concepts and ideas to them. This enables them to ask questions if there is anything they do not understand. From a very young age children like to have stories read to them. This gives them an early insight into the value of the spoken word and the importance of listening carefully to ensure they do not miss vital information. Early years workers will explain to children what they want them to do, children listen to this information and respond accordingly. When a child is given praise and encouraged to learn, they are motivated to do well.

Oral

As soon as a child has mastered language and communication, they constantly ask questions, especially 'why?'. This is in response to their naturally inquisitive nature and desire to learn. Children enjoy talking about their experiences and sharing ideas with others. They can learn a great deal from each other when they talk informally whilst playing. Children also enjoy adults talking to them and learn from the information they are given.

Experiential

Experiential learning takes place when a child actually carries out an activity. They learn through practical activities which involves them thinking for themselves and solving any problems that occur. A baby learns that when they push a button on a toy something happens; the pleasure this gives them encourages them to repeat the activity until they have perfected the action. A toddler learns that when they push a toy it moves along. They like to be active and therefore keep doing this. A child will not learn how to write if they do not hold the pencil and try it out for themselves.

Children learn by their achievements and mistakes. If they do something and it hurts, they are less likely to repeat the same actions. When they experience success, the sense of pleasure ensures they like what they did and repeat it. Play is a key contributor to a child's learning. When playing, they carry out practical activities which enable them to experience physical skills, intellectual knowledge, emotional pleasure and social interactions.

Children learn in different ways

Factors that affect learning and development

Children's development can be affected positively and negatively by a range of different factors. Early years workers should have an understanding of the factors affecting the learning and development of the children in their care.

Social factors

Social factors are those which involve interaction with others. Children are very sociable and mix with others in various situations.

Family

A child's family has the responsibility to provide for a child's needs. These needs include:

- food and drink
- a home or shelter
- warmth and clothing
- love and companionship
- protection and support
- care and training
- a safe, secure environment in which they can develop
- encouragement.

A child relies on their family to provide them with the care and support needed to develop. The **bond** formed between a baby and his/her parents or primary carer has a definite impact on development. Children who have a secure bond usually develop into happy, well-balanced individuals. Those who have poor **attachments** can experience problems with their development. A child who lives in a happy, reassuring family, where the parents give encouragement, will benefit in their learning and development.

Extended families

Nuclear families

Foster families

Family structures

Shared-care families

One-parent families

Step-families

Families help children learn

In modern society the structure of the family can vary. This can also have an impact on a child's learning and development.

A child who lives in a one-parent family will not receive the same level of attention as a child who lives in an **extended family**, where grandparents live in their home together with their parents. A child whose parents have separated may experience stress, which a child living happily in a **nuclear family** does not. **Step-families** can create problems for children because they have divided loyalties and may not get on with their step-parent due to resentment. **Shared-care families**, where children spend time with each of their parents in different homes, can create a sense of insecurity and not knowing where they belong. **Foster families** care for children on a temporary basis and children may have suffered some form of trauma before going there. Not knowing whether they will stay or return to their natural parents can cause children to become upset and confused.

Whoever the child lives with should ensure that they have the care, education and support they require. The culture, beliefs and values of a family have a definite impact on the learning and development of a child. Behaviour and moral values are learnt through socialisation within the family. **Norms** of behaviour are often copied from other members of the family. As a child grows and develops, they reflect their upbringing in their personal characteristics.

Siblings

Sibling rivalry can emerge when a new baby arrives in the family causing an older brother or sister to be jealous. Older children may feel that they have to compete for their parents' attention and be afraid that the new baby is going to replace them. A child who has been used to having their parents' undivided attention up until the baby's arrival may feel left out because the new baby is getting a lot of attention not only from the parents but also from other relatives. This can have a negative impact on a child's development and may cause them to regress to **stages of development** they had overcome, for example using nappies again or using a bottle.

Siblings can also have a very positive impact on a child's development. A child will always have someone to play with if they have older or younger brothers and sisters. They may look upon siblings as a role model and learn and develop skills by copying their actions and behaviour. If siblings are much older, they may take an active role in the parenting aspect and learn in the same way as they would from their parents. Siblings can teach children how to play with toys, read stories to them, help them with washing and dressing, teach them the rules of new games. Having the company of siblings means that a child will not be lonely and will feel a sense of security from belonging to a larger family unit.

Play

Play stimulates a child's inquisitive nature and enhances their learning and development in all areas: physically, through the development of fine and gross motor skills, co-ordination and balance; intellectually, through the learning of concepts, understanding and language. Their interactions with adults and other children when playing provide opportunities for the development of social skills. Children feel **empowered** when playing as they are in control and can make individual choices over what they want to play with.

A child who is deprived of play opportunities is likely to experience difficulties in one or more areas of their development. Delay in development is generally not permanent; however, children who suffer serious problems with no **stimulation** and are neglected may never regain the time that has been lost. A variety of play activities in different environments both indoors and outdoors are essential to ensure children develop according to the norms.

Education

Education begins from the time a baby is born. The way parents interact with their baby is an educational process which teaches skills and understanding. The toys toddlers play with all contribute to their education. Attending a nursery or playgroup provides an excellent foundation for a child's formal schooling.

All early years education requires the influence of the parents who initiate the process through their attention, buying toys or sending the child to a particular setting. Parental co-operation with early years workers ensures that activities at home build on their experiences to enable a **partnership approach** to the education of their child. Everyone who educates a child has a role to play in the holistic learning and development. Children who experience a range of educational activities in different settings and are given encouragement make rapid progress in their development.

Education supports the development of children

A child who misses a large proportion of their education through illness or other circumstances may suffer from delayed development because they have not had the same learning opportunities as other children. It is a challenge for children who have experienced difficulties in this way to catch up.

Environmental factors

Environmental factors are those linked to where a child lives, plays or attends for activities and education.

Location

The location where children live and grow up plays an important part in their learning and development. It determines the facilities they can access, the activities they can participate in, the ease with which they can visit friends and extended family members, their education, visits they can go on and opportunities they have for social interaction.

Children who grow up in a **rural** area may have limited facilities and have to travel to access early years education settings or other learning environments. However, they have access to many natural learning environments which can enhance their learning and development. Their interaction with nature and wildlife may compensate for any lack of facilities they experience.

However, children who live in an **urban** area may experience social deprivation and have to cope with high crime rates and vandalism. Children living in high rise flats have limited space to play in and may not experience playing outdoors because it is difficult for parents to supervise them. They may have access to a wide variety of facilities and activities close to where they live which could enhance their learning and development.

Location can deprive children of play facilities

Children do not choose the location they live in and have to rely on the opportunities they have to aid their learning and development. Parents have a responsibility to ensure that, wherever they live, their children do not feel deprived and can have a range of experiences to aid their development. This may involve taking them to activities in the car or on the bus if there is a distance to travel, supervising them wherever they are and being inventive with the activities they provide themselves.

Learning environments

Children learn in a variety of different environments. The types of learning they experience may differ according to the amount of space, facilities and equipment available. The adult supervision will also have an impact through the planning, preparation and facilitation of learning activities.

Primary school
Child's own home
Nursery school
Crèche
Childminder's house
Garden
Learning environments
Swimming pool
Park
Leisure/sports centre
School
Playgroup
Beach
After-school clubs
Day nursery

All learning environments should provide suitable stimulation for the learning and development of children. Safety and security are of paramount importance. The décor, layout, toys and equipment available should be chosen to give children the best opportunities and maximise their learning. Activities, whether planned or spontaneous, help children to develop different skills, learn various concepts, interact with others and improve their emotional well being.

Learning in a variety of different environments can help a child to develop a wider range of skills, concepts, knowledge and understanding. Physical and intellectual development are usually the **overt** intentions. They also meet and interact with other adults and children which will have an impact on their social and emotional development. Learning in a range of environments generally has a positive impact on children's whole development.

Resources

The resources children have to aid their learning and development ensure a variety of experiences and opportunities. Children learn skills and knowledge by playing with and using equipment and materials. They can also develop their skills and abilities by participating in activities using the resources available in their locality.

Quality and safety need to be considered when choosing resources for children. Resources should not put children at risk in any way and should be relevant to their age and stage of development. Children will demonstrate **natural talents** if they are provided with the right resources to enable this to happen. For example, a child who is musical would not be able to demonstrate this if they did not have access to musical instruments.

Radio/CD player

Videos/DVDs/CDs   Toys

Television   Games

Crayons/   Computer
paints   **Resources
for children**   Games station

Parks/play   Pen and pencils
areas
Community centre   Books

Swimming pool   Adult support
Musical
instruments

Discussion point

What factors should be considered when choosing resources for children to use?

Economic factors

Economic factors can have a huge impact on the development of a child. Children cost money as they require housing, food, clothes, toys and activities.

Income

The income of families can vary considerably. One family may have two incomes, if both parents are working, where another may be relying on benefits. The children in both families have basic needs which have to be met. A family has to balance their income with essential expenses which involves careful budgeting. The amount of disposable income is the money which is left after the essentials of food, housing and clothing have been paid for.

Buying or renting a house or flat is one of the largest expenses a family has. Some children may live in damp, overcrowded conditions where there is little room for play. Others may have a large house with central heating and a garden where they can play safely. These differences will affect the development of the child and the experiences they have to enhance their learning.

Diet can be affected by the income of a family. A child needs a balanced diet with all the required nutrients for growth and development. Some children may be deprived of essential nutrients if their parents cannot afford to buy fresh healthy foods. Children whose parents both work may have

a diet which includes convenience foods which are not particularly healthy. A child's diet can also affect their ability to learn. If they do not eat breakfast they may be lethargic and not able to concentrate in school. A child who eats a healthy diet will be alert and motivated to learn.

Clothing is essential to maintain **dignity** and keep children warm. Young children grow quickly and often grow out of their clothes before they are worn out. Fashionable clothing can be very expensive and children may experience peer pressure or bullying if they do not follow the trends. This can have a direct influence on their social and emotional development. Children demanding expensive clothing put pressure on their parents who may be having difficulty budgeting their income; this can affect the relationship between them and may cause arguments.

The amount of money available for 'wants'

'Wants' are the non-essential items which many children desire and can be extremely expensive. Media, advertising and other children raise a child's awareness of items available to buy. Children may put pressure on their parents for the latest toy because their friends have got it. This can create unnecessary friction if the parent says 'no'.

'Wants' are non-essential items

Working in Early Years Care and Education

6.2.4 The ways children learn and factors that affect performance / Assessment activity (AO3) /
6.2.5 How to plan and implement activities for children in care and education settings

A family coping on a limited budget may not be able to afford to buy 'wants' as there will be very little money available after the essentials have been paid for. The children may have to play with toys that have been bought second-hand or passed down in the family. Children whose parents buy them everything they want will not develop an appreciation for the cost of things and may demand **preferential treatment** throughout their lives.

Assessment activity (AO3)

Factors affecting learning and strategies that aid learning
CASE STUDY

Streetville College has a group of students who are training to become early years workers. The students need to understand the factors which can affect the learning and development of the children in their care. They also need to find out about strategies that can be used to aid learning.

You have been asked to carry out research using a range of sources to provide information which the students can use.

1 Produce a questionnaire to use with early years workers to find out how **two** factors from each of the following groups affect children's learning and development:

   a social
   b environmental
   c economic.

2 Use your questionnaire with parents and early years workers.

3 Research using books and the Internet to gather information about your chosen factors which affect children's learning and development.

4 Write up your findings to provide comprehensive information for the students.

5 Produce a questionnaire to use with early years workers to find out about **two** strategies that could be used to aid learning in **two** different ways, i.e directly and indirectly.

6 Design an observation chart to record your observations of children participating in activities which use your **two** chosen strategies.

Continued...
CASE STUDY

7 Visit an early years setting to carry out your observations and complete your questionnaire.

8 Research using books and the Internet to find out about the **two** strategies which can be used to aid learning in different ways.

9 Analyse your findings of the **two** strategies that could be used in **two** different ways, i.e. directly and indirectly.

10 Record all your sources of information in your bibliography and make sure they are referenced appropriately within the text.

You must make sure your information is accurate and interesting to read. You should use the correct specialist vocabulary.

6.2.5 How to plan and implement activities for children in care and education settings

Role of adults in helping children to learn and develop

The role of adults in supporting children's learning is the key to success. Adults have the knowledge and understanding which can be utilised to ensure children have access to play and activities that will develop their skills, knowledge and understanding. Adults can recognise any strengths and/or weaknesses a child may have and plan activities to help them develop their strengths further or overcome any weaknesses.

Planning an activity that will aid learning and development

When planning activities adults must consider the needs of the child/children who are going to participate. Children acquire skills and knowledge in different ways, therefore consideration should be given to their preferred learning style(s). The equipment used must be checked for safety. An activity should be planned to extend play opportunities and encourage learning.

Activity types	Activities	Impact on development
Physical – usually involves some form of physical activity. Physical activities involve a child using most or all of their bodies. They use their large muscles and exercise their bodies. They are often very active and involve moving around, strength and stamina.	Team games, outdoor play using equipment like bicycles, push and pull along toys Dancing, Gymnastics Ball games Music and movement	**Physical** – children can develop fine and gross motor skills, balance and co-ordination. **Intellectual** – children can develop understanding of size, speed, distance, awareness of the world around them, how equipment works. **Emotional** – boosts confidence and self esteem, promotes pride in their achievements and allows children to release tension. **Social** – taking turns, sharing, interacting with other children and the importance of rules.
Creative – children use a range of materials to make something using their own ideas. Children can experiment with different ideas and find out what is or is not successful. A child's achievements through creative play are their own work and may not be easily recognised by an adult – to the child it means a lot.	Painting, drawing, colouring Cutting out and sticking Collage Junk modelling Sand and water play Play dough Writing stories or poems Construction toys Sewing Clay modelling	**Physical** – it helps children to develop fine motor skills, sensory skills and hand-eye co-ordination. Writing and drawing skills are also developed. **Intellectual** – helps language skills, colour recognition, shapes, children learn about different materials and their properties. Develops their imagination and helps understanding of various concepts including size and shape. Language is developed by talking about what they are doing, listening to others. **Emotional** – children can express their feelings without using words, builds their self esteem and confidence. Children take pride in their achievements no matter how small or unrecognisable they are. **Social** – when playing with other children aids the development of social skills like manners and patience.
Imaginative – pretend play or role play. Children pretend they are somebody or something else and take on that role. They may use toys or clothes or pretend boxes are objects, like cars or rockets, and use them as props. The child is completely engrossed in a 'fantasy world'.	Dressing up Role play Home corner Dens Puppet shows Cardboard box toys Shops Kitchen	**Physical** – encourages fine and gross motor skills. **Intellectual** – develops the child's imagination and encourages their use of language. Raises awareness of job opportunities and possible careers. **Emotional** – develops confidence and enables a child to act out real fears and emotions in an 'unreal' situation. **Social** – helps children to learn how to share and think of others in different situations to themselves, for example different cultures and adult roles.
Manipulative – involves children using their hands to manipulate objects into different positions, through holes or joining them together in some way. The hands, eyes and brain have to co-ordinate to be able to achieve a successful result.	Jigsaws Shape sorters Construction toys Play dough Rattles Soft toys Water sets Sand pits Model making Threading beads onto laces Tool kits Cars and garages Dressing and undressing dolls	**Physical** – development of fine motor skills, hand-eye co-ordination and sensory skills. **Intellectual** – encourages development of language skills, colour recognition, logical thinking, concepts of size, shape, volume, numbers and understanding of the world around them, valuing culture and diversity. **Emotional** – builds confidence and self esteem, gives satisfaction for their achievements, enables children to cope with success and failure and teaches them to keep trying if they want to succeed. **Social** – develop social skills of sharing, taking turns, supporting each other and interacting, develops independence in being able to dress and feed themselves.

Activity types	Activities	Impact on development
Competitive – when children are playing together in joint activities or games. They are in competition with each other to 'win'.	Board games Card games Team games Party games Table top activities Memory games	**Physical** – fine motor skills, gross motor skills, sensory skills, balance and hand-eye co-ordination. **Intellectual** – the meaning of rules, winning and losing, the consequences of anti-social behaviour, concepts of time, space, size and distance. **Emotional** – how to deal with conflict, what happens to someone who cheats, satisfaction of team work, confidence, self esteem. **Social** – children develop social skills including conversation, taking turns, the importance of following rules, manners, sharing, honesty, co-operation, responsibility and friendships.
Musical – activities which encourage children to develop an appreciation of music.	Singing Playing instruments Dance	**Physical** – develop co-ordination, gross and fine motor skills, rhythm and balance. **Intellectual** – naming musical instruments, reading music, understanding of different types of music, awareness of different cultures, improving memory and understanding. **Emotional** – improving self esteem and confidence, allowing children to express themselves freely and release any tension they may have. **Social** – interacting with others, taking turns, sharing responsibility, developing friendships.
Reading – can be purely for relaxation and enjoyment or for gathering information.	Reading for themselves Story time	**Physical** – relaxation, development of fine motor skills through turning pages. **Intellectual** – developing imagination and awareness of the world around them. **Emotional** – enjoyment, pleasure, pride in their achievements. **Social** – interaction with adults and other children, sharing, taking turns to read parts of a story.

Activities help children to develop in various ways

An activity plan

An activity plan should be set out in a logical manner which is easy to follow. The plan should include the following information:

- the title of the activity
- the number of children participating
- the ages of the children
- aims of the activity
- the objectives to be carried out during the preparation, and facilitation of the activity to ensure the aims are met
- the outcomes to be achieved from the activity – how the activity will help the child/children to develop, which may include links to the early learning goals

- a time plan for the preparation of the activity
- the timing for the implementation of the activity covering all stages
- how the activity will be carried out, delivery methods and learning strategies
- extension activities which may be utilised to further extend the learning and development of the children
- sources of feedback to be used for assessing the success of the activity – these could include early years workers, the child/children, assessor, peers and yourself
- criteria which will be used to judge the success of the activity, these should reflect the aims of the activity and the learning outcomes to be achieved
- a bibliography of all sources of information used to plan the activity.

Writing an evaluation

After the activity has been implemented an evaluation must be completed using the feedback gathered and personal judgement to assess the success of the activity. When considering the effectiveness of the activity you should consider your role in the whole activity. Look back at the original aims of the activity and decide if the activity achieved the aims. If the aims were met you should assess how successfully they were met. If they were not achieved you must consider why they were not met – perhaps the activity was too difficult or too easy. Consider what could be changed about the activity to ensure the aims would be met if the activity was repeated in future.

Check whether the objectives were achieved. If they have been then the anticipated learning will have taken place. If children enjoyed the activity and understood what they had to do, this would have contributed to the achievement of the objectives. Matching the learning outcomes to the anticipated outcomes in the plan will help to evaluate thoroughly. Highlighting any unanticipated outcomes will demonstrate synthesis within the work.

Improvements which could be made if the activity was repeated should also be included. When considering improvements you should think about the overall benefits to the children involved. Consideration of the costs, timing, safety and organisation of the activity would be useful. Should the activity be repeated in the future the recommendations for improvements would be essential to prevent the same mistakes being repeated. Improvements could include the following:

* if too many children were involved, try the activity with fewer children
* if the timing of the activity was incorrect, try allowing more or less time as appropriate
* if the activity was too difficult, try simplifying certain aspects or if it was too easy, try making the activity more challenging
* if the activity was not appropriate for the age of the children, try carrying it out with older/younger children
* perhaps the location needed changing – could it have been carried out better outside/inside.

If the activity was a complete success, the children would enjoy repeating it – early years workers should be careful not to repeat the same activity too regularly as the children would easily get bored with it and the activity would lose its impact.

Assessment activity (AO4)

Plan and implement an activity for children in an early years setting — CASE STUDY

Happy Days Nursery provides care for children from 0–4 years and has an after-school club for children from 4–8 years.

You have been asked to plan and implement an activity which will encourage learning and development.

1 Choose an activity to do with children that will have an impact on their development. The activity should be challenging to enable the children to progress and should last for at least **ten** minutes and have more than **one** stage in the process.

2 Produce a detailed plan for your chosen activity which must include:

   a Aims
   b Objectives
   c Learning outcomes
   d Methods to be used
   e Accurate timescales for the stages of how the implementation is to be achieved
   f Reasons for actions to be carried out.
   g Criteria to be used to make judgements about success.

3 Prepare feedback questionnaires/observation charts.

4 Carry out the preparation and implementation of the activity.

5 Collect feedback about the activity.

6 Complete an evaluation of the activity which includes:

   a Reflection of your performance
   b Analysis of the component parts of the activity
   c Reasoned judgements
   d Realistic and thoughtful recommendations for improvements.

You must make sure your information is accurate and interesting to read. You should use the correct specialist vocabulary.

Contents

About this unit

Within this unit you will investigate:

- nutritional value of food and the dietary function of nutrients
- current dietary guidelines to promote the health of individuals
- positive effects of exercise
- health and safety considerations when designing an exercise programme
- how diet and exercise interrelate to affect health.

Taking part in a healthy lifestyle

Introducing this unit

Staying healthy has to be a lifestyle choice, as for most of us it does not just happen by chance. In this day and age people have to make a conscious effort to remain fit and healthy. With the variety of fast foods that are available and the potential of a sedentary lifestyle, it is often difficult to follow a lifestyle that is healthy.

This unit allows the exploration of good health as a choice in life, through all of the life stages. Consideration of current dietary guidelines and the effect that exercise can have on individuals will form part of the work. Looking at different types of physical activity and the effect that they can have on health, physically, intellectually, emotionally and socially, will be another important aspect of study. The concepts involved in designing exercise programmes are an important feature and these will be explored in detail within the unit.

This unit is designed to help in the understanding of:

- The positive effects of exercise on the physical, mental and social health of individuals.

- The effect of an individual's diet and how improvements can be made based on current dietary guidelines.

- The effective use of research and planning when designing a three-week exercise programme.

- How monitoring and evaluation of the exercise and diet programmes can show success and effectiveness for an individual.

The use of these ideas and concepts will help to provide a sound knowledge of how others can be directed to follow a healthier lifestyle that will promote better physical and mental health, and increased lifespan, as well as helping individuals to become more socially interactive.

7.2.1 Nutritional value of food and the dietary function of nutrients

One of the best ways to healthy living is to eat a balanced diet containing the five major food groups. Diet plays a significant role in maintaining our health. A good diet helps to prevent disease and can also alter the duration or outcome of an illness or disease. It can also contribute to having a longer lifespan. So what should a good diet contain to help maintain good health?

Macro nutrients

Building blocks

Proteins

Proteins are the building blocks of our body. For children they are very important for building the brain, muscle, skin, blood and others tissues. Proteins also provide the materials needed to repair body cells.

Proteins are made up of complex chemicals called **amino acids**. To function properly the human body needs 21 different amino acids. The body can make 12 of these itself through complex chemical processes. The other nine are obtained from the food that we eat.

There are two types of protein, animal protein and vegetable protein. Animal proteins are obtained from products such as meat, fish, eggs, milk and cheese. These products contain all of the remaining nine amino acids that our body requires. Vegetable proteins come from plant products such as peas, beans, lentils and nuts. They are a very good source of protein especially for vegetarians. The remaining nine amino acids that the body needs can be found in vegetable proteins.

Fats

Different types of fat

Fats are very good at providing energy and are found in both animal and vegetable products. There are three main types of fat, saturated, monosaturated and polyunsaturated, all of which are important sources of energy and also allow the human body to have the ability to store energy in the form of subcutaneous (under the skin) fat layers.

Saturated fats

These are found in both animal and vegetable products. Products like meat, milk and eggs are high in saturated fats. **Saturated fats** are also found in some vegetable products like coconut oil. Saturated fats are important but the amount eaten must be regulated. This is because too much saturated fat can produce high levels of blood cholesterol leading to an increased risk of heart disease. The increase in **cholesterol** causes a build up of fatty deposits in the arteries known as atheroma. This can narrow the coronary arteries and lead to a **myocardial infarction** that stops oxygen getting to the heart muscle. This will stop heart muscle functioning and can cause irreversible damage.

Unsaturated fats

These are found in vegetable products and some fish. Vegetable oils, sunflower oil, olive oil, herrings and cod liver oil are valuable sources of unsaturated fat. These fats do not raise blood cholesterol. They also contain a group known as **polyunsaturated fats**, which are very good at helping the body repair itself.

Carbohydrates

Carbohydrates also provide the body with energy but their energy value is not as high as fat. Most carbohydrates come from sugars, starches and fibre. Foods such as biscuits, chocolate, cakes, honey and jams are high in carbohydrates. A second source of carbohydrates is foods such as pasta, rice and potatoes. These also provide a high energy source. In both fat and carbohydrate we can measure this energy in units known as kilojoules or calories. These are the same calories that people count in their diets.

Micro nutrients

Vitamins

Vitamins are found in most of the food that people eat and there are six different types (see Vitamins table below). Their main function is to regulate the chemical processes that take place in the body.

Vitamins must be obtained from everyone's daily diet. If any of the vitamins are absent then vitamin deficiencies will develop that can cause health problems. In Britain the 17th and 18th century's sailors constantly suffered from a disease called scurvy. Scurvy was a deficiency in vitamin C, which gave them skin problems, bleeding gums and caused their teeth to fall out. It was eventually stopped when they noticed that Spanish sailors did not have this problem because they ate oranges as part of their diet onboard ship.

Scientists only recently, in the 20th century, managed to isolate the various vitamins in experiments. They have managed to identify their structure and it is now known that there are thirteen of these organic substances that are commonly found in the food and drink that everyone consumes.

There are two ways that vitamins are recognised: by their name and by their letter coding. The vitamin listed as retinol is also known as vitamin A. However, there is always the odd exception! Vitamin B is not just one vitamin but a collection of vitamins known as a complex. Most have their own name and are also recognised by a letter and a number, for example cobalamin or B12.

Vitamins fit into two categories by the way that the body absorbs them. The first category is soluble in water and is needed by the body on a regular basis. The regular need is because they are easily **excreted** in the urine and need to be replaced. Vitamins B and C fit into this category, as they are water-soluble. The remaining vitamins A, D, E and K are all fat-soluble and form the second category. As these vitamins are fat-soluble they can remain in body fat for months and sometimes years.

Below and on the next page is a table that lists the main vitamin groups, where they are found and the problems you can get when they are absent from your diet.

Vitamin	What it does	Found in	Effect if absent
Vitamin A	Necessary for new cells to grow and to fight infection, gives healthy skin, blood, strong bones, healthy teeth, kidneys, bladder, helps good eyesight	Fish liver oils, liver, dairy foods, carrots, peaches, tomatoes, sweet potatoes, apricots, green and yellow fruit & vegetables	Unable to see in the dark, skin problems
B-Complex	The B-Complex vitamins help in energy production. They are important for the way the nervous system works, healthy hair, skin, eyes, liver, mouth, muscle tone and blood production and nerve damage	Brewers yeast, liver, whole grain cereals	Problems in the nervous system, muscle weakness and skin problems, **beri-beri**, **anaemia**, mouth ulcers
Vitamin C	Helps in the production of red blood cells and in healing. Fighting of bacterial infections. Stress increases the need for vitamin C	Citrus fruits and berries, green vegetables, onions, tomatoes, rose hip syrup, green peppers	Scurvy, cuts and wounds are slow to heal, helps prevent infections

Vitamin table

Vitamin	What it does	Found in	Effect if absent
Vitamin D	Promotes strong bones and teeth, helps in prevention of rickets, protects against muscle weakness, helps regulate the heart and contributes to good health	Fish, fish liver oil, egg yolks, milk, dairy products	**Rickets** in children, weak bones and muscles
Vitamin E	Helps muscles use oxygen, improves circulation, helps normal clotting and healing, Extends life of red blood cells, makes skin soft, keeps eyes healthy	Most vegetables, raw seeds & nuts, eggs, leafy vegetables, beef, liver, milk, eggs, butter, rice and wholemeal bread	
Vitamin K	Needed for blood clotting, essential for normal liver function, helps calcium to be absorbed	Leafy green vegetables, milk, yogurt, egg yolks, polyunsaturated oils, fish liver oils	Bruising

Minerals

These are simple elements such as iron, calcium and potassium. They are found in most of the foods that are eaten, some foods being higher in some minerals than others. Minerals find their way into the food chain by being integrated into the soil in which plants are rooted. This means that there are two ways that we can absorb minerals, either by eating the plants or by eating the animals that eat the plants.

Minerals are also needed by the body in small quantities so that it can function correctly.

There are 22 minerals that are essential in remaining healthy. Minerals such as calcium help to build strong bones and teeth, and iron helps in the formation of red blood cells.

Minerals are divided into two main groups:

- minerals that are needed in relatively large amounts; major minerals
- elements and minerals that are needed in much smaller amounts; **trace** minerals or elements.

The table below shows where most of the different elements are grouped:

Major minerals	Trace minerals
Calcium, magnesium, potassium, chloride, sodium, sulphur, iron and phosphorus	Copper, chromium, fluoride, iodine, manganese, molybdenum, silicon, selenium and zinc

As with vitamins, any deficiency of minerals can often lead to disease. For example, a lack of iron in the diet may lead to anaemia (low red blood cell count). Conversely, excessive consumption of certain minerals can also be dangerous. Excessive doses of magnesium can lead, for example, to paralysis, nausea and sickness. Doses in excess of 3,000 to 5,000mg a day can be fatal. Deficiency, however, is associated with heart attacks.

The table below and over the page shows exactly what the main minerals are called, what they do and the foods that are the best sources.

Mineral	Use	Found in
Calcium	Builds strong bones and teeth, muscle growth, aids blood clotting, heart rhythm, transmission of nerve impulses, prevents bone loss associated with osteoporosis	Milk and milk products, yogurt, cheese, whole grains, green vegetables, sardines, salmon, soybeans, peanuts
Chromium	Helps bring protein to where it is needed. Necessary for energy production and the proper use of cholesterol, fats and proteins	Meats, clams, brewers yeast, unsaturated fats. vegetable oil, liver, whole grain cereal, chicken, shellfish

Mineral	Use	Found in
Iron	Required for the production of red blood cells, builds up blood quality, increases resistance to disease as well as increasing energy production	Lean meats, brewers yeast, liver, eggs, whole grain breads and cereals, vegetables, heart, kidney beans, peas, fish, poultry, prunes, prune juice, oysters
Magnesium	Functioning of nerves and muscles, maintenance of bones, helps protect the arteries, helps the body form its bones and proteins. Aids in blood clotting, creation of new cells	Peas, dark green vegetables, nuts, whole grain foods, dry beans, soy products
Manganese	Necessary for normal skeletal development, helps maintain sex hormone production, nourishes the nerves and brain	Egg yolks, sunflower seeds, wheat germ, whole grain cereals, dried peas, brewers yeast
Phosphorus	Maintenance and repair of cells and energy production. Necessary for skeletal growth and tooth development	Fish, whole grains, meat, seeds, nuts
Potassium	Required for muscles, nerves and heart. Aids in maintenance of mineral balance of blood as well as a stable blood pressure. Helps to regulate the body's water balance	Whole grains, green leafy vegetables, sunflower seeds, potatoes (skins preferably), bananas, lean meats, avocados, apricots, orange juice, dried fruits, cooked dried beans, peas
Selenium	A required trace mineral. Selenium supports the body's immune system, helps the body produce antibodies and helps your heart stay healthy	Broccoli, bran, onions, tomatoes, tuna, wheat germ, swordfish, salmon, cracked wheat bread, selenium-rich yeast, sunflower seeds, oysters
Zinc	Required for healing and development of new cells. Helps enzymes in digestion and metabolism. Needed for general growth, reproductive organs, and normal functioning of prostate gland. Zinc is thought to help the body repair wounds, synthesise protein, preserve vision and boost the immune system	Bone meal, fish, brewers yeast, beans, nuts, seeds, wheat germ, meat, liver, oysters, lean meats, poultry, organ meats, whole grain bread and cereals, pumpkin seeds

Water

Water is probably the most important part of the diet. A person can go without food for weeks and still survive. However, if the supply of drinkable water is cut off, death will occur in a matter of days.

Water is the medium in which many of our body processes take place. It helps us digest our food and dispose of our waste products. The value of water should not be underestimated.

Different ways that water can be packaged

How much water do we need?

A good rule to follow for drinking water is to drink half your weight in 'fluid ounces' of water every day.

For this calculation 1 fluid ounce = 28.4 ml

So, if you weigh 98 pounds (44.5 kg), you would benefit by drinking 49 ounces (approx 2.5 pints or 1.36 litres) of water each day.

Example: 98 lbs = 49 ounces of water daily
(approx 2.5 pints).

44.5 kg = 1.36 litres of water daily

If you are using metric measurements then you can divide your weight in kilograms by 33. This will give you the amount of water needed in litres.

These methods are approximate guides.

Activity 1

1 Check to see if you are eating five pieces of fruit and vegetables a day.

2 How much salt is there in your weekly diet? Remember pre-packed and processed meals can contain high levels of salt.

3 Carry out a vitamin and mineral check and see if you are getting all of the vitamins and minerals that you require.

4 How much junk food are you eating, how is it affecting your diet?

Did you know?

Most people can live without food for several weeks but the average human can survive for only three to four days without water.

Water is in fruit juices, teas, sparkling water and other fizzy drinks. Drinking pure water allows the body to wash out toxins without having to put stress on the digestive system. Water consumption is one of the single most important tasks undertaken daily in order to live a long and healthy life.

Fibre

Fibre in the diet adds bulk to the food that we eat. This helps the digestive system to move the food through the bowel. Without these muscular movements it is easy to become constipated.

Fibre is found in a variety of different foods such as:

- bran
- rice
- cereals
- wholemeal bread
- fruit
- vegetables (peas, beans, greens).

Lack of fibre in the diet can cause poor digestion of food, which can lead to **constipation**.

Did you know?

The average burger meal (burger, fries and milk shake) can contain between half and two-thirds of the daily calorie intake required by the average 16-year-old student.

Where do daily nutrients come from?　　Activity 1

Monitor everything that you eat on a daily basis for one week. To do this, make sure that you keep a record of the types and amounts of the different foods that you consume. Make sure that you keep the packaging of the products consumed. This will help you work out the nutritional value of the meals and snacks that you have eaten. You will now be able to assess whether your diet is healthy and if there is anything missing. You will also be able to see if you are consuming too much of any one food group or product.

What is a healthy balanced diet?

A healthy diet contains all of the nutrients needed by the body. Nutritionists and the government have worked out a rough guide to show what a healthy diet should include.

Getting the balance right

The Department of Health has produced 'The Balance of Good Health' which includes the government's eight guidelines for a healthy diet. The first of these is very important: 'Enjoy your food'. Diet is an important component of good health but it should not be a battle or be making you miserable. A healthy attitude to food is an important part of a healthy diet.

Remember, it is diets, not foods, which are unhealthy. It is the food that is eaten over months and years that will influence your health. People don't have to strictly follow a healthy diet every day but they should try and make sure it applies to their diet over a week. It's no great disaster if one day they don't eat five portions of fruit and vegetables or eat lots of cake on their birthday – things should be kept in perspective, making sure that the diet is balanced over the long term.

A diet rich in fruits, vegetables and wholegrain foods with the occasional cream cake or fry-up is still a healthy diet; people just have to be realistic about how often they make those small **irregularities**.

It is important to make changes for life, and not to be influenced by 'fad' diets. All diet changes should be thought about carefully; they have to be sensible changes that can be lived with. It may make more sense to make small changes over time rather than radically altering the entire diet, especially if the changes are likely to be part of a permanent lifestyle change.

Be adventurous and put as much variety in the diet as possible. This way people are bound to meet all their vitamin and mineral requirements without needing extra **supplements**.

Diet is not the only component of good health. Don't forget about exercise, stress and smoking and think in terms of healthy lifestyles for maximum benefits.

Food for Life Pyramid — CASE STUDY

Food for Life Pyramid

It is important to remember that it is a person's diet that is healthy or unhealthy and not individual foods. A healthy diet is not just about eating 'good' foods and completely cutting out 'bad' foods. This is because all foods have benefits in certain circumstances, depending on the individual's needs. Look at the person's whole diet and see where beneficial changes need to be made. Complete change is not always necessary; small changes can give major improvements in a person's health.

From the pyramid it is clear that most of our diet should consist of:

- cereal products, potatoes, and fruits and vegetables will provide energy, fibre, most vitamins and minerals and some protein.

- choose wholegrain cereal varieties and reduce the use of salt when cooking vegetables.

- all forms of fruit and vegetables are beneficial (dried, juice, unsweetened, canned, frozen and fresh).

- meat, fish and vegetarian alternatives, and dairy products: these two groups complement the protein provided by the cereals and provide more vitamins.

- dairy products are an excellent source of calcium and are very important, full fat products are rich in saturated fat, your age should dictate how much of these you eat.

- oily fish (mackerel, herring, sardines, etc.) are rich sources of omega-3 fatty acids which are associated with a reduced risk of coronary heart disease. (A medium-sized portion of mackerel will provide the recommended weekly intake of omega-3 fatty acids.)

- spreadable fats and oils and sugary foods should be a small part of our diet as they are very rich in energy. The choice of margarine and oil is important as there are different types of fat. Use olive or a seed oil and an unsaturated margarine, rather than butter or lard, when saturated fat needs to be cut down.

- fluid intake is a very important part of a healthy diet and intake should be at least two litres of fluid a day. Fruit juice is a good source of vitamin C but coffee is a diuretic and can actually dehydrate you. Always follow the recommended safe intakes of alcohol (21 units per week for women and 28 for men).

Additives

Substances that do not occur naturally in a particular food are additives. Many substances occur naturally in one food but could become an additive when they are used in the manufacture of another. Sodium propionate can be in the list of ingredients in a loaf of bread, but if you eat certain cheeses you will be eating ten times as much sodium propionate. It will not be on the label because it is a natural part of the cheese.

Additives have a variety of functions when used in the food that people eat. They can be used to replace nutrients lost in processing. An example of this is that white flour must have thiamine, riboflavin, niacin and folate put in to replace what is lost when the wheat germ is removed. Some vitamins are added to breakfast cereals once they have been processed. Some additives slow the rate that foods go off; another term for this is slowing spoilage. BHA (butylated hydroxyanisole) and BHT (butylated hydroxytoluene) are antioxidants that keep fat from turning **rancid**.

Additives are also used to improve texture or consistency. They can make the product thicker, smoother, or more free-flowing, or keep ingredients from separating. Flavourings and colourings are considered to be additives. They can be common spices such as salt and pepper, or strange-sounding chemicals such as tartrazine (a yellow food dye) or monosodium glutamate (which preserves the colour of food).

Most additives are used in such small amounts that they have no significance in the diet unless huge quantities of a single food are consumed. People should be more concerned about what's taken out of food than what's added in. Processing a food may mean that vitamins, minerals, other nutrients and fibre have been removed. What is added back may be only a small part of what was taken away.

When fibre is removed, our intestine will be the loser as less fibre means a higher risk of constipation and bowel disease. By eating **unprocessed** fruits, vegetables, whole grains and beans, food processors do not get the chance to remove the good nutrients that nature provides.

So why did manufacturers start putting additives in our food? Food additives came into being because mass food production has different requirements to those of the household kitchen. Problems in maintaining the quality of food increased when they started to be produced a long way from their point of sale. Food additives came into use to allow the production of processed foods. In some products, additives are so essential that they are retained even in some organic foods.

In less developed countries the losses that occur between farm and table, due to **microbiological deterioration**, are very high. In countries such as the UK, the high incidence of food poisoning indicates the extent of this threat. As many as one in five of the UK population probably suffers one bout of food poisoning per annum. This figure would be much higher without preservatives. Preservatives, colours and flavours are the best known additives but, in fact, there are many categories of additives, each having a specific purpose.

Below and on the next page is a table of common additives and their uses:

Additive	Action	Effect	Safety rating
Artificial colours	Man-made dyes. Impart colours to foods to offset colour losses, correct natural variations in colour, enhance naturally occurring colours and prevent bacterial growth (especially in wine).	Some animal studies suggest they create a small risk of cancer or tumours; possible link with hyperactivity and learning disabilities in some sensitive children.	Mild allergic reaction (itching or hives) possible in those sensitive to Yellow No. 5; Red No. 3 may be banned due to health concerns derived from animal studies.
Aspartame	Artificial sweetener, low-calorie sugar substitute (Equal and Nutra-Sweet). Made by combining aspartic acid and phenylalanine, amino acids that occur naturally in protein-containing foods.	Digested and absorbed like any other protein.	**Anecdotal** reports of dizziness, headaches and behaviour changes are unconfirmed in controlled studies. People with the rare disease **phenylketonuria** must avoid.
BHA (butylated hydroxyanisole) BHT (butylated hydroxytoluene)	Preservatives, antioxidants. Added to fats, oils and foods that contain oil (baked goods and snacks) to prevent rancidity.	Prevent the oxidation of dietary fats and oils. Low doses in food may help prevent stomach cancer by mopping up reactive molecules that can damage tissues in food.	Most studies indicate they're safe; **carcinogenic** in some animal studies using high doses.

Additive	Action	Effect	Safety rating
GUMS (alginate, arabic, carrageenan, ghatti, guar, karaya, locust bean, tragacanth, xanthan)	Stabilisers, thickening agents. Replace fat in low-fat foods; modify texture.	Recognised by the body as mixtures of digestible sugars.	Derived from natural sources (plant fluids, seeds, seaweed and bacteria).
MSG (monosodium glutamate)	Used to flavour foods, especially various types of meats.	Emphasises natural flavours in certain foods. Glutamate is a salt in protein-containing foods. Also produced by the body for metabolism and brain function. The body can't distinguish between glutamate in food and glutamate in MSG.	May precipitate reactions in sensitive individuals; headache, **nausea**, weakness, difficulty breathing, and burning sensations in the back of the neck and forearms.
OLESTRA (Olean)	Fat substitute. A synthetic fat that adds no fat or calories to foods.	Made from everyday ingredients (vegetable oil and table sugar), but the molecules are too large to be digested or absorbed by the body.	Reduced absorption of cancer-fighting, fat-soluble carotenoids from fruits and vegetables that help maintain a healthy heart. Can cause a laxative effect, gas, abdominal cramps and diarrhoea.
Sodium nitrates	Colouring, flavouring, preservative. Stabilise red colour, and enhance flavour of cured meats; help prevent the growth of bacteria that causes botulism.	In the acidic environment of the stomach, as well as during intensive heating (frying bacon to crisp stage), nitrites can be converted into potentially cancer-causing compounds (**nitrosamines**).	Higher levels than used in food found to be carcinogenic in animals; ascorbic acid (vitamin C) is routinely added to cured meats to inhibit formation of nitrosamines.
Sterol esters	Added to margarine to promote healthy blood cholesterol levels.	Extracted from wood pulp or soybean oil extracts. Not absorbed by the body. Inhibits cholesterol absorption in the intestine.	Studies originally used three portions of margarine per day to assess safety. Approved for use in 1999.
Sucralose	Artificial sweetener. Only low-calorie sweetener made from sugar. Adds no calories when used to sweeten foods and beverages. Can be used virtually like sugar, including in baked goods.	Not recognised by the body as sugar, sucralose molecules pass through the body unchanged and are eliminated.	Approved for use in the United States in 1998.
Sulphites	Preservative. Prevent discolouration (in dried apricots, raisins and other dried fruit, and some dried, fried or frozen potatoes); control 'black spot' in fresh shrimp and lobster.	Destroy any of the vitamin thiamin (vitamin B1) present in food.	Can cause reactions such as hives and breathing difficulty. Those with asthma and aspirin allergies should avoid due to risk of **anaphylactic** shock, indicated by swelling of airways.

Health as a Lifestyle Choice
7.2.1 Nutritional value of food and the dietary function of nutrients /
7.2.2 Current dietary guidelines to promote the health of individuals

Did you know?

In the Middle Ages the only way of preserving food safely was to use salt or vinegar. Meat and fish would be dried and preserved in salt and some vegetables would be pickled. Is it any wonder that they looked forward to summer coming!

The underpinning knowledge for the unit has not been arranged within the specifications in the same order as the Assessment Evidence Grid. The Assessment activity is, therefore, more appropriately placed at the end of Unit 7.

Jack   Activity 2

Jack is 19 and needs some serious help. His diet is probably the worst that you have heard about in a long while. This is because Jack is addicted to fast food. Jack's only healthy meal is breakfast when he has a bowl of cereal and a cup of tea.

The remainder of his daily meals are made up of fast foods such as burgers, pizza and other fried foods. He has very few fruits and vegetables other than the salad that is in his burger and the chips that accompany it.

The beverages that Jack consumes are mainly carbonated drinks and milk shakes. Jack would not know what fruit juice was if it fell out of the sky and hit him on the head.

It is obvious that Jack needs some serious help. If he des not get help, his health and social well being will suffer. Your job is to stop him from being a junk food junkie.

1. Look at the average 'burger meal' (burger, fries and a soft drink) and explain to Jack why it is not a good meal to eat on a regular basis.

2. Jack's burger meal will contain a variety of additives. Explain to Jack the types of additives that he is consuming and the effect that they could have on his health and well being.

3. Looking at Jack's overall diet, estimate what vitamins and minerals may be missing from his daily food intake.

4. Explain to Jack why it is essential to eat fruit and vegetables on a daily basis.

5. As Jack is only consuming soft drinks and milk shakes, he will need to be shown what effects this will have on his body. What liquids should Jack be consuming and in what quantities?

6. Generally, what should be in Jack's daily diet to keep him fit and healthy?

7.2.2 Current dietary guidelines to promote the health of individuals

Current dietary guidelines

In the United Kingdom the government has initiated various healthy eating initiatives. These have been delivered through government approved agencies. Examples of such initiatives are:

- The Healthy Eating Plate
- Take Five
- UK Dietary Guidelines for Saving Lives (Our Healthier Nation 1999)

The Healthy Eating Plate was a government strategy set up to help people discover how a balanced diet could be achieved. One of its aims was to demonstrate that a plate of food could not only be healthy but interesting especially when the content was balanced.

Fruit & Vegetables   **Bread, cereals & potatoes**

Meat, fish & alternatives   **Fatty & sugary foods**   **Milk & dairy foods**

The Healthy Eating Plate

Take Five was an initiative that was designed to persuade more people to eat fresh fruit and vegetables each day. The whole idea was to eat five portions a day making the diet healthier.

In Our Healthier Nation new dietary guidelines were put in to place to make it clearer to everyone what a balanced diet was and the nutritional values

235

they should receive. All initiatives produced are always designed to improve our health but they are not compulsory, people have to be willing to try.

How DRVs help us with our diet.

A set of guidelines have been developed so that people are able to monitor and regulate their intake of vitamins and minerals. The system is known as the 'Recommended Daily Amount' or RDA. The RDA represents the amount of vitamins or minerals needed by an average adult man in order to maintain good health. In addition to RDA, individual countries will set their own recommendations for nutrients. These are more specific and will take into account the age and sex of the population and are known as DRVs (dietary reference values).

The Department of Health introduced DRVs in 1991. DRVs are benchmark intakes of energy and nutrients – they can be used for guidance but shouldn't be seen as exact recommendations. They show the amount of energy or an individual nutrient that a group of people of a certain age range (and sometimes sex) needs for good health.

Although DRVs are given as daily intakes, people often eat quite different foods from one day to the next, and their appetite can change so, in practice, the intakes of energy and nutrients need to be averaged over several days. DRVs apply to healthy people only and don't apply to children under five years old.

DRV is a general term used to cover:

- Estimated average requirement (EAR): this is the average amount of energy or a nutrient needed by a group of people.

- Reference nutrient intake (RNI): the amount of a nutrient that is enough to meet the dietary needs of about 97% of a group of people.

- Lower reference nutrient intake (LRNI): the amount of a nutrient that is enough for a small number of people in a group with the smallest needs. Most people will need more than this.

- Safe intake: this is used when there isn't enough evidence to set an EAR, RNI or LRNI. The safe intake is the amount judged to be enough for almost everyone, but below a level that could have undesirable effects.

Healthy eating initiatives – specific needs

Infants

From the moment a baby is born it needs nutrients to help it grow. These are provided by the mothers milk or milk that is made up from a formula that contains all of the nutrients the baby needs. This will continue until the mother weans the baby off milk and on to solid foods.

Children

We do not always like eating what is good for us

Children grow very quickly and are usually very active, so they need plenty of calories and nutrients. A healthy and varied diet should provide all the nutrients the toddler needs. Everyday requirements should include:

Milk and dairy foods – these provide calories, protein, vitamins and minerals.

Meat, fish, eggs, beans, peas and lentils – these are rich in nutrients such as protein, vitamins and minerals. Boys can be given up to four portions of oily fish a week, such as mackerel, salmon and sardines, but it's best to give girls no more than two portions of oily fish a week.

Bread and other cereals such as rice, pasta and breakfast cereals, and potatoes, yams and sweet potatoes – these starchy foods provide calories, vitamins, minerals and fibre.

Fruit and vegetables – these contain vitamin C, and other protective vitamins and minerals, as well as fibre.

Although toddlers can eat the same food as adults, before they're two years old children can't eat large amounts of food at one sitting. So, until then, child meals and snacks should be packed with calories and nutrients (nutrient-dense foods) such as:

- full-fat milk and dairy foods, meat, eggs.

It must not be forgotten that they must have fruit, vegetables and starchy foods as well.

Although adults eat high-fibre foods, young children's stomachs can't cope with large amounts of foods such as wholemeal pasta and brown rice. Also, too much fibre can sometimes reduce the amount of minerals such as calcium and iron that children can absorb.

By the time they're five years old, young children should be eating family food, which is more bulky as it contains lots of starchy foods and plenty of fruit and vegetables. But make sure it doesn't contain too much saturated fat, which is found in butter, hard-fat spreads, cheese, fatty meat and meat products, biscuits, pastry and cakes.

It should be remembered that certain foods should be avoided, these include:

- Raw eggs and food that contains raw or partially cooked eggs because of the risk of salmonella, which causes food poisoning. When eggs are given to a toddler, make sure the eggs are cooked until both the white and yolk are solid.

- Whole or chopped nuts for children under five years old because of the risk of choking. It's a good idea to crush or flake them.

- Shark, swordfish and marlin because these fish contain relatively high levels of mercury, which might affect a child's developing nervous system.

- Avoid giving raw shellfish to a toddler to reduce the risk of food poisoning.

There's no need to add salt to a toddler's food. From the age of one to three, children should be having no more than 2g of salt a day. If buying processed foods, even those aimed at children, remember to check the information given on the labels to choose those with less salt.

Don't give sweet drinks such as fizzy drinks and fruit squash because they cause tooth decay. When fruit squash or sugary drinks are given make sure they're well diluted with water, and drunk at mealtimes. Between meals, it's better to give water or milk to drink. There's no need to add sugar or honey to a toddler's food.

Adolescents

We do not always make the correct decisions

Young people need lots of energy and nutrients because they're still growing.

These are estimates of the average amount of energy young people of different ages need. Energy is measured in calories (kcal).

- Boys aged 11 to 14 need about 2,220 calories a day.

- Girls aged 11 to 14 need about 1,845 calories a day.

- Young men aged 15 to 18 need about 2,755 calories a day.

- Young women aged 15 to 18 need about 2,110 calories a day.

But remember these figures are only a guide, and young people might need more or less than these estimates, depending on a number of things, such as how physically active they are.

Young people often have big appetites, so it's important for them to have a healthy balanced diet, rather than filling up on sugary or fatty foods, such as crisps, sweets, cakes, biscuits, and fizzy drinks. These foods tend to be high in calories but contain few nutrients, and they can also reduce appetite for healthier foods.

A healthy, balanced diet should include

Foods rich in starch and fibre, such as bread, rice, pasta, cereals and potatoes, are good examples. As well as being low in fat they are good sources of other essential nutrients: protein, vitamins and minerals. The fibre from these helps to prevent constipation, which reduces the risk of some common disorders in the **intestine**. Don't be tempted to buy raw bran and sprinkle it onto food to increase fibre as this may prevent the absorption of some important minerals such as calcium and iron. Oats, beans, peas, lentils, fruit and vegetables are also sources of fibre.

Iron-rich foods

Iron-rich foods help maintain the iron store in your body. The best source of iron is red meat. It can also be found in pulses (peas, beans, lentils), oily fish like sardines, eggs, bread, green vegetables and in fortified breakfast cereals. Iron is very important, especially during pregnancy.

Foods and drinks rich in vitamin C

These help the body to absorb iron, so you could have some fruit or vegetables or a glass of fruit juice with an iron-rich meal. Fruit, especially citrus fruit, green vegetables, peppers, tomatoes and potatoes are all good sources of vitamin C. Avoid drinking tea with iron-rich meals as this can affect how much iron the body absorbs from your food.

Adults

Foods containing folic acid

These help maintain good health in older age. Good sources are green vegetables and brown rice, as well as fortified bread and breakfast cereals.

Calcium-rich foods

Osteoporosis is a major problem for older people, particularly women. This is where bone density reduces and so the risk of fractures increases. The best sources of calcium are dairy products such as milk, cheese and yoghurt. Remember to choose lower-fat varieties if you are young. In older adults full-fat products are less of an issue unless you have

a serious medical problem such as a heart condition or high cholesterol. Calcium is found in canned fish with bones, such as sardines and pilchards.

Cutting down on salt

Blood pressure appears to increase with age and it is thought that this may be related to our relatively high salt diets. Having high blood pressure increases the risk of stroke. On average, you should aim to keep salt intake to less than 6g per day (equivalent to about 2g of sodium). Most of the salt we eat is already in foods, and so it is important to be aware of the salt content of ready-prepared foods, which can be a major source. Also avoid adding salt to your food when cooking and at the table.

Potassium, on the other hand, has a beneficial effect on blood pressure, and fruits and vegetables such as bananas, tomatoes and avocados are a good source of potassium.

Too much salt can be dangerous to health

Vitamins

Like calcium, vitamin D is important for good bone health. Most vitamin D comes from the effect of sunlight on our skin but good dietary sources include oily fish, eggs, and **fortified** foods such as breakfast cereals, bread and margarines.

People should consider taking a daily 10 microgram vitamin D supplement if they:

- rarely get outdoors or are housebound,
- wear clothes that cover all your skin when you are outdoors,
- eat no meat or oily fish.

People should avoid taking potassium supplements unless on medical advice. This is because, as we get older, our kidneys become less able to remove potassium from our blood.

Older adults

As with all adults, the basic principles of diet should be followed. As people get older there are certain changes that we have to accommodate. The following is a set of principles that can be applied to older adults:

1 Eat a wide variety of foods, including those with high nutrient density.

2 Energy intake should be balanced with regular physical activity.

3 Starchy foods should be eaten throughout the day. For people with an acute or chronic illness, who have a limited appetite, intake of starchy foods should be modified to suit their individual needs.

4 Four or more portions of fruit and vegetables should be eaten daily. People with acute or chronic illness should modify their fruit and vegetable intake to suit their individual needs.

5 An adequate intake of high-fibre foods and fluids should be maintained.

6 Meat, poultry and fish should be eaten regularly. Dairy foods such as milk, yogurt and cheese should be eaten daily. For those with an acute or chronic illness, an increased intake of dairy foods may be recommended. Fortified milk is also recommended for older people.

7 For those who are healthy, a moderate fat intake, with a mixture of fats, should be included in the diet. For those who have an acute or chronic illness, fat intake should be modified to suit their individual needs.

8 At least eight cups or glasses of fluids should be drunk each day.

9 Enriched foods, fortified foods and dietary supplements should be used where specifically indicated by a GP or dietician. The use of dietary supplements should be reviewed regularly.

10 Alcohol can be consumed in moderation, if acceptable.

Pregnant women and nursing mothers

Even before pregnancy begins, nutrition is a primary factor in the health of mother and baby. Eating a well balanced diet before becoming pregnant will lead to only a few changes to meet the nutritional needs of pregnancy.

It is recommended that pregnant women should increase their usual servings of a variety of foods from the four basic food groups to include the following:

- Four or more servings of fruits and vegetables for vitamins and minerals
- Four or more servings of wholegrain or enriched bread and cereal for energy
- Four or more servings of milk and milk products for calcium
- Three or more servings of meat, poultry, fish, eggs, nuts, dried beans and peas for protein
- Eating a well balanced diet while pregnant will help to keep both mother and baby healthy. Most physicians agree that the Recommended Daily Allowances (RDAs), except those for iron, can be obtained through correct diet.

The following table shows the recommended dietary allowances especially during pregnancy:

Recommended daily allowances	Female RDA (by age)				
	15-18	19-24	25-50	51+	Pregnant
Calories	2200	2200	2200	1900	+300
Protein	44	46	50	50	60
Vitamin E	8	8	8	8	10
Vitamin K	55	60	65	65	65
Vitamin C	60	60	60	60	70
Thiamin	1.1	1.1	1.1	1.0	1.5
Riboflavin	1.3	1.3	1.3	1.2	1.6
Niacin	15	15	15	13	17
Vitamin B6	1.5	1.6	1.6	1.6	2.2
Folate	180	180	180	180	400
Vitamin B12	2.0	2.0	2.0	2.0	2.2
Iron	15	15	15	10	30
Zinc	12	12	12	12	15
Selenium	50	55	55	55	65

In addition there are certain foods that should be avoided:

Liver is rich in vitamin A. Too much of this vitamin may be harmful to your baby, particularly during the first trimester.

Fish liver oil supplements such as cod liver oil.

Raw eggs. Ensure that the yolk and white are solid when having a boiled or fried egg and eat only manufactured mayonnaise.

Undercooked meat. Meat must be cooked evenly and thoroughly. Cooking it until it is pink is not enough.

Unpasteurised milk and milk products such as cheese and yoghurt (both cows and goats milk products).

Soft cheese such as Camembert or Brie and blue-veined cheese.

Unwashed fruit and vegetables. Take extra care when eating out, especially on holidays abroad, and only choose cooked fruit and vegetables.

Peanuts. It is recommended that you avoid nuts and products containing nuts during pregnancy and lactation to help avoid allergy.

Alcohol. The balance of evidence suggests that drinking alcohol should be avoided.

All drugs should be avoided unless specifically prescribed by a doctor or midwife who knows about the pregnancy. Almost all drugs cross the **placenta** and many are capable of harming the unborn baby. Some over the counter drugs are also unsuitable for pregnant women.

A recent study has shown that smoking during pregnancy has a long-term negative effect on growth. Children whose mothers smoked while pregnant were lower in stature and weight and they also had lower bone density.

It's still sometimes difficult to know what is safe

Jenny   Activity 3

Jenny is just starting the third month of her pregnancy; she is not overweight but is conscious that she should have a healthy diet.

One of her main concerns is that she feels that she might be anaemic. Jenny wants to have the healthiest possible pregnancy and has asked for help.

1 Design a two-week healthy diet plan for Jenny who is in the third month of her pregnancy.

2 Explain how the diet will differ from the conventional diet that she was used to before she became pregnant.

3 Explain why you have made the changes.

4 Explain to Jenny why it is important that she does not:
   * drink alcohol
   * smoke
   * take unprescribed drugs or medications.

Religious beliefs and lifestyle choice

In the free society in which we live, people have the freedom to follow the religion and lifestyle that they choose. Diet is often affected by religion and often for good reason; people who follow the Jewish and Islamic faiths are not allowed to eat pork products – this is for health reasons as pork is very difficult to store safely in hot weather. Others may be vegetarians because of religious beliefs or out of the principle that eating meat may be a cruel act. Whether it is due to religion or lifestyle choice a person's diet may vary and this often has to be taken into account when new diets are being suggested to them.

Specific diet-related disorders

Many people suffer from diet-related disorders which can be aggravated by the food they eat. In the table below are some diet-related disorders, the effects that they can have and ways that diet can avoid making the symptoms worse.

Disorder	Effect	Dietary action taken
Diabetes mellitus	The body does not produce enough insulin to help metabolise sugar. This can lead to hyperglycaemic coma and restricted peripheral circulation in later life.	The intake of sugars has to be dramatically reduced and closely monitored so that it can be balanced against any injected insulin that is taken to maintain the body's homeostatic levels.
High blood pressure (Hypertension)	This is where blood pressure exceeds 150/90 (normal is 120/80). This can lead to stroke (cardiovascular accident) or heart attack if the pressure remains high.	Salt intake is a major cause and has to be reduced. Caffeine and alcohol also have an effect and are to be avoided. Some foods such as grapes and celery have a diuretic effect that makes a person pass water. This helps maintain fluid levels and helps reduce blood pressure.
Osteoporosis	This is where the bones start to lose their calcium. This can be due to reduced dietary calcium intake or changes bought on by menopause or old age.	Increase in dietary calcium helps reduce the problem. Post-menopausal women may need to take hormone replacement therapy.
Irritable bowel syndrome	IBS can lead to wide changes in bowel habit from constipation to diarrhoea. It can also be heavily influenced by stress.	Individuals will come to recognise the foods that cause the most problems and then avoid them to reduce their symptoms.

All of the above disorders have a noticeable effect on diet and have to be taken into account when altering an individual's daily diet.

Prepared foods

In this modern age and fast lifestyle people have become more reliant on prepared foods. Prepared foods can affect us because they often have a higher level of salt than fresh foods. This increases the risk of high blood pressure. There may also be higher levels of additives and preservatives. Some of these have been shown to affect the way we act and feel. Some food colorants in soft drinks have been known to cause hyperactivity in children, so fresh is always best.

> The underpinning knowledge for the unit has not been arranged within the specifications in the same order as the Assessment Evidence Grid. The Assessment activity is, therefore, more appropriately placed at the end of Unit 7.

7.2.3 Posiive effects of exercise

Everyone needs exercise; it's no good saying, 'I've had a very busy day, I've had enough exercise for one day'. It doesn't quite work like that. Failure to exercise on a regular basis causes people to suffer from one or more of the following:

- coronary heart disease
- **cardiovascular problems**
- obesity
- osteoporosis
- muscle and joint problems.

Exercise helps to keep people fit. It strengthens the body, helps to control weight and burns off extra energy. It has a great many other health benefits, too, because it:

- improves our circulation
- helps our heart work more efficiently
- improves the strength in our muscles
- improves our **stamina**
- reduces the risk of heart attack

- improves our mobility
- helps in building up our **immunity**.

Support when exercising always helps

Exercise changes the body's composition. It increases the amount of muscle the body has and reduces fat levels. Babies, from the moment that they are born, begin to exercise their muscles. Children exercise in all of their activities and sport is a major part of growing up. It protects our physical as well as our emotional well being. It also helps protect us against diseases in later life such as osteoporosis.

Aerobic exercise

Aerobic exercises include:

- walking
- jogging
- swimming.

They involve muscles moving through their full range over set time periods (15–20 minutes). These activities are in addition to our normal daily routine. During the activities the heart and respiration rates will increase. This type of exercise is used to improve cardiovascular fitness. It also increases blood flow to the muscles and benefits the whole body.

Aerobic exercise is the most commonly used method of increasing and maintaining fitness. It must be remembered that exercising above the safe rate can be dangerous.

Anaerobic exercise

Anaerobic exercise is the body builder's method of building muscle. It involves high-intensity activity. It is aimed at developing the muscles. It is only done for short periods of time.

Getting fit can become addictive

Physical health

Fitness

Physical activity is natural. Building more activity into daily life is an easy way to keep fit. The type of activities and the level at which they are done means that a person can start off at a very low level and build the exercises up gradually. The activities that are good to start off with are everyday ones, like walking.

A person can only become fitter and maintain fitness by being physically active regularly. The more active you are, the fitter you will be and the better your body will work. It has been recommended that five sessions of exercise of 30 minutes a week has great benefits to the system. Two sessions of this should be brisk exercise.

Research has been done into the benefits to the body of doing regular activity. It shows that:

- it helps to relieve stress and depression
- it helps keep you supple and more mobile
- it helps strengthen your muscles, joints and bones
- it helps your heart work more efficiently
- it improves your circulation
- it helps protect against heart disease and bowel cancer.

Muscular strength

Appropriate exercises have been shown to improve muscular strength and **endurance**, improve range of motion, and reduce functional deficits associated with many disabilities. The effects of exercise are seen at two levels:

- the cellular level, or in the muscle fibre
- throughout the cardiovascular and **respiratory** systems to meet the physiological demands of the muscle fibres.

Strength is the ability of a muscle or a group of muscles to exert an amount of force, typically in a one-time burst of effort. Weightlifting (or resistance training) is a classic example of strength training because it increases muscle strength and mass, as well as bone strength, by placing more strain on muscles and bones than they are used to. When you lift weights, muscles are forced to meet that challenge by generating more force-generating proteins to feed the 'fibres' that grow during exercise.

Most muscles have a combination of two types of fibres that are challenged during strength-training activities:

- **Fast-twitch fibres** provide the explosive force needed for weightlifting or activities such as sprint racing.
- **Slow-twitch fibres** are for endurance, such as the ability of muscle to withstand fatigue. Most muscles have a 50-50 blend of fast- and slow-twitch fibres, but others have an advantage one way or the other. When the muscles are made to work harder, these fibres are actually torn. As they rebuild, they get stronger and bigger, resulting in harder, tighter and larger muscles.

Muscle endurance is the ability to resist fatigue and continue to exercise over long periods of time. Whereas strength training is needed to maintain muscle strength, endurance training is required to achieve stamina. Muscular endurance is the ability of muscles to continue working strongly without rest, such as the ability of a rugby player to throw long pass after pass.

Flexibility

Flexibility is the ability of joints and muscles to achieve a full range of motion. This results in the prevention of injuries and helps keep the body feeling comfortable after exercise. Despite popular opinion, there's no evidence that flexibility will be lost as the muscle is built.

Flexibility exercises can help to:

- improve posture
- improve the ability to do everyday activities
- prevent muscles becoming sore and injured.

Flexibility can be improved by stretching the muscles. Each stretch, if held still for 10–30 seconds, will help improve flexibility. This is called static stretching and is normally done three to five times to start with.

To get the most out of stretching, people should not overextend themselves, as this helps to keep the exercise safe. Benefit can be gained by including a range of stretches that will stretch different muscle groups. There are many different stretches that can be used; the physical education coach will have some examples. Certain activities such as **tai chi** and yoga actually promote flexibility.

We cannot all be this flexible

Weight control

Exercise is one method that can be used to help control weight. The first thing that must be remembered is that one kilogram of body fat is equivalent to 7700 kcal or calories. On average this is about three days' calorie intake for the average person. This means that exercise alone is not the easiest or the best way of controlling weight. It is a myth that exercise will suppress hunger. A person who exercises may not feel hungry immediately; it will just catch up with them about two hours later. For exercise to work in weight control, calories used in exercise must exceed those consumed in diet. This will be a slow process because as we exercise we will strengthen our muscles and they may increase in mass. This will mean that the net weight loss may be lower than expected.

Coronary heart disease

The heart is a pump and the coronary arteries are its fuel supply pipes. The fuel is oxygen, which is carried in the blood. Coronary arteries may narrow due to a thickening of their walls and this reduces blood flow to the heart muscle. The process is called arteriosclerosis. In its early stages this does not affect the heart's function. When the narrowing gets worse, the lack of oxygen may cause pain called angina. If the narrowing becomes critical, it can cause a complete blockage and lead to a heart attack (properly called a myocardial infarction). In the early stages of the narrowing process, there are no symptoms. Sometimes a myocardial infarction is the first sign that there is any problem. It is all the more important, therefore, to prevent or limit the narrowing process before it causes problems. There is no simple test to screen people for their risk of early narrowing of their arteries. However, even once a heart attack has occurred, the risk of a further attack can be reduced and exercise can be used to help.

An inactive lifestyle is one of the top risk factors for heart disease. Fortunately, it is a risk factor that can be reduced. Regular exercise, especially aerobic exercise, has many benefits. It can:

- Strengthen your heart and cardiovascular system.
- Improve your circulation and help your body use oxygen more efficiently.
- Improve your heart failure symptoms.
- Increase energy levels so you can do more activities without becoming tired or short of breath.
- Increase endurance.
- Lower blood pressure.
- Improve muscle tone and strength.
- Improve balance and joint flexibility.
- Strengthen bones.
- Help reduce body fat and help you reach a healthy weight.
- Help reduce stress, tension, anxiety and depression.
- Boost self image and self esteem.
- Improve sleep.
- Make you feel more relaxed and rested.
- Make you look fit and feel healthy.

Almost all of these benefits will help reduce the incidence of heart disease.

Exercise can be divided into three basic types:

- *Stretching*: slow lengthening of the muscles. Stretching the arms and legs before and after

exercising helps prepare the muscles for activity and helps prevent injury and muscle strain. Regular stretching also increases the range of motion and flexibility.

- *Cardiovascular or aerobic*: steady physical activity using large muscle groups. This type of exercise strengthens the heart and lungs and improves the body's ability to use oxygen. Aerobic exercise has the most benefits for the heart. Over time, aerobic exercise can help decrease your heart rate and blood pressure and improve your breathing (since the heart won't have to work as hard during exercise).

- *Strengthening*: repeated muscle contractions (tightening) until the muscle becomes tired. For people with heart failure, many strengthening exercises are not recommended.

Aerobic exercises include: walking, jogging, skipping, bicycling (stationary or outdoor), cross-country skiing, skating, rowing and low-impact aerobics or water aerobics.

In general, to achieve maximum benefits, those exercising should gradually work up to an aerobic session lasting 20 to 30 minutes, at least three to four times a week. Exercising every other day will help to keep a regular aerobic exercise schedule.

High blood pressure

Each time the heart beats (about 60–70 times a minute at rest), it pumps out blood into the arteries. Blood pressure is at its greatest when the heart contracts and this is called systolic pressure. When the heart is at rest, in between beats, your blood pressure falls giving the diastolic pressure.

Blood pressure is always given as these two numbers, systolic and diastolic pressures. Both are important. Usually they are written one above or before the other, such as 120/80 mm Hg, with the first number the systolic, and the second the diastolic. Different actions make your blood pressure go up or down. For example, if a person runs for a bus, their blood pressure goes up. When they sleep at night, their blood pressure goes down. These changes in blood pressure are normal.

Some people have blood pressure that stays up all or most of the time. Their blood pushes against the walls of their arteries with higher-than-normal force. A reading of 120/80 mm Hg (or '120 over

80') is normal for a healthy adult. The abbreviation 'mm Hg' is a unit of measure for pressure and is short for 'millimetres of mercury'.

Different factors can affect blood pressure, such as how nervous the person is or the medication that is being taken. If their blood pressure reading is consistently 140/90 or higher, they have high blood pressure. The higher the numbers are above 140/90, the more serious the hypertension (high blood pressure).

Systolic	Diastolic	
Less than 130	Less than 85	Normal blood pressure
130–139	85–89	High-normal blood pressure
140–159	90–99	Stage 1 (mild) hypertension
160–179	100–109	Stage 2 (moderate) hypertension
180–209	110–119	Stage 3 (severe) hypertension
210 or higher	120 or higher	Stage 4 (severe) hypertension

Many recent studies have shown that regular aerobic exercise (workouts like brisk walking that use large muscles for an extended period) over several months may lower blood pressure. Exercise reduces resting blood pressure in people who have hypertension by an average of 11 points off their systolic and 9 points off their diastolic readings. That could be enough to lower high blood pressure to normal.

Assessing blood pressure is a good place to start before exercising

Before starting an exercise programme, an overall assessment needs to be made. Depending on how high the blood pressure is, there may need to be other changes such as less salt or less caffeine. The body diverts blood to working muscles; exercise typically raises blood pressure, although this effect is only temporary. Exercise, for people who have mild or moderate hypertension, is generally safe. Most people would prefer to control their hypertension without drugs – or minimise their need for medication – if possible. Therefore exercise should be taken on most days of the week.

Start slowly – Those taking part in exercise should aim to build up to about half an hour of moderate activity a day. Remember that every little bit counts. Any activity that can be done will help on the road to a healthier lifestyle. An individual might start by taking the lift to the floor below and walk one flight of stairs; then increase it to two, and so on, until they are walking up the whole way without thinking.

Aerobic exercise:

Frequency – 3–5 days per week

Intensity – 55–60% of maximum heart rate

Time – Building up to 15–40 minutes of continuous or intermittent aerobic activity.

Current recommendations for regular aerobic activity are for 30 minutes of moderate aerobic exercise which can be accumulated in three 10-minute periods of activity over the course of the day, for the same health benefits as one continuous 30-minute session. Improved strength, endurance, flexibility, and better ability to walk and perform daily tasks are all benefits of exercise.

All exercise taken will help strengthen heart muscle and the muscles in the vascular system. Having a fitter more efficient vascular system will help control blood pressure, helping it to remain within normal limits.

Osteoporosis

Osteoporosis literally means 'porous bone'. It is a condition where the bones gradually become more fragile, which can lead to fracture. Both men and women are at risk of developing osteoporosis. Men have larger and stronger bones than women, which partly explains why osteoporosis affects fewer men than women. The risk increases with age, especially after the menopause in women.

Bones grow in length and density until you reach your maximum height, usually in your teens. They also continue to become more dense until you are aged about 30 years. After this age, bones slowly start to lose density and strength. Throughout life, bone density is affected by the following factors:

- genes
- diet
- sex hormones
- physical activity
- lifestyle choices
- the use of certain **medications**.

If bones are not 'used' they weaken. It is well known that regular weight-bearing exercise, which exerts a loading impact and stretches and contracts the muscles, stimulates bone to strengthen itself.

Modern scientific techniques make osteoporosis protection much easier

The National Osteoporosis Society recommends exercising at least three times a week for a minimum of 20 minutes. If a person is healthy, but hasn't exercised for a while, start gently. If people have other health problems, they should check with their doctor before starting to exercise. If they have already been diagnosed with osteoporosis, they should ask the doctor or physiotherapist for advice about an exercise programme, because some twisting motions and impact activities might not be good for them. Exercises that are considered useful for most people include:

- stepping on the spot while holding on to a steady surface – this is good for people who are less active;
- walking, especially if it is brisk;
- skipping;
- gentle jogging (or running if you are able);
- racquet sports (e.g. tennis);
- stair climbing or step-type exercises;
- team sports;
- lifting weights or using resistance machines, which strengthen your bones and muscles;
- aerobics (if you are able);
- tai chi is useful for posture, leg strength and balance.

Mental health

The changes experienced in lifestyle in recent times suggest that increased levels of activity across the population could have significant mental and physical benefits. The use of exercise in the treatment and prevention of psychological illness is relatively safe, inexpensive and without side effects when tailored to individuals. Fun is an important ingredient to taking exercise as well as improving health. Exercise may not only bring benefits for mental health but may also provide an important channel of communication. The interaction in an exercise class may provide an important outlet to meet people and make friends.

The use of exercise in the treatment of mental disorder is not a new concept. The ancient Greeks first explored the link between physical and mental health. In England around the early 1900s exercise was an important part of the patients' daily programme in most large psychiatric hospitals.

Before the discovery of **tranquillisers** in the 1950s, exercise had a vital role to play in the routine of patients receiving inpatient hospital treatment. There was emphasis on the patients' physical health as well as the relief of symptoms. Depression is by far the largest reason for admission to **psychiatric hospitals** in the UK today. It has been estimated that one in five of the population suffers from a serious affective (mood) disorder at some time in their lives. Individuals with depression frequently are low in mood, less active, lethargic and apathetic. Individuals feel intensely sad, intensely isolated, lonely and withdrawn and often say they cannot go on with their life. Often individuals are not motivated as a result. They can now benefit from the evidence that regular exercise alleviates negative mood states such as depression and anxiety.

It is, therefore, now known that physical fitness:

- is positively associated with mental health and well being

- builds confidence
- helps relieve stress
- improves self esteem
- gives a general feeling of well being
- exercise has been associated with a decreased level of mild to moderate depression
- current **clinical opinion** holds that exercise has beneficial emotional effects across all ages and in both sexes.

Benefits of exercise   **Activity 4**

You have been asked to give a talk to your local community centre on the benefits of exercise. Your audience will contain people of various ages and levels of fitness. Your focus will be to ensure that they understand how they can improve their health with the use of exercise.

1. Create a set of handouts that explain the benefits to physical health from exercise.

2. Design a PowerPoint presentation that will show the audience how exercise can be positively beneficial to mental health.

3. Design a friendship network for the community that will help individuals with similar interests in exercise to form groups. The idea here is to stop them feeling isolated, so they will be encouraged to exercise together.

Social health

Despite the strong case for staying active, many people find it difficult to adapt their daily lives to incorporate physical activity. With cars on most driveways and the decline in the number of physically active jobs, it is becoming a big problem. It is estimated that 70% of the adult population is sufficiently inactive to be classed as 'sedentary'. They can also become isolated and this is where exercise can help.

Exercise is the ideal vehicle to allow people to mix and meet. People give many reasons for not taking up exercise:

- lack of time due to work or family commitments
- cost of equipment or gym membership
- lack of facilities nearby
- personal safety when exercising outdoors alone
- poor weather or night-time lighting.

All of these excuses simply disappear if they decide to take up exercise in a group or with a friend or relative. Regular activity can also improve the way that people look and feel. In combination with a balanced diet, regular activity can help to maintain a healthy weight. It can even boost self confidence and reduce the risk of depression. This in turn makes the person feel more **gregarious** and acceptable to others and leads to an increase in social interaction, namely making friends.

Trying out new sports or activities helps improve social well being. The overall interest can stimulate conversation even during exercise, especially if it is at a pace that still allows them to talk. Activities that can be done as a family or with friends may often help with motivation when considering other exercise **regimes**. In short it is beneficial for our social and emotional make-up to take part in group activities or with friends.

Team sports not only make you fit but encourage friendship

The underpinning knowledge for the unit has not been arranged within the specifications in the same order as the Assessment Evidence Grid. The Assessment activity is, therefore, more appropriately placed at the end of Unit 7.

7.2.4 Health and safety considerations when designing an exercise programme

Assessment of fitness level

Most people do not exercise as much as they should. Every adult should accumulate 30 minutes or more of moderate-intensity physical activity on most days of the week. The health benefits gained from increased physical activity depend on the initial physical fitness level. Beginners are expected to benefit most from increasing their activity to the recommended level.

If all adults who lead inactive lives adopted a more active lifestyle, there would be enormous benefit to the public's health and to individual well being. An active lifestyle does not require a regimented, vigorous exercise programme. Instead, small changes that increase daily physical activity will enable individuals to reduce their risk of chronic disease and may contribute to enhanced quality of life.

In general, to **enhance** long-term participation in regular physical activity, several factors should be considered:

- The person, including gender, age, occupational status, health status, education, prior exercise experience.
- The exercise programme, especially the intensity and type of activity.
- The environment, including the weather, community facilities, home-based programmes, travel distances, time barriers, family and spousal support, employer and co-worker support, government, economic and public-policy support.

Assessment must also take into account the physical condition of the individual and this can be done in a variety of ways. A good method of assessing cardiovascular endurance is the Harvard step test.

The Harvard step test is a sub-maximal fitness test, as it predicts cardiovascular fitness (endurance) from the rise of heart rate during moderate exercise, rather than exercise to exertion. This makes it a very popular fitness test with health clubs, schools and colleges, as it may be used with individuals who are not fit to exercise to maximal exertion. Many different versions of the step test are available for use. Probably the most commonly used is the five minutes test. An accurate measurement of the heart rate is necessary if the results of this test are

to be meaningful. Heart rate may be counted most easily by pressing with the fingertips on the arteries of the wrist. When the pulse rate is taken, each individual is asked to step up and down on a bench 41 cm high (standard gym bench) at a rate of 22 steps a minute for women (up, up, down, down) and 24 steps for men. The same foot must start the step-up each time. The pulse rate is taken exactly one minute after the last step is completed.

The step test is based upon the idea that a client with a higher level of cardiovascular fitness will have a smaller increase in heart rate, and that following the exercise, the heart rate will return to normal faster than a client who has a much lower level of cardiovascular fitness. This is known as pulse recovery rate.

The recovery heart rate can then be used to predict Vo2 max, using the following formulae:

Men: Vo2 max (ml.kg-1. min-1) = 111.33 – (0.42*pulse rate)

Women: Vo2 max (ml.kg-1. min-1) = 65.81 – (0.1847*pulse rate)

Note that pulse rate is in bpm (beats per minute).

Body composition can be used to assess fitness. Body composition refers primarily to the distribution of muscle and fat in the body, and its measurement plays an important role in both sports and health. Excess body fat may lead to obesity and increases the risk of getting many diseases.

Assessment does not have to be complicated

In sports, excess fat hinders performance as it does not contribute to muscular force production, and it is additional weight that requires energy to move about.

Body composition is often represented as a two-compartment system; lean body weight and fat weight. The fat weight is then expressed as a percentage of total body weight, where percentage body fat = (fat weight/total body weight) × 100. The table below gives general guidelines for body fat percentage levels.

	Non-athletes		Athletes	
	Males	Females	Males	Females
Lean	<12	<17	<7	<12
Acceptable	12–21	17–28	7–15	12–25
Moderately overweight	21–26	28–33		
Overweight	> 26	> 33	> 15	> 25

Many training or exercise programmes are geared solely to modify body size and composition in some way. The tests described below provide a way of measuring current levels and determining changes over time.

Body Mass Index

This is commonly used and easy to calculate:

- description/procedure: calculation from body mass and height.

  BMI = M / (H × H),

  where M = body mass in kilograms and
  H = height in metres.

  The higher score normally indicates higher levels of body fat.
- scoring:
Healthy	20–25
Overweight	25–30
Obese	> 30

- equipment required: scales and tape measure for weight and height.
- target population: BMI is often used to determine the level of health risk associated with obesity.
- advantages: simple calculation from standard measurements.
- disadvantages: BMI can be inaccurate, for example, large and muscular though lean athletes score high BMI levels which incorrectly rate them as obese.

Waist to hip ratio

- description/procedure: a simple calculation of the ratio of girth measurements of the waist to the hip.
- scoring: the table below gives general guidelines for acceptable levels for hip to waist ratio.
- equipment required: tape measure.
- target population: this measure is often used to determine the coronary artery disease risk factor associated with obesity.
- advantages: a simple measure that can be taken at home by people to monitor their own levels.

The basis of this measure as a coronary disease risk factor indicator is that fat stored around the waist poses a greater risk to health than fat stored elsewhere.

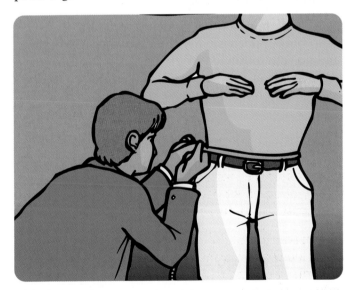

Size does matter

Waist to hip ratio	Excellent	Good	Average	High	Extreme
Male	<0.85	0.85–0.90	0.90–0.95	0.95–1.00	> 1.00
Female	<0.75	0.75–0.80	0.80–0.85	0.85–0.90	> 0.90

Exercise　　　　　　　　　Activity 5

Ask a friend or relative if you can assess their level of fitness. Make sure you pick a person who is not totally fit as this will be of benefit to them if they start exercising.

1　Use as many different tests as you can to assess their level of fitness.

2　Present your findings to the person in a format that is appropriate to their age and level of understanding.

3　Using your results start them on the road to fitness by offering them an exercise plan that will improve their fitness.

4　Design the plan so that it can fit into their daily life.

Safe environments

Whenever exercising, safety must always be taken into consideration. If there is a risk then do not proceed.

Inclement weather

If exercise is to take place outside then weather conditions must be considered. For example, to participate in mountain climbing when there is deep snow, poor visibility, poor weather conditions and no safe footholds would not only put the participants at risk but also the lives of those who may end up having to rescue them.

Condition of pitches

For football matches, hockey matches and any other sport that uses a 'pitch' you must ensure that the surface is safe and unlikely to cause people to trip or fall.

General safety – personal suitability of exercise

By taking a few simple precautions, people can make sure any physical activity taken part in is safe and enjoyable:

- Only work within personal limits: physical activity does not have to be strenuous to have a beneficial health effect.

- Always warm up if the activity is more intense than normal. When going for a walk, for example, people should gradually ease into it. Never start off too briskly or go straight in to a steep uphill climb. Start off slowly, gradually building up to hill climbing or a faster pace.
- Never stop exercising suddenly. If the activity or exercise has been more intense than usual then cooling down will be necessary – do this by gradually easing back down to a comfortable level.
- Choose an activity that is enjoyable as it is more likely to be incorporated into the daily routine.
- Do not suddenly attempt activities that you are not used to. Take things steadily and learn to enjoy being active.
- Gradually build up the amount of activity done on a daily basis.
- A helpful guide for starting out is that a person should be active enough to feel warm and slightly breathless but still be able to have a conversation while they are active.
- When worried about being active alone or in the dark, stick to well lit areas or enlist a friend or a group of friends to join in.
- Ask a GP for advice if uncertain about health matters or the ability to be active.

Safety tip

- Try to avoid walking alone at night.
- Keep to well lit areas.
- Carrying a personal alarm is a good safety precaution. They can be bought from hardware or DIY stores.

Where people have been fairly inactive, they should not go to extremes and rush straight into being very active. Being active too quickly might also make them more **vulnerable** to injuries from over-using the muscles and joints. Building up gradually over time is the aim.

When exercising, common sense is also the rule:

- Don't try aerobic dancing in the middle of a cluttered living room. Activities like this require space to move around in.
- Don't skate inline down the middle of a road.
- Don't ride a bike on a busy road or dual carriageway.
- Don't run after dark.
- Give safety a little thought.
- Each exercise activity has its own rules. Rules are good. They exist to help prevent injury and ensure best results.

- Take a class or join a club to learn the ins and outs of whatever activity is chosen.

Safety should always be of great importance

When leaving the home to exercise, carry a small card with emergency information, just in case.

Include on the card:

- name
- blood type
- doctor's name and number
- family contact information and
- any special medical conditions.

Hopefully it will never be needed but it could save a person's life in an emergency.

Correct equipment

Using and selecting the correct equipment is very important if the exercise routines are going to be successful, and thought should be given to this. The following guides apply to all equipment.

Will the equipment be used regularly? Perhaps the most critical issue is commitment. If it is important to have it for safety reasons, for example a safety helmet, then purchase it. Do not buy equipment if the only reason is that it is fashionable.

Will the equipment help me meet my goals? Disregard false claims, like those that say abdominal exercise equipment melts flab from your waistline. A reasonably fit person can burn about 400 to 600 calories per hour in rhythmic exercise that involves major muscle groups (especially the legs). This can occur without expensive equipment.

Is the equipment well made? It's hard to tell from just looking. Take advice and ask others or professionals what they think of the suitability of the item. It should feel usable and durable.

Is it comfortable? An item of clothing can be well made but still feel awkward. A seat on a piece of equipment should stay comfortable during a long exercise session. Bars or pull-handles should be padded and feel comfortable, even after many minutes. Also, note things like noise level and ease of using the controls.

What type is best? Test each type of exercise equipment and choose the one that feels best.

Suitable clothing

Choose comfortable clothes, simple in style, streamlined to avoid tripping or catching on objects. Fabrics with built in stretch provide lots of give and take when moving, and stay in place.

Good quality shoes and absorbent, breathable socks will help prevent blisters and they will also add a little bounce to your step. In the winter, dress in layers so you can remove clothing as you warm up. In the summer, a towel you can tuck into your waistband and a cotton cloth headband will help keep perspiration out of your eyes. Some sports require protective padding or headgear, don't overlook these. A £10 bike helmet can save a life; elbow and kneepads for skating can cushion a fall preventing cuts and breaks, which could take weeks to heal. Don't skimp on safety, it will lead to regret.

Remember, in the interests of safety:

- Remove all jewellery as it might catch or cause injury.
- Tie hair back so that it does not affect concentration or **obscure** vision.
- Always be aware of the surrounding environment.

OK, I think this one is durable enough

Safety   Activity 6

The local community group that you gave the talk to have decided to set up a club so that its members can exercise together. They have decided that the three most popular exercises are:

- swimming
- jogging
- cycling.

1 Design a set of safety guidelines for each of the three activities mentioned above.

2 Make suggestions as to the types of clothing and safety equipment that they will require to take part in the exercises.

Suitability of exercise for the intended purpose

The first step in setting up a routine is to choose exercises that target the muscle groups to be exercised. One way to make sure of doing this correctly is to work with a programme specifically designed for the muscle groups. Another option could be to rent or buy a workout DVD/video. DVDs and videos can give visual instruction without the cost of a personal trainer. The only limitation is that once the person adjusts to that workout they might have to get another video to progress.

For beginners, choose at least one exercise per muscle group. The list below offers some examples:

- Chest: bench press, chest press machine, push-ups, pectoral deck machine
- Back: one-armed row, seated row machine, back extensions, lat pull downs
- Shoulders: overhead press, lateral raise, front raise
- **Biceps**: bicep curls, hammer curls, concentration curls
- **Triceps**: triceps extensions, dips, kickbacks
- **Quadriceps**: squats, lunges, leg extension and leg press machines
- **Hamstrings**: dead lifts, lunges, leg curl machine
- **Abdominal muscles**: crunches, reverse crunches, oblique twists, pelvic tilts.

Sequence of exercises

- Make sure at least one exercise is chosen for each major muscle group.
- The muscles to work include: chest, back, shoulders, biceps, triceps, quadriceps, hamstrings, calves and abdominal muscles.

- If any muscle group is left out, this could cause an imbalance in your muscles and possibly lead to injuries.

Most experts recommend starting with the larger muscle groups and then proceeding to the smaller muscle groups. The most demanding exercises are those performed by the large muscle groups and the smaller muscles will also need to get the most out of these exercises.

You do not have to take it this far. If you stop exercising, muscle can turn to fat

For example, in a bench press your shoulders and triceps are involved in stabilising the arms, they need to be strong to stop the weight dropping on the person. The bonus? By the time the person gets to the shoulder and triceps exercises, their muscles will be warmed up and ready to go.

However, this is not a hard and fast rule so do what works for the individual.

In addition, you don't necessarily need to do as many sets with your smaller muscle groups since they're used so much in other exercises.

Correct preparation

No matter what activity has been chosen, start slow, whether it's running, walking, biking, weight training or another sport. Rein in the enthusiasm to jump in full force. Overworking muscles which are not used to specific actions can cause muscle strains, ligament tears and a great deal of pain. Any **consistent, repetitive** movement can cause unusual strain. Walking for exercise is different from start and stop strolling through the local park.

Even if no real damage is done, waking up in pain can be a big turn off to resuming a new exercise regime. Sustaining an injury may require weeks or months of recovery, making it difficult to start again. Plan a reasonable schedule – ten or fifteen minutes, two or three times a week for the first week or two, and gradually increase the length of time spent working out. In just a few weeks, adding a few minutes more each week, the time spent in exercise will grow to a reasonable thirty minutes to an hour.

For those who have never exercised, or have been out of shape for a long time:

- see your doctor for the go-ahead
- get recommendations for:
  - type of exercise
  - how often exercise should take place
  - a proper schedule.

Principles of training

The basic training principles help to design programmes that are specific and safe for an individual. The training principles below focus mostly on fitness training:

- *Individual differences* – all people respond differently to the same training. This is due to factors such as those inherited from their parents, their personal commitment and their level of physical and mental maturity.
- *Adaptation* – is the way the body responds to the training programme. The parts of the body that are actively stressed during exercise adapt to those stresses, leading to an increase in performance.
- *Overload* – for the body's systems to make these adaptations, they must be overloaded. Just taking part in an activity will not cause any improvements in fitness, as the body will not be stressed enough to change.
- *Progression* – the overload imposed on an athlete must be progressive. If a training programme stays at the same intensity for a whole year, adaptations will only occur at the beginning, as after this the body will no longer be overloaded.
- *Reversibility* – the adaptations that take place as a result of training are all reversible. Adaptations to endurance training can be lost more quickly than it takes to achieve them, while strength gains are lost more slowly.
- *Specificity* – is the least complex training principle. In order for a training programme to be effective it must be specific for the muscle groups to be exercised.
- *Recovery* – is one of the most overlooked principles of training. It is during the recovery sessions that the adaptations to training take place. Recovery sessions may not necessarily mean complete rest. Periods of lower intensity activity will allow the body to adapt without increasing the stress placed on it.
- *Variation* – if training programmes are repetitious, people can soon become bored and lose their motivation.

The table below and on the next page provides examples of the training principles described above:

Principle	Description	Example
Frequency	How often a training exercise is carried out; usually the frequency of sessions.	Three sessions per week is typical for weight training.
Intensity	How hard a session of exercise is.	Intensity measures could be: weight or resistance used in strength training; speed of completion of a run; 'perceived rating of exertion' (PRE).
Duration	How long a particular exercise takes.	Time for a jogging session; number of 'sets' and 'repetitions' in resistance training.
Overload	You get little body development unless you stress the body beyond its current capability; it's as if you develop only just enough to do what you usually do. So fitness training needs to push you beyond your current limits – to 'overload' the current capability.	To run a mile comfortably, you might practise running two miles. To shoot 60 arrows easily, you might practise regularly with 100, shoot 50% faster than competition rate, or do muscle training that substantially tires the shooting muscles.

Principle	Description	Example
Reversibility	What training can achieve, disuse can undo. Use it, or lose it!	The classic example is the main energy store (specifically, your glycogen reserve). This reserve is very susceptible to training, and trained reserves can be triple the normal reserve. But on disuse of even a few weeks, the extra reserve just fades away. Easy come, easy go. *Implication*: Training programmes should avoid long breaks; long breaks (injury, holidays...) mean restarting at a lower level of effort.
Progression	If overload is necessary, what happens when your fitness improves with training? To keep developing, you need to keep overloading, and that means the training load has to increase, or 'progress'.	Examples: beginners start with a light bow and 'progress' to heavier bows. A weights regime progressively increases weights, repetitions, or cuts rest time, depending on the intent.
Specificity	Substantial research shows that training is extraordinarily *specific* in its effect. Strength training does not add much endurance and vice versa; training one muscle group has little effect on others; training for one movement pattern often does not transfer to even quite closely related movements.	Training to lift dumbbells makes you a better dumbbell lifter. It may have little or no effect on your shooting. *Implication*: The intensity and duration of training must match the sport closely, and it's important to train the right muscle groups.

Appropriate monitoring techniques

Whereas the techniques that were mentioned earlier could be used as monitoring techniques, there are other general physiological measurements that can be used to monitor the progress of a person using an exercise program.

Resting heart rate usually improves as people get fitter and lighter. This is due to the increase in cardiac competence, the heart becoming stronger and more efficient.

Blood pressure will also show signs of improvement for the same reasons. Peak flow will also improve as the lungs get stronger and the resting respiration rate will also show signs of improvement.

All of the above measurements can be carried out throughout the exercise programme to show improvement and to motivate the individual by the indication of their success.

Aerobic exercises are planned to increase the heart rate to 70% of Its maximum. This is 220 beats per minute (bpm), minus the person's age. This provides a safety barrier that will help reduce any danger from excessive exercise and allow the person exercising to be monitored.

Example:

The maximum heart rate for a 45 year old will be:

220 – 45 = 175

70% of 175 = 120

Therefore a fit 45 year old should be able to exercise safely at 120 bpm.

Another personal best

Q What should your maximum heart rate be when you are exercising if you are 19 years old?

Aim of programme

The overall aim of the programme must be to accommodate the fitness needs and wishes of the person taking part. To do this we can use various types of training.

Fartlek, developed in the 1930s, comes from the Swedish for 'Speed Play' and combines continuous and interval training. Fartlek allows the athlete to run whatever distance and speed they wish, varying the intensity, and occasionally running at high intensity levels. This type of training stresses both the aerobic and anaerobic energy pathways.

Continuous training is when an athlete exercises in a steady aerobic way and interval training is characterised by repetitions of work with a recovery period following each repetition.

Circuit training is an excellent way to simultaneously improve mobility, strength and stamina. The circuit training format utilises a group of six to ten strength exercises that are completed one exercise after another. Each exercise is performed for a specified number of repetitions or for a prescribed time period before moving on to the next exercise. The exercises within each circuit are separated by brief, timed rest intervals, and each circuit is separated by a longer rest period.

Resistance training involves working against a weight, force or gravity. Weight lifting is one form of resistance training and weight training affects the body in different ways. It all depends on the weight you are lifting and how many times you lift it without a period of rest. If you lift weights that are heavy for you, you will only be able to perform a few lifts without resting. This form of weight training develops muscular strength. When you lift weights that are light for you and you perform lots of lifts without stopping for a rest (say 10 or 15), this form of training develops muscular endurance.

A good training programme will make use of one or more of these methods.

Time available

Time is not always the most readily available resource. When it is in short supply the exercise plan has to be adapted to accommodate this. The good thing about exercise is that it can be done anywhere at any time. So the plan has infinite possibilities for variation of when it can happen and how.

Keeping up with the pace of life can be rather pressing

Two aspects of fitness to improve

In your programme you need to be able to justify what you are doing. This can be achieved by creating an assessment table for a service user that shows you:

- who the service user is
- what aspects of fitness you will be working on
- when the exercises will take place and for how long
- types of exercise
- where it is to happen
- why they need to be done.

The table can also help you monitor their progress, an example is given below:

Service user:	
Aspects of fitness to be improved:	Aspect of fitness 1:
	Aspect of fitness 2:
Exercise time plan:	Mon:
	Tue:
	Wed:
	Thu:
	Fri:
	Sat:
	Sun:
Types of exercise:	Description:
Location:	Place:
Rationale for inclusion or omission:	Explanation to service user:
Monitoring of progress:	

The table above is a basic idea and can be modified or augmented to suit any other needs.

Evaluation

To assess performance it is necessary to:

- think back and consider what we have done
- think about how the activity was carried out
- analyse against theory how well we did the task
- draw conclusions
- plan for improvements.

Questions that could be asked when evaluating include:

- Was the plan suitable? If not why not?
- Were the correct skills used?
- Were the aims and objectives met?
- How could the activity be improved?
- What were the strengths?
- Was time managed efficiently and effectively?
- What were the benefits?
- What changes should be made?

Strengths

Considering strengths means looking at the positive effects of the activity. Was the activity beneficial and if so what made it so? An example might be that we organised time well. This meant that everything was in place and the whole activity ran seamlessly from beginning to completion. Looking at strengths can often result in highlighting weaknesses. By looking in a critical way at what happened it is often possible to see things that would help improve the overall quality of the activity. For example:

Type of benefit	Actual benefit to an individual
Physical	Using energy, toning muscles, developing fitness
Intellectual	Feeling stimulated, more alert
Emotional	Satisfaction, feeling good about ourselves
Social	Working together with someone, being part of a team

From one short activity a whole range of benefits emerge.

The underpinning knowledge for the unit has not been arranged within the specifications in the same order as the Assessment Evidence Grid. The Assessment activity is, therefore, more appropriately placed at the end of Unit 7.

7.2.5 How diet and exercise interrelate to affect health

How diet and exercise work together

When diet and exercise are combined effectively there are a number of definite benefits to the individual:

More energy. It's odd, but a good diet and exercise actually makes people feel more energetic. Sitting around not doing much, on the other hand, makes people feel sluggish and unable to do anything.

Improved sleep patterns. Regular exercise and a good diet will also make the body and mind feel as though they've done something. This will help improve the quality of sleep that is experienced.

Stable weight. Having stable weight will help improve personal self esteem. If a person feels good and looks good there is a great psychological and emotional effect.

Mirror, mirror on the wall, who's the thinnest of them all?

Protection against heart disease. Not smoking, sensible eating and taking regular exercise all help to boost the immune system. This in turn helps improve resistance to disease, making it less likely that illness will take hold.

Improved circulation. Exercise and a reduced intake of saturated fats can also lower blood pressure and help with other conditions such as clinical depression.

Delayed aging. Keeping active strengthens the muscles, joints and bones as well as helping mobility and balance. This is more important the older you get, as it helps to prevent falls, which are among the most common reasons for older people having to go into hospital. Anti-oxidants found in certain foods are also reputed to slow down the aging process.

There are also other social and emotional rewards:

Meeting and making new friends. Taking exercise with others is great for developing social contacts.

It's time for you. Work, family or friends all take up time. Sometimes doing something alone is just what's needed.

Developing a sense of achievement. There's nothing like completing an exercise activity to boost spirits and lift emotions.

Reaching goals. Exercise and diet can provide something specific to aim for. Run a marathon, enter a dance competition, or walk to a friend's house across town – something to be proud of.

Stress relief. Bad day, bad week or annoying relatives? Exercise helps people to remain calm and put things in perspective.

Feel and look better. Many people who exercise regularly look younger than people of the same age who aren't so active.

Finally what better reason than:

It can be great fun

Assessment activity (AO1–AO4)

Robert

Robert leads a very sedentary lifestyle and works in a busy office. His hours at work are long and irregular and he has no real leisure activities. While at work his diet is poor, it usually revolves around fast food and beer; this has made him overweight. His alcohol intake is currently 42 units a week.

His wife is worried that he could be compromising his cardiac health. She is determined to help him and is also prepared to take part in the diet and exercise plan that you design.

1 Prepare a guide that could be used to explain to Robert and his family the effects of exercise on an individual's physical, mental and social health.

Make sure the information is detailed and shows a high level of understanding. You should include a bibliography and record sources within the actual text.

Make sure you draw conclusions relating to the effects of daily living.

2 Choose an individual. Describe the dietary needs of the individual giving a comprehensive understanding of the nature of dietary function of all macro and micro nutrients.

Include a detailed analysis of foods that provide the main sources of nutrients, including the roles of water and non-starch polysaccharide (NSP/dietary fibre).

3 Re-design Robert's weekly diet to help him lose weight and maintain his ability to exercise, showing how this will meet Robert's needs. Justify the recommendations.

4 Explain to Robert the various types of exercises he could follow.

5 Design a three-week exercise programme for Robert, showing evidence of a wide variety of sources. Explain, giving a detailed rationale as to the selection and duration of the activities.

6 Produce grids that can be used by Robert to show the monitoring of **two** types of fitness programmes selected for Robert's improvement.

7 Use score tables to indicate standards and levels of fitness of the individual and to identify strengths and weaknesses.

8 Evaluate in depth, forming reasoned judgements, showing a high level of understanding of the likely effects of the diet recommendations and exercise programme, as evidenced in the detailed account.

Reflect on the three-week programme and its strengths and areas for improvement.

Provide comprehensive advice to the individual for the future, making accurate reflections and reasoned judgements.

Unit 8 Complementary Therapies

Contents

About this unit

Within this unit you will investigate:

- the history and development of complementary therapies
- their use and provision
- meeting physical, emotional and social needs
- the value of complementary therapies.

The term 'complementary therapies' may also refer to alternative, non-conventional, holistic and natural medicines or therapies

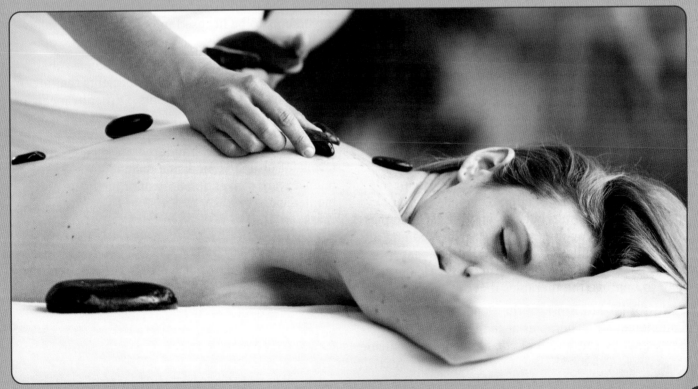

Introducing this unit

The term 'complementary therapies' refers to a number of products and health care practices that are not currently recognised as a part of orthodox medicine. Some complementary therapies are often used alongside mainstream medicine, however, and treatments may even overlap. There are no fixed guidelines about which therapies are complementary, i.e. those that are used in conjunction with conventional medical practice; and those that are alternative, or used on their own. This can sometimes lead to confusion for people wishing to explore different approaches to improving health and well being.

The term 'complementary therapies' is frequently used for both complementary and alternative therapies – as is 'complementary medicine'. Increasingly, they are now often referred to as 'complementary and alternative medicine' or CAM.

New therapies are constantly being developed and need to be carefully monitored and reviewed to ensure safe practice. An organisation called 'The Cochrane Collaboration' monitors and evaluates reviews of **controlled trials**. This is a quote from their definition of complementary medicine:

'… includes all such practices and ideas self-defined by their users as preventing or treating illness or promoting health and well being.'

The definition also emphasises that

'the boundaries between complementary and alternative medicine and the orthodox system are not always clear or fixed'.

Finding a single definition or criteria for all therapies is almost impossible. However, there have been many attempts to try to do this during the last fifteen years.

There is a major concern about the generally **uncritical acceptance** that users often display towards complementary or alternative medicine. Persuasive sales literature and marketing techniques can fool many people into falsely believing that all therapies have been thoroughly researched and tested and are therefore safe to use. It would be wise to bear in mind that some healthy **constructive criticism** may help to improve the therapies that are available.

Professor Edzard Ernst, of the Department of Complementary Therapies at the University of Exeter, states 'the future of complementary medicine critically depends on the intensity of research in the years to come'.

There has been an upsurge in the popularity of complementary therapies and accordingly an important need to regulate the field more closely, primarily to safeguard public health, and to increase research into their effectiveness.

Statutory self regulation for chiropractic and osteopathy is the result of a recent Act of Parliament. Acupuncture, herbal medicine and homeopathy are also likely to follow soon.

Discussion point

Which two complementary therapies are currently self regulated and which other therapies are expected to be regulated soon?

The House of Lords Select Committee on Science and Technology published a report in 2000 which stated that 'better regulation of complementary therapies is essential to protect the needs of the public'. As a result of this report, the government concluded that 'complementary medicine does have a role to play within the NHS, but must meet the same standards as other NHS requirements'. Regulations at European level are also planned, under the EU Directive for traditional, herbal and medicinal products. These regulations will require all over the counter medicines made from herbal ingredients to be licensed in order to ensure safety and quality.

These terms are broadly used to encompass the whole range of therapies and treatments that are not part of orthodox treatments. Orthodox medicine refers to treatments that are carried out by medical practitioners and other health professionals such as psychologists, nurses, physiotherapists, etc. Other terms for orthodox medicine include: Western, mainstream, conventional, regular medicine and biomedicine.

Discussion point

Why is regulation of therapies important?

8.2.1 History and development of complementary therapies

The father of modern medicine, Hippocrates (460–370BC), was actually a herb practitioner. The beginnings of complementary therapies go back a very long way.

Mesopotamia 3000BC

Plant medicine used for fever, stroke, lung and liver disease.

Egyptian Medicine 2900–1550BC

Imhotep identified approx. 500 herbs used for rheumatism, diabetes and infections.

Traditional Chinese Medicine 2900–2600BC

Yin-Yang philosophy, diet, acupuncture and 1,800 herbs to restore health.

Ayurvedic Medicine 800BC–1000AD

This Indian healing system used diet, herbs, exercise, meditation, massage and light.

Greek Medicine 500BC

Hippocrates advocated treating the patient and not just the disease, firstly with diet and then with herbs if diet alone was not enough.

Aztec and Mayan Medicine

Over 1,200 medicine plants were used for treatment.

Inca Medicine

Used botanical medicines including the coca plant.

Native American Medicine

More than 500 medicinal herbs and natural products known to be used.

Naturopathy

Herbal and spa cures used in the European tradition.

The World Health Organisation estimates that 80% of the world population still rely on plant-based medicine for their **primary health care**.

Ayurveda is the traditional medicine of India and has been around for 5,000 years. The Ancient Egyptians were known to have used fragrant oils in what may have been an early version of aromatherapy, and hydrotherapy was practised in ancient Greece and Rome to promote healing and well being. Homeopathy is one of the newer techniques, but even this is more than 200 years old.

The development of the modern **pharmaceutical industry** started by examining plants that were used in traditional medicine.

Aspirin (developed from a tree bark) was the first drug to be produced **chemically** and put on the market in 1899. Until then treatment in Western medicine was mainly based on the use of herbs with some metals and animal preparations. The use and development of new chemical drugs has increased steadily since the introduction of aspirin. There are currently an enormous number of drug remedies that are available for the treatment of illnesses and diseases. Although many of these new drugs are now developed from in-house research, analysis of plants continues to play an important part in the search for more effective treatments.

Before the introduction of the National Health Service in 1948, the provision of **primary medical care** in the UK was spread unevenly. It was common practice for many family doctors to spend ample time with their patients, often visiting them regularly at their homes, both for medical purposes and socially. 'Tender loving care' (often referred to as TLC), was for many doctors the main method of care, apart from using a range of herbal remedies. This resulted in a trusting relationship between doctor and patient and confidence in the prescribed treatments.

The last one hundred years have seen remarkable developments in surgery, as well as a vast increase in the number of drugs available for treatment. Improvements in the use of **effective anaesthesia** have made previously difficult surgery possible. These developments have led to successful cures for many **acute and chronic** conditions. Major improvements have also occurred in detecting illnesses and diseases through other investigative procedures such as blood tests, scans, x-rays and the use of DNA testing.

Some conditions do not seem to respond particularly well to drug or surgical treatments, however. Arthritis, low back pain, asthma and some forms of cancer are examples of conditions where it is claimed that complementary therapies may provide more effective results.

Without doubt, there are now more pressures and demands on the average GP than there were 50 years ago. He now has much less time to spend with each patient (an average consultation time at GP surgeries is currently about ten minutes per patient), and the opportunities to provide TLC for the patient are far less. At a group practice, patients may not see the same doctor consistently and this lack of continuity may mean that a close **therapeutic** relationship does not develop.

The use of drugs and surgery can be troublesome for some patients, causing distressing side effects and occasionally even death. These adverse reactions are less common with complementary therapies, and the **benefit–risk** ratio of each form of treatment is often taken into account when choosing treatment.

It is not surprising, therefore, that complementary therapies in the UK are more popular than ever before. It is estimated that between 4 and 5 million people in the UK see a therapist each year. Between 1981 and 1997, the number of non-medically qualified **registered practitioners** trebled to about 50,000.

> **Note:**
>
> 'A person should never stop or change prescribed medication without seeing their GP first.'

Types of complementary therapies

There is no universally accepted method of grouping complementary therapies, but the most common grouping is by types, as illustrated by the diagram below.

Cognitive
Hypnotherapy, meditation, yoga, visualisation

Sensory
Aromatherapy, massage, shiatsu, reflexology, music therapy

Examples of complementary therapies

Expressive
Art therapy, music therapy, stress management

Physical
Yoga, Alexander technique, acupuncture

Medical
Chinese medicine, Ayurveda, herbal medicine, homeopathy

Somewhat confusingly, many therapies can be placed in more than one category and others have superficial similarities in **philosophy**, but are, in fact, quite distinct. For example, acupuncture and yoga are both concerned with energy systems, but vary in the way that energy is boosted. Each therapy needs to be approached individually.

- *Sensory* are complementary therapies that work in conjunction with the five senses, i.e. sight, hearing, smell, taste and touch.

- *Cognitive* are complementary therapies that promote mind-body healing by using the powers of positive thinking.
- *Expressive* are complementary therapies where people are encouraged to express their thoughts.
- *Physical* are complementary therapies that release endorphins (mood-elevating hormones) and promote better general health.
- *Medical* systems are complementary therapies using different, alternative, or non-traditional medicines.

Activity 1

The general public are not fully aware of the different types of complementary therapies that are available or what to expect from using them.

1. Describe briefly the history and development of complementary therapies.

2. Produce a list of the most popular therapies and identify two conditions that users may seek help with.

3. Give four reasons why a patient may choose to use a complementary therapy.

4. Name the complementary therapies that are currently **self regulating**, and identify the ones that are likely to be so in the near future.

Did you know?

Professor Ernst of the Department of Complementary Medicine at Plymouth Peninsula Medical School advises:

'If it sounds too good to be true then it probably is.'

The Select Committee on Science and Technology received evidence from various disciplines that were considered to be either complementary or alternative to **orthodox medicine**. The Committee then categorised the disciplines into three groups:

1 The First Group includes osteopathy and chiropractic that are regulated in their professional activities. Others in this group are acupuncture, herbal medicine and homeopathy. These are known as 'the Big 5' and claim to have a diagnostic approach.

2 The Second Group are those therapies that are used to complement conventional medicine but do not use diagnostic approaches. These are Alexander technique, massage, counselling, stress therapy, hypnotherapy, reflexology, shiatsu, meditation and healing.

3 The Third Group claims to offer diagnostic information and treatment and is sub-divided into two groups:

a includes Ayurvedic medicine and Traditional Chinese Medicine.

b covers alternative disciplines which lack credible evidence, such as crystal therapy, iridology, radionics and kinesiology.

Different cultural attitudes

People from different cultural backgrounds react in different ways to life change events and even illness. Western medicine tends to focus on the **external factors** that cause the symptoms of disease but Eastern medicines and complementary therapies focus more on rebalancing the body's internal energies. Western approaches also focus more on treating the disease, while complementary therapies focus more on restoring the balance between the physical, mental, social and spiritual well being of the person.

In Western medicine, all drugs are governed and tested in clinical trials before being approved for use. Many complementary therapy practices are not clinically tested, but are learned from ancient practices and experience.

Most complementary therapists agree that the purpose of **therapeutic intervention** is to restore balance and to facilitate the body's own healing processes to stop troublesome symptoms. Therapists frequently offer a 'package of care', therefore, that may include changes or modifications in lifestyle, diet and exercise, as well as a specific treatment. For example, a herbalist, apart from prescribing herbs, may also offer counselling, suggest an exercise programme, guidance on how to improve breathing patterns and teach ways to improve relaxation skills.

The philosophy that users of complementary therapies are involved in their own care is as important as the therapy itself.

Florence Nightingale also used complementary therapy as well as traditional medicine in her work

Florence Nightingale (1820–1910) described the use of a number of complementary therapies, including music, in the holistic care of patients.

More users are taking control of their own care and looking for therapies that will relieve their symptoms of chronic or acute illnesses. Others may be seeking a complementary therapy that will help to prevent illness, for example a person may go for a massage on a regular basis to prevent a build-up of stress.

How complementary therapies work alongside orthodox medicine

Most complementary services have traditionally been offered by non-medically qualified practitioners and this is still generally the case. The last few years, however, have seen a change in that several thousand health care professionals now practice some form of complementary therapy and are registered with their own **professional organisation**.

The main service providers are in the private sector, with clients paying out of their own pockets or through their private health insurance. The increase in the provision of complementary services within the NHS has been quite significant in the past 15 years. Homeopathy has been available since 1948, but other therapies have become more accessible within the NHS only since the late 1980s. In December 1991, the Department of Health acknowledged the public demand for NHS access to complementary therapies and gave family doctors permission to employ complementary therapists as **ancillary** staff.

A study at the University of Sheffield in 1995 showed that four out of ten GPs in England were providing some form of complementary therapy for their NHS patients. Sixty-five per cent of hospital doctors in the UK think that complementary therapy has a place alongside orthodox medicine. Nurses play a major role in promoting therapies within NHS hospitals. The Royal College of Nursing has a Complementary Therapies Nursing Forum with over 2,000 members.

Local Health Authorities are also funding therapists for the elderly in **sheltered accommodation** and nursing homes and also for Community Drug and Alcohol Units. Hospices are also major providers, with one survey of 18 hospices in England finding that all of them offered aromatherapy and massage.

Complementary therapists often spend more time talking to their patients as well as offering therapy

The Guide 1	CASE STUDY

Case Study 1: Malik

Malik is experiencing stress. He is overworked and has little free time for any recreational activities. He has been to see his GP who has prescribed medication to help Malik sleep. He has now decided to try some complementary therapies to see if these would help. Malik is a Muslim and will not do anything that interferes with his faith.

Case Study 2: Marion

Marion has back problems. She also has difficulty with mobility. She is receiving medication to reduce the pain in her back. Marion gets upset very easily because she cannot do the things she used to be able to do previously. She becomes depressed and withdrawn and sits looking at the TV all day but does not really see the programmes.

Case Study 3: Sheema

Sheema has mental health problems. She gets confused and wanders around the streets in her area. The house is in a mess. This all started two months after the death of her son.

1 Produce a comprehensive Guide to help each of the three service users in the case studies to understand a wide range of complementary therapies that are available.

You must include the development and purpose of each complementary therapy included, showing the similarities and differences between them.

2 Produce information to show the global use of complementary therapies explaining how they work alongside orthodox medicine, how they are used and the settings in which they are used.

8.2.2 Use and provision of complementary therapies

There is evidence of a rapid increase in the use of complementary therapies in the UK. In the 1960s complementary therapies were of only minor interest, but by the 1980s, interest really started to grow, not only from the general public but also from the medical and health care practitioners. The number of people in the UK who see a complementary therapist each year is approximately 4–5 million.

One study showed that about 8.5% of adults had received a main complementary therapy in the previous year, with acupuncture, chiropractic, homeopathy, hypnotherapy, herbal medicine or osteopathy being the main therapies named. Five years later, this had increased to 10.6%, and more recently, a similar study showed that 25% of the general public had used one of the six main therapies.

In 1995, the **Consumers Association** conducted a survey and 9,000 subscribers responded. Almost one in three respondents had used a complementary therapy at some time previously. Women showed a greater tendency to use complementary therapies than men. Other surveys have shown that people living in the south of England are more likely to use complementary therapies than people who live in Scotland and the north of England. Most users are between the ages of 21 and 60 and tend to be from the **higher socio-economic** group.

Recent surveys show a wide range in the extent that these therapies are used, but emphasise that this may be due in part to the different methods used to **implement** the surveys.

Discussion point

When did complementary therapies grow in popularity in the UK and who is more likely to use them?

In 1999 Mr Simon Mills and Ms Sarah Budd, at the Centre for Complementary Health Studies at Exeter University, were commissioned by the Department of Health to conduct a study of the complementary therapy organisations in the UK.

Their survey indicated that there were approximately 50,000 therapy practitioners in the UK and that there were approximately 10,000 **statutory registered health professionals** who practise some form of complementary therapy. With up to five million patients consulting a practitioner each year, there are obvious developments in the use and provision of the complementary therapy services. Service users can access the various therapies through the professional bodies for registering the practitioners (where such exist), through health professionals such as doctors, nurses and physiotherapists, who provide complementary therapy within their practices, or directly through over the counter preparations and literature.

In 1999, the BBC commissioned a telephone survey whereby a group of British adults were **randomly selected**. A total of 1,204 people were contacted by telephone and asked 'if they had used alternative or complementary medicine within the last year'. They were then asked to define the complementary therapy that they used. These were the results:

BBC telephone survey of 1,204 randomly selected British adults in the UK	Percentage users
Use of any complementary therapy in past 12 months	20
Of which: *	
Herbal medicine	34
Aromatherapy	21
Homeopathy	17
Acupuncture/acupressure	14
Massage	6
Reflexology	6
Osteopathy	4
Chiropractic	3

Percentages of those who had used complementary therapies.

Source: nationally representative random telephone survey of 1,204 British adults, commissioned by the BBC

N.B. Some individuals had used more than one therapy and thus the numbers do not add up to 100%

How are complementary therapies used?

The same BBC telephone survey asked respondents what were their main reasons for using this approach. The results were as follows:

Reason	Percentage who used a complementary therapy
To relieve an injury or condition	25
Just like it	21
Find it relaxing	19
Good health or well being	14
Preventative measure	12
Do not believe that conventional medicine works	11
Doctor's recommendation	11
To find out other ways of life or doing things	11
Way of life or part of lifestyle	8
Cannot get treatment under conventional medicine	7

Did you know?

An increasing number of medical practitioners are choosing to provide limited access to complementary therapies within their practices.

(British Medical Association, 2003)

It is clear that more individuals are now making a choice between conventional and/or a complementary therapy. It is less clear, however, how many appreciate that they should tell their GP if they are receiving a complementary therapy, because they may be at risk if their complementary therapy **interacts adversely** with any other treatment that they may be receiving.

Some of the main reasons for people choosing a complementary therapy may be:

- They do not believe that conventional medicines will work.
- To avoid the effects of conventional medication that they perceive to be worse than the condition itself.
- They want a care provider who can spare the time to listen as well as prescribe.

- The person seeks an **holistic** approach
- They want to be a partner in their own care plan.

People choose complementary therapies for many different reasons, illnesses, symptoms and conditions. Some well-known therapies, with some of the conditions that frequently cause people to use them, are listed below. The listing of therapies and conditions is not comprehensive.

Therapy	Condition
Aromatherapy	Acne, insomnia, headaches and reducing tension.
Acupuncture	Addictions, back pain, cancer care, migraine, nausea and vomiting, osteoarthritis, stroke and tennis elbow.
Hypnotherapy	Asthma, cancer care, eczema, headache, irritable bowel syndrome, stress and anxiety.
Relaxation	Asthma, mild depression, high blood pressure, insomnia, menopausal symptoms, migraine, stress and anxiety.
Yoga	Asthma, back pain, diabetes, high blood pressure and osteoarthritis.
Herbal medicine	Congestive heart failure, enlarged prostate, constipation, depression, erectile dysfunction and heart disease.
Massage	Cancer care, constipation, tension and headaches.
Osteopathy	Back pain, headache and musculo-skeletal pains.
Biofeedback	Constipation, headache, high blood pressure, incontinence, pre-menstrual syndrome, stress and anxiety.
Chiropractic	Back pain, headache and musculo-skeletal problems.

If a person is taking any prescribed drugs or medication, consultation with their GP is strongly recommended before any complementary treatment is accessed.

Service users should find out as much as possible about their selected therapy beforehand and also ascertain the costs of each session. Care should also be taken to find a knowledgeable, sensitive and qualified practitioner. Information on the various therapies is available from the different complementary therapies' professional bodies, who will usually provide a list of their qualified and trained members in any particular geographical area.

Activity 2

After examining evidence of recent surveys and research, quote some of the findings:

1 Approximately how many people in the UK are accessing a complementary therapy each year?

2 What are some of the main reasons/conditions given for using a complementary therapy? List five.

3 Why do people choose complementary rather than conventional medicine? Name three main reasons given.

4 What risks can you identify if a patient does not inform their doctor about any complementary therapy received while also taking prescribed medicines or treatments?

Therapists work in a number of settings both in the public and private sectors. Here are some venues that are frequently used:

Hospices

Private clinics

Private and NHS hospitals

Own home

Over the counter therapies

Settings in which therapies are used

Care homes for the elderly

GP surgeries

Community centres

Private leisure centres

Discussion point

Where is complementary therapy available?

Costs of complementary therapies

The cost of the many therapies varies enormously and a user would be wise to ascertain the fees and estimated total costs of treatment before attending for therapy. Salaries for employing practitioners can currently vary from about £17,000 to £30,000 per annum. If the therapist is practising within a clinical role such as a nurse, then she may be paid according to the nursing scale from grade E to grade H. Self-employed therapists may charge fees ranging from £20 to £75 per session.

The Royal Pharmaceutical Society quotes that in 1999, £2,318 million was spent on non-prescription medicine and that this market continues to increase in turnover and profitability each year. Whilst many people spend less than £5 per month, the average amount of money each complementary therapy user spends is estimated to be approximately £14 per month. This particular survey estimated that the annual expenditure on complementary therapies in the UK is £1.6 billion. *This level of expenditure equates to £26 p.a. for each man, woman and child.*

According to another recent survey the most frequently consulted therapists are as follows (the fees they may charge have been added).

Osteopaths 4.3%

£30–£70 for the first session and £20–£50 for subsequent sessions

Aromatherapists 3.5%

£20–£40 for 60 to 90 minutes

Acupuncturists 1.6%

£20–£60 initially and follow up sessions may be £5–£15

Chiropractors 3.6%

£20–£50 per session (depending on location)

Reflexologists 2.4%

£25–£40 per session

A total of 8.6% of the respondents in this study had bought over the counter homeopathic remedies and 19.8% had bought herbal remedies.

The Royal Pharmaceutical Society reported that retail sales of complementary medicine, i.e. herbals, homeopathic preparations and aromatherapy essential oils, totalled £93 million in 1998. The breakdown showed £50 million was spent on herbal remedies, £23 million on homeopathic remedies and £20 million for aromatherapy essential oils. Overall retail sales for the year 2000 were predicted to reach £109 million and £126 million by 2002.

The World Health Organisation (WHO) published their first 'Traditional Medicine Strategy' for the period 2002–2005 and stated that the **global market** for traditional therapies is at present around £60 billion per year and growing steadily.

Accredited training leading to a recognised qualification is vital to maintaining standards

Training and qualifications of practitioners

A recommendation in the report on Complementary and Alternative Medicine by the House of Lords Select Committee on Science and Technology was '… that only those CAM therapies which are **statutorily regulated**, or have a **powerful mechanism of voluntary self regulation**, should be made available for reference from doctors and other health care professionals working in primary, secondary or tertiary care, in the NHS.'

It seems that most complementary therapies are, in fact, regulated by one or more voluntary bodies. Osteopathy and chiropractic are statutorily regulated therapies with their courses **standardised and accredited** by their appropriate regulatory body. Other complementary professions are also working towards common standards of education and training in order to provide accreditation.

Complementary practitioners are strongly recommended to register with an organisation that ensures all members are suitably qualified and insured to practise. The professional organisation should have in place:

- a list of members and their qualifications
- identification of standards for membership that include competence and insurance
- evidence of **continuing professional development**
- a **code of ethics**
- a complaints and disciplinary procedure
- methods for involving members in decision making
- an AGM and publication of annual accounts.

Health care professionals such as doctors, nurses and physiotherapists, who may also wish to practise complementary therapies, are bound by the code of conduct of their own profession. They are, however, advised to consult their regulatory body, their professional body and their employer for specific guidance before introducing complementary therapy into their clinical work.

Note:

'It is vital to know about the qualifications, training and experience of practitioners before accepting therapy.'

The Royal College of Nursing and the Nursing and Midwifery Council have issued guidelines on practice for nurses thinking about using complementary therapies in their work. These guidelines include information on the following issues:

- **indemnity insurance** for practitioners using complementary therapies
- **product liability cover**
- self-employed practitioners using complementary therapies
- nurses who work as homeopaths
- choosing a complementary therapy course
- advertising
- homeopathic substances and herbal preparations.

The House of Lords Committee recommended that complementary therapy training for conventional health care professionals should be to standards agreed with the appropriate complementary therapy regulatory body (Department of Health, 2001). Standards may be developed for training and practice at different levels.

Qualifications may be:

- a Diploma, or other qualification, awarded by a private college or training institute
- a nationally recognised qualification, such as a Diploma, from an awarding body that is regulated by one of the four UK statutory regulating authorities.

Details of the external awarding bodies for complementary therapy qualifications currently regulated by QCA can be obtained on their website www.qca.org.uk.

Health and safety aspects

As a practitioner, employer, employee, service user or service provider, everyone has a responsibility for health and safety and for maintaining a safe working environment. Some aspects to consider are illustrated by the following chart.

We are all responsible for health and safety. The utmost care must be taken to reduce and eliminate all risks

All employers and self-employed practitioners need to be aware of the health and safety **legislation** to protect employees and the public. The legislation and the various aspects and key points covered are summarised in the table on the next page.

Risk assessment

Training in manual handling

Critical incident reporting and management

Health and safety

Safe disposal of equipment

Procedure for dealing with spillages

Storage of resources

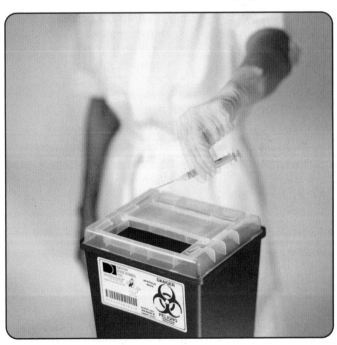

Always dispose of sharp items properly

Complementary Therapies
8.2.2 Use and provision of complementary therapies / Assessment activity (AO2) /
8.2.3 Meeting physical, emotional and social needs

Legislation	Key points
Management of Health and Safety at Work Regulations 1999	• Identify **hazards** • Assess risks and who is at risk • Eliminate risks and train staff to deal with risks
Workplace (Health, Safety and Welfare) Regulations 1992	• Maintenance of workplace and equipment • Ventilation, temperature and lighting • Cleanliness • Sanitary and washing facilities • Drinking water • Rest, eating and changing facilities
Personal Protective Equipment at Work (PPE) Regulations 1992	• Storage of materials • Care of electrical equipment • Storage and use of heated instruments
Control of Substances Hazardous to Health Regulations 1999	• Risks if in contact with the skin or eyes • Risks if **inhaled or ingested** • Risks if injected • Risks if in contact with broken skin
Electricity at Work Regulations 1989	• Electrician's name and contact details • Itemised list of equipment and serial numbers • Date of inspection • Date of purchase and disposal
Health and Safety (First Aid) Regulations 1981	• Records of date and time of incident and treatment • Name and occupation of injured person • Details of injury and treatment given • Details of aftercare, e.g. home or hospital • Name and signature of person providing care
Fire Precautions Act 1971 and Amendment Regulations 1999	• Assessment of fire risks • Suitable detection equipment • Warning systems and fire-fighting equipment • Adequate training
Health and Safety (Display Screen Equipment) Regulations 1999	• Covers the use of computers and similar equipment
Manual Handling Operations Regulations 1992	• Risk of injury assessment • **Manual handling** training

Assessment activity (AO2)

The Guide 2 — CASE STUDY

Choose one service user, either one who is actually using complementary therapies or one from the case studies previously given. If you use the case studies you will still need to prepare questions for the service user in order to produce the information required for the Guide:

1. Choose two complementary therapies suitable for the service user, giving a detailed account of how they meet the service user's physical, intellectual, emotional and social needs (P.I.E.S.).

2. Describe the roles of the practitioners, who work with the service user, giving a detailed account of what they actually do and how this is beneficial to the service user. Also include information about:

   • training and qualifications of practitioners
   • health and safety related to each complementary therapy
   • how lifestyle choice and beliefs influence the choice
   • cost compared to the service user's means.

8.2.3 Meeting physical, emotional and social needs

Service users are often influenced by marketing strategies and the pressures of advertising through the media. Their knowledge of each complementary therapy may be vague and often confused. This is a brief description of the various complementary and alternative therapies.

Mary — Activity 4

Mary is a local district nurse, and she wishes to train as an aroma therapist and to practise her new skills in the surgery with patients referred to her by the practice GPs.

In your opinion, what should Mary consider, when looking for a suitable training school and qualification? And what does she need to consider about resources, insurance and a working contract as a member of the primary health care team?

Group 1 (The Big 5)

These therapies use **diagnostic systems**, treatments and are professionally organised:

Chiropractic

Treats mainly **musculo-skeletal** complaints, by adjusting muscles, tendons and joints. May use massage and manipulation.

Osteopathy

Focuses on musculo-skeletal problems, mainly by **manipulation**. Theory is to improve impaired blood supply.

Acupuncture

Involves inserting small needles to stimulate nerve impulses. May also be used as an **analgesic**. Based on the idea of 'Qi' (vital energy).

Herbal Medicine

Uses various remedies, derived from plant extracts, to treat disorders and maintain health. Also referred to as phytotherapy.

Homeopathy

Based on the theory of treating like with like. Uses highly diluted substances to treat cause of symptoms. Diagnoses consider physical, emotional and lifestyle factors.

> **Discussion point**
>
> Why are these called 'the Big 5'?

Complementary therapies in Group 2

Alexander Technique

This technique encourages the person to sit, move and stand according to the body's natural design and function. This technique is taught rather than a therapy.

Aromatherapy

This therapy uses essential oils extracted from plants. They may be used under professional guidance to inhale, as massage oil and even occasionally ingested. They can also be used as a **relaxant**, or to relieve certain symptoms.

Bach and other flower remedies

The theory is that flowers contain the life force of the plant and this is imprinted into water through sun infusion. This therapy is often used to help patients experiencing negative thoughts.

Massage and body work therapies

These therapies use rubbing, kneading and pressure to deal with aches, pain and musculo-skeletal problems. They are also used to aid relaxation.

Counselling stress therapy

This helps people to work through their thoughts, using a problem-solving approach to recognise signs and symptoms of stress and to apply appropriate remedial strategies.

Hypnotherapy

This therapy uses hypnosis to treat behavioural problems, dysfunction and disease.

Learning to relax is a psycho-motor skill

Meditation

In this therapy, relaxation techniques are used to help a person to relax the body and the mind and to reflect.

Reflexology

This therapy involves massage of the feet and is based on the idea that there are zones running vertically through the body that locate with each organ. Massage of these zones is claimed to improve blood supply to the corresponding organ.

Shiatsu

This is a massage that aims to stimulate the body's healing by applying light pressure to various points of the body. Relies on the meridian system of 'Qi' as in Traditional Chinese Medicine.

Healing

This therapy refers to a system of spiritual healing, sometimes based on prayer and religious beliefs, that attempts to tackle various illnesses through non-physical means. It is often referred to as 'the laying on of hands'.

Maharishi Ayurvedic Medicine

This system uses herbal preparations and promotes transcendental meditation. It is derived from the Vedic tradition in India.

Nutritional medicine

This therapy uses diets and nutritional supplements to prevent disease and often examines allergies and chronic digestive problems. Nutritional therapists work independently, using **naturopathic principles**. They focus on disorders that they believe are due to nutritional deficiencies, **food intolerance** and **toxic overload**. Dieticians usually work under medical supervision, using diets to encourage healthy eating. Nutritional therapists often use exclusive diets and herbal remedies.

Yoga

This therapy uses various postures, breathing techniques and relaxation to promote spiritual and physical well being.

Group 3a

These are long established and traditional systems of health care, including:

Anthroposophy

This system looks at people in terms of their physicality, soul and spirit and aims to stimulate a person's natural healing forces.

Ayurvedic Medicine

This is an ancient therapy from India that uses natural herbs in treatments and looks at the mind, spirit and body interaction.

Chinese Herbal Medicine

This therapy has been used for thousands of years in China. It has its own system of diagnosis and uses herbs for a wide range of health problems.

Eastern Medicine (Tibb)

This therapy uses elements of health philosophy from Egypt, India, China and Greece, in which wholeness and balance are essential concepts and imbalance is thought to cause disease. Physical, emotional, mental and spiritual well being are all assessed. Treatments include massage, manipulation, dietary and herbal medicine. **Psychotherapeutic** approaches are also used.

Naturopathy

This therapy utilises treatments that are based on the natural laws of life, using diet and herbs whilst encouraging exposure to sun and fresh air.

Traditional Chinese Medicine (TCM)

The basis of TCM is that it sees the body as a dynamic energy system, with two types of energy, Yin Qi and Yang Qi. It believes that if there is an imbalance between the Yin and Yang Qi, symptoms will occur. TCM uses acupuncture, herbal medicine, massage and the exercise technique known as Qigong.

Group 3b

This group consists of therapies which lack credible evidence of success, including:

Crystal therapy

Crystal therapists believe that crystals absorb and transmit energy and help to tune the body's **fluctuating energy levels**. Crystals are placed around the patient's body to produce an energy network to adjust the patient's energy field or aura.

Dowsing

This technique has been used by practitioners for many years to identify underground water sources. It is not a therapy as such and is often used with radionics.

Iridology

In this system, a patient's health status is diagnosed by studying the iris of the eye.

Kinesiology

This practice uses manipulation to assess a patient's physical, chemical, emotional and nutritional imbalances by testing the muscles and measuring variations in stress resistance. Deficiencies and imbalances are diagnosed and treatments include strengthening the body's energy through acupressure points.

Radionics

This practice uses an instrument to detect disease before it has physically **manifested** itself. The belief is that everyone is surrounded by an invisible energy field, which the practitioner tunes into and attempts to correct the problem or problems.

Discussion point

A service user seeking help through complementary medicine may have a range of physical, emotional and social conditions that you will need to be aware of and be familiar with.

Joy   Activity 5

Joy is a 65-year-old lady, who lives alone in a bungalow on a quiet estate in the south of England. She lost her husband when he died of a heart attack quite suddenly two years ago. Joy has two children, a daughter who lives five miles away with her husband and two of Joy's grandchildren, aged 6 and 8. Her daughter has a part-time job with a busy life and a young family, but she tries to visit or see her mother once a week.

Her son lives in Scotland, with his wife and young family of three children. She sees him once a year and speaks on the telephone to him every few weeks.

Joy felt the loss of her husband greatly and even with the help of her family she remains depressed and grief stricken at times. Her GP has prescribed an **antidepressant** which is helping a little, but Joy is also finding that her sleep patterns are very disturbed, due to pain caused by **osteoarthritis**. She has heard about complementary medicine and feels she would like to try something else other than using pills all the time.

1   Why is it important to assess Joy's needs carefully?

Activity 5

2   How do you evaluate her physical, social and emotional well being?

3   What advice would you give her regarding the use of a complementary therapy in view of her current depression and medication?

4   What should Joy look for when choosing a therapist?

5   Debate some of the benefits and risks for Joy if she accepts treatment from a complementary therapist.

It is important to have a broad understanding about the range of conditions, illnesses and symptoms that may affect a service user. For discussion, these may be broken down into physical, emotional and social. The following diagram offers some guidelines of conditions that the user may present to the therapist where he/she needs help.

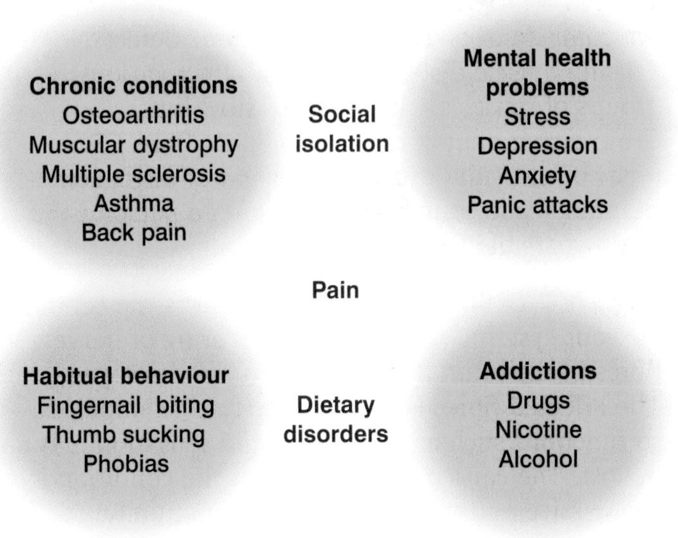

Chronic conditions
Osteoarthritis
Muscular dystrophy
Multiple sclerosis
Asthma
Back pain

Social isolation

Mental health problems
Stress
Depression
Anxiety
Panic attacks

Pain

Habitual behaviour
Fingernail biting
Thumb sucking
Phobias

Dietary disorders

Addictions
Drugs
Nicotine
Alcohol

These may all be linked or inter-linked.

Defining a range of terms

Pain can be defined as a localised sensation, varying in feeling and intensity from a mild discomfort to an unbearable and even **excruciating** experience. It is the result of the stimulation of special **sensory nerve endings**, usually following an injury or caused by a disease. The mechanism of pain exists to act as a warning of possible injury and to provide caution. Where certain diseases exist, such as arthritis or extensive cancer, the mechanism of pain may be triggered and chronic pain sets in. This has no apparent function.

The following illnesses and conditions are ones that complementary therapies are often used to treat.

Referred pain is the type that is felt in a part of the body away from the injury or disease. This happens when sensory nerves transmitting the feelings of pain to the brain converge and cause confusion about where the source of pain could be located.

Osteoarthritis is a common **degenerative** disease of the joints of the body. It results from excessive wear on the joints and differs from rheumatoid arthritis in being **non-inflammatory** and has a better outlook for treatment and control. Osteoarthritis occurs in almost all people over the age of 60, although not everyone has symptoms. It affects three times as many women as men. Symptoms include pain, swelling, creaking and stiffness in one or more joints. The hips, knees and spine are the main areas that are affected.

Muscular dystrophy is due to a genetic defect causing muscle disorder that can affect various groups of muscles. This leads to slow but **progressive degeneration** of muscle fibres. Some types of muscular dystrophy appear at birth, some in infancy and some as late as when a person is 50 or 60 years old, but all forms are rare.

Multiple sclerosis is a disease that affects the central nervous system. The protective covering of nerve fibres in the brain and spinal cord are destroyed. The affected fibres cannot conduct nerve impulses, so functions such as movement and sensation may be lost. The cause is unknown, but the condition is progressive and symptoms range from numbness and tingling to paralysis and **incontinence**. Multiple sclerosis is the most common acquired (i.e. not present at birth) disease of the nervous system in young adults and usually starts in early adult life. It may be active for a while then recess and become active again in later life. Symptoms vary according to which parts of the brain and spinal cord are affected. Some of these may be weakness, heaviness, **rigidity** and paralysis.

Asthma is caused by inflammation of the bronchi or air passages to the lungs. This results in recurrent attacks of breathlessness and wheezing. Severity of attacks may vary from hour to hour and day to day.

The condition often starts in childhood and tends to clear in adulthood, but it can develop at any age. The most common **allergens** are pollens, house dust, house dust mites, animal furs, feathers and dander. Asthma may also be triggered by a viral or bacterial infection, or induced by exercise, tobacco smoke or other pollutants found in certain foods or drugs. About one adult in twenty is asthmatic, but amongst children the frequency is about one in ten.

Back pain is something that most people experience at times. In most cases the pain gets better with rest. Back pain is one of the main causes of sickness absence from work. **Non-specific** back pain is thought to be due to a mechanical disorder, affecting one or more structures in the back. This may be ligament strain, a torn muscle or damage to a spinal joint or the prolapse of an **intervertebral** disc. If the reason for the back pain is found, then treatment will depend on the identified cause. Acute non-specific back pain is treated with rest and analgesia.

Stress may be defined as any interference that upsets a person's healthy mental and physical well being. A person may experience (or perceive) stress in response to a wide range of physical or emotional stimuli. These may include physical violence, internal conflicts and significant life change events (such as death of a loved one). The Health and Safety Executive definition of stress is: 'The adverse reaction people have to excessive pressures or other types of demands placed on them' (Health and Safety Executive, 2000).

Continued exposure to stressful situations often leads to mental and physical symptoms such as increased anxiety and depression, indigestion, palpitations and/or changes in behaviour.

Did you know?

13.4 million working days are lost each year in the UK due to stress (HSE, 2000)

Depression is a problem associated with feelings of sadness, hopelessness and general loss of interest. Most people experience some of these feelings occasionally and in many cases this is a normal response to a particular event in life. For example, dealing with a loss, or a major sudden change in life may trigger a **reactive depression**. The symptoms may include tearfulness, anxiety, mood swings, tiredness, etc. Clinical depression is more serious, however, with symptoms such as loss of appetite, difficulty in sleeping, loss of interest, social withdrawal and loss of concentration. Movement and thinking may also be slow. In cases of severe depression people may have suicidal thoughts. Some 10–15% of people in the UK are said to suffer from depression at sometime in their lives, especially the milder forms of depression.

Anxiety can be defined as an emotional state, causing a range of unpleasant feelings, from mild unease to intense fears. A person suffering from anxiety may complain of a sense of impending doom, even though there is no obvious threat. A certain level of anxiety in certain situations is considered normal. This may help to focus thoughts and to improve performance. Extreme feelings of anxiety can become a problem when they start to disrupt normal everyday activities. Symptoms can include palpitations, throbbing or stabbing pains in the chest, a feeling of tightness and an inability to take in enough air. There may also be signs of over breathing, sighing and **hyperventilation**.

Panic attacks can be described as a brief period of acute anxiety, often associated with an intense fear of dying or losing control. They may occur unpredictably at first, but also tend to be associated with certain places and feelings, e.g. **agoraphobia** (fear of open spaces). Symptoms often occur suddenly, together with breathing difficulties, chest pains, dizziness, sweating, trembling and faintness. These attacks can be very unpleasant, but often only last a few minutes and cause no physical harm. They are rarely associated with physical illness. The cause is unknown, but treatment with behavioural therapy is successful, especially if the attacks are associated with specific **phobias**. Relaxation training may also help.

> ### Did you know?
>
> Relaxation is a psycho-motor skill. This means we need to practise regularly before it becomes 'second nature'.

Social isolation. Whilst isolating oneself socially may be a sign of ill health or unhappiness, it is not always the case. Some people choose their own company at times and may withdraw from social activities to meditate or take stock of their lives.

Persistent reclusive behaviour may mask deeper problems of mental ill health and inability to communicate with people.

Dietary disorders. Diet and associated disorders were originally concerned with deficiencies in the diets of the poor. Today, however, deficiency diseases are very rare in developed countries, although in poorer developing countries they remain a major concern.

Today the groups of people in the UK who cause concerns with dietary disorders include those who are alcoholic, those who have difficulties with food being absorbed from their bowels and people on extremely restricted diets (such as anorexics), who may all develop dietary disorders associated with poor nutritional habits. Conversely, many common disorders are due to over-consumption of certain foods and alcohol.

Poor dietary habits are associated with developing coronary heart disease and obesity diabetes. Over-consumption of alcohol can lead to cirrhosis of the liver, brain damage, pancreatitis and many other conditions.

Fingernail biting. This is common, but does not indicate any underlying problem. Many children bite their nails during their first years at school and most grow out of the habit. It can sometimes continue as a nervous habit into adolescence and into adulthood. The problems associated with persistent nail-biting are that it makes the fingers unsightly and may cause pain and bleeding. This may also lead to extreme soreness and infection.

Thumb sucking. The sucking of a thumb is very common in children. It provides comfort and oral gratification, especially before falling to sleep. At other times, children may also suck their thumbs if they are bored, need reassurance or comfort. The habit usually decreases after the age of three, with only a few children continuing to the age of six or seven.

Phobias are an irrational fear that is often persistent and associated with a specific object, place, or situation. Quite a number of people may have minor phobias that cause them some distress, but not enough to impair their quality of life. If the phobia interferes with or disturbs their social well being, then it is considered a psychiatric disorder. Simple disorders may be a fear of dogs, snakes, spiders, mice, etc. These often start in childhood.

Agoraphobia is a more serious type of phobia and often disrupts family life. It is the most common phobia for which treatment is sought.

Drug addiction. This is due to a compulsion by the addicted person to continue to take a drug, either for the desired effects that result from taking it, or to prevent the ill-effects that occur when it is not taken. The dependency may be physical or psychological. The symptoms for a person who is psychologically dependent may cause cravings or emotional distress when they no longer have the drug. In physical dependency, the symptoms and signs of **withdrawal syndrome** occur when the drug is withdrawn, resulting in severe physical and mental distress. Addiction develops as a result of regular and/or excessive use of a drug.

More choices are available nowadays for traditional or complementary therapies

8.2.4 Value of complementary therapies

Activity 6

Many of the cancer care units offer complementary therapies alongside orthodox treatment.

1 Which of the therapies may be the most popular with these patients?

2 Why do you think they are helpful?

3 What in your opinion are the main benefits?

4 What precautions may be necessary when treatment is being done?

The stereotypical image of the use of complementary therapies has changed dramatically over the past 15 years. Whereas previously, both health professionals and the general public were sceptical about the use and benefits of the various therapies, the trend now is towards increased use and participation in self care. It is estimated that a quarter of the population in the UK now use some form of non-conventional therapy.

The Consumers Association and the Patients Association have both suggested that patients' satisfaction with their complementary therapy is very high and partly accounts for the surge in the use of complementary therapies. Patients who were interviewed by the Select Committee expressed 'high levels of satisfaction', whilst none expressed dissatisfaction with their treatment. In addition to relieving the conditions for which they accessed therapy, patients often reported improved feelings of well being.

Professor Edzard Ernst, of Exeter University, looked at arthritis sufferers to compare satisfaction levels with complementary therapies and conventional approaches (the patients had accessed both types of treatment). He found that there was a trend whereby patients felt that complementary therapists were friendlier, spent more time with them and offered more information about their treatments and conditions. Some even found the therapies more effective in relieving their symptoms.

Consultations with complementary therapists often last an hour (sometimes longer with treatments). The therapists usually have excellent communication skills and are good listeners. In addition to taking details of the present symptoms, they usually obtain a detailed history concerning the whole of the patient's life, which is seen as essential to put the patient at ease.

Improvements in general lifestyle benefits after attending yoga, aromatherapy, massage and reflexology have been recorded in a survey by the Consumers Association in 1997. All these factors contribute towards the increased use of complementary therapies and improved patient satisfaction.

Current public and medical opinions have been brought about for many reasons. The increasing pressure on conventional medical practitioners means that a GP may only have ten minutes consultation time with his patients. This can lead to the patient feeling that their doctor has not given them enough time or attention.

There is a tendency for medical practitioners and other health professionals to accept only conventional treatments, because they have been thoroughly tested with documented proof of their effectiveness. Further evidence seems to show that there is a bias against the use of complementary therapies among many practitioners. Sir Iain Chalmers, Director of the UK Cochrane Centre, suggests:

> 'many in the "orthodox" medical world remain either sceptical about the desirability of this trend [towards increasing use of complementary therapies], or hostile to it. This scepticism seems to result partly from unwillingness within the "orthodox" mainstream to apply a single evidential standard when assessing the effects of health care.'

To offset the above somewhat, the Select Committee report notes that current medical training now includes more emphasis on looking at behavioural science, communication skills, counselling, patient–doctor interaction and patient partnership activities. These are regarded as important skills in all fields of complementary therapy. Another significant factor is that there is also an increased trend towards many medical doctors choosing to practise holistic as well as orthodox medicine. From these indications, it is possible, therefore, that any **entrenched** attitudes against complementary therapies will diminish with time, as the newer medical graduates take over from the older generation.

It is clear that many service users are choosing complementary therapy, as opposed to conventional medicine, because of easier access, more consultation time (often in more comfortable, relaxing surroundings), and because complementary therapists are very welcoming and positively encourage long consultations.

General demands for professional changes and accountability have the medical profession under even more pressures. The medical profession is perceived to be resistant to change whilst deterioration in customer service has occurred for some of the following reasons:

Risk of GP being sued for malpractice

Fewer general practitioners

Patient wants a second opinion or a change of GP

GPs want to keep clinical information to themselves

Increased paperwork within the NHS

Increased costs and rationing of services

Deterioration in customer services in orthodox medicine

- The increased risk of being sued for **malpractice** has made doctors more cautious and less relaxed with patients.
- With fewer general practitioners and more specialists, long-term doctor–patient relationship is less likely to develop.
- Patients find that changing their doctor or getting a second opinion is a struggle, often leaving them with feelings that there is little option other than the medical proposals offered.
- There is a perceived feeling that doctors want to keep clinical information to themselves and are reluctant to share it with patients.
- Changes in procedure within the medical service (difficulties in getting appointments, revised out of normal hours emergency services, changes in service provision to meet nationally set targets, etc.), often leave patients feeling that the internal administration and paperwork are more important than ensuring they receive prompt and appropriate treatment.
- Increased costs and rationing of services has led to feelings that services are being cut back or withdrawn.

Discussion point

What can GPs do to improve their image and the services they provide?

277

Some of the controversial aspects relating to the use of complementary therapies in health and social care settings may be examined under the following headings:

Poor communication between the patient and the GP is often identified as a problem that affects the patient–doctor relationship. With medical practitioners under enormous time pressures and trying to assess a patient's needs with only ten minutes on average for a consultation, patients often feel that their symptoms are more important than they are as a whole person. There is also a general feeling that GPs are reluctant to share the clinical findings with patients and do not explain treatment and diagnosis in terms and language that patients easily understand. Patients are also guilty of not always explaining clearly how they feel and what they want. They may have an expectation that their doctor has an all-seeing crystal ball or that they have the power to read their minds. It is a well recalled pattern that many patients say as they are about to leave 'Oh! One other thing doctor' and this is often their main reason for attending the surgery in the first place.

When a patient is considering accessing a complementary therapy, whether it involves seeing a therapist or taking an **'over the counter'** remedy, it is vital that they inform their GP. Prescribed medication may interact adversely with herbal medicines and some over the counter medicines.

False expectations may account for patients' dissatisfaction with either complementary or orthodox medicine. Some orthodox remedies for back ache, myalgic encephalomyelitis (ME), or arthritis, for example, do not always appear to be effective. Equally a false expectation of a complementary therapy may also lead to unhappiness and disappointment. A service user should be aware of **bogus practices** that promise to 'cure' illnesses and disease. There is a lack of evidence and research to prove their effectiveness. However, this does not mean that many therapies are not effective.

Contraindications are ignored. Complementary therapists who are qualified and are members of a professional body are well aware of certain conditions and illnesses where prescribed medication is essential to life. Where a patient has a condition such as diabetes, heart disease or thrombosis (where medication is known to be an important part of that person's treatment), a qualified therapist would not advise stopping or changing that treatment. Some herbal remedies can have an adverse effect on other drugs. An example is St John's Wort, which is often taken to change mood and is particularly used for mild depression. A patient self administering St John's Wort may affect the reliability of the contraceptive pill. Warfarin (taken for controlling the thickness of the blood) may be similarly affected.

An inappropriate therapy for the patient's needs. Once patients have been given a diagnosis, they should be encouraged to research treatments and to discuss the options with their medical practitioner, looking at both orthodox and complementary therapies. It may be possible to integrate both approaches. This does not mean ignoring conventional practice, but massage, for example, may work well for a patient undergoing treatment for cancer. Acupuncture for a patient who has an extreme fear of needles may not be the right complementary therapy for him.

Under-qualified or inexperienced therapist. The only way a service user will know if practitioners are qualified is to ask them. Patients need clear information about their therapists, their training and qualifications and whether they are competent to practise. Do they belong to a professional body and abide by the organisation's code of ethics? The lack of nationally recognised standards for some therapies is a major problem in deciding whether therapists have been appropriately trained and, consequently, whether they are competent to practise. In such cases it is important to establish how long they have been practising and to enquire whether there are previously satisfied customers who would recommend them.

Excessive costs. Nearly 40% of NHS general practices in England provide access to complementary therapies (not necessarily free of charge) and some have employed therapists as part of the primary health care team. The majority of people who use complementary therapies, however, pay for the treatments privately. These people are strongly advised to discuss costs with the provider before attending for treatments. It is also wise to enquire about the number of recommended sessions, the time required to complete the treatments and establish a realistic estimate of the final cost. The therapist should be asked to include any 'add on costs', e.g. for any tests or materials required.

Lack of health and safety regulations. Some observations of a poorly managed clinic may be:

- dirty or soiled equipment
- essential oils and other resources that are not kept safe
- lack of washing facilities or changing rooms
- excessive noise or interruptions
- lack of privacy
- poor lighting
- poor access
- broken stairs, furniture, etc.

A practitioner has a **statutory obligation** to meet the health and safety regulations. This obligation applies to all practices whether within the NHS or in private practice.

No evidence of effectiveness. The British Medical Association states that there is still a great deal of scepticism over the credibility of some forms of complementary therapy, due to lack of sufficient evidence to support the many claims of efficacy. They contrast this with orthodox medicine which has a sound base of evidence. The BMA feel that without evidence it is impossible for the public and medical profession to assess the risks and benefits of the different therapies. Although there are proposals at national and European levels to improve validation and regulation of complementary therapies, supporters of these therapies suggest that the lack of **scientifically**

proven evidence of efficacy is unreasonable since there is ample evidence of patient satisfaction.

> **Note:**
>
> 'Complementary therapy is not an alternative to seeing a GP, nurse, hospital doctor or other medical practitioner.'

The use of complementary therapies

The use of complementary therapies alongside or instead of orthodox treatments has increased considerably over the past 15 years.

A survey of users shows that about 80% are satisfied with the treatment they received. The increase in availability and demand for complementary therapies is indicative of their popularity, although service users may be confused about treatments and what to expect. The following questions may act as guidelines before accessing treatments:

- What benefits can be expected?
- Are there any side effects?
- Will there be any adverse reactions with existing health problems or current treatments, e.g. surgery, chemotherapy, radiotherapy?
- Are side effects or interactions common?
- If there are side effects, are they mild, moderate or severe?
- Are the side effects temporary or permanent?
- Will the treatment cause any adverse reactions with other drugs or foods?
- Do the benefits outweigh the risks?
- Can this treatment be used alongside conventional medicine?
- Will the treatment be covered by health insurance?

Where complementary therapies are used within a conventional medical setting, as part of prescribed treatment, this is known as 'integrated medicine'. Complementary therapies play a big part in NHS cancer care units and palliative care, but they tend to be the 'touch' therapies such as aromatherapy, reflexology and mind-body techniques such as relaxation, visualisation and methods for reducing anxiety in patients.

More women than men access complementary therapy, although more men use osteopathy. Users tend to be between 35 and 60 years of age, are better educated and are more affluent than average.

The term 'complementary' describes those therapies that can be used alongside conventional treatments.

Therapies such as osteopathy, chiropractic, massage, yoga or relaxation and meditation comfortably work with orthodox approaches. In fact both the patient and the therapists expect orthodox methods and treatments to continue. According to the British Medical Association survey in 2000, almost half of GPs (47%) arrange acupuncture for patients and 79% think it should be available on the NHS – 86% of NHS pain clinics offer acupuncture to their patients.

Assessment activity (AO3)

The Guide 3   CASE STUDY

For the Guide you will need to find out, by using a range of appropriate sources, the views of the public and health care professionals of the value of complementary therapies. You should use both primary and secondary information.

1. Consider the sampling methods that are available to be used to gather the information required. These could include:

   - questionnaire
   - interview
   - observation
   - experimentation.

   Compare the differences between each method, giving advantages and disadvantages.

2. Produce questions that could be used with the public and professionals to find out their views about the value of using complementary therapies.

3. Trial the questions and make any adjustments necessary.

4. Use the questions to collect the information required.

5. Analyse the results of the survey/interview, presenting the information in spreadsheets, pie charts, graphs, etc. Remember to refer to the results of each question asked.

6. Collect secondary information to find out about the views of the public and professionals on the use of complementary therapies.

7. Compare the service users' opinions with those of the professionals to show the similarities between their opinions. Draw conclusions.

Acupuncture for service users

The term acupuncture derives from the Latin words **acus** (needle) and **puncture** (to prick). This describes a technique in which needles are used to puncture the skin at certain points in order to restore the balance of 'Qi' energy, which acupuncturists believe is essential to good health.

In China, acupuncture developed as a key part of Traditional Chinese Medicine (TCM) together with the use of herbs, diet, exercise, massage and meditation. Its true origins are unknown but similar techniques were developed independently in several communities.

Acupuncture has been practised in China and other Eastern countries for thousands of years. Some tribal communities practised a therapy known as 'scarifying' the skin. This process gave similar relief to that obtained from scratching an itch. The use of acupuncture in China can be traced back 5,000 years and sixth-century BC Chinese medical text books show reference to the use of acupuncture.

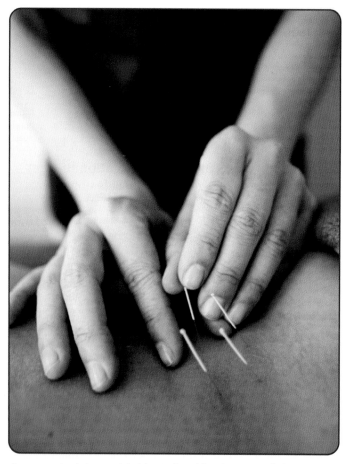

Acupuncturists are highly trained in the use of the needles for treatments

The theory of acupuncture was first documented in an ancient Chinese text: the Tyellow Emperor's Classic of Internal Medicine (the Nei Ching). This is thought to have been compiled about 2,500 years ago. It was the missionaries who returned from China in the seventeenth century who introduced it to the Western world. History also writes about physicians who attended the battlefields, observed that some soldiers with arrow wounds appeared to be cured of chronic conditions and injuries. More interest was taken about the precise positions of the wounds, and in these early days experiments with pieces of fish bone and flint were tried and tested.

It is important, when trying to understand Chinese medicine, that we have a basic concept of Qi (pronounced Chee). This term is often interpreted as 'energy', 'vital energy', or 'life force'.

Acupuncture is used to re-establish harmony in energy. The Chinese see disharmony as the cause of the symptoms that may be indicative of illness. These are just some conditions that acupuncture can help to cure or modify:

- Pain
- Tonsillitis
- Bronchitis
- Sinusitis
- Asthma
- Menstrual problems
- Digestive disorders
- Weak bladder
- Fibro-myalgia
- Addictions
- Eating disorders
- Headaches
- High blood pressure
- Night sweats
- Musculo-skeletal problems.

Basically any condition may be treated with acupuncture, but there are a few conditions or exceptions regarding the patient that should be mentioned, which usually mean that acupuncture is not an appropriate complementary therapy.

- If the patient is a **haemophiliac**
- If the patient is pregnant (because certain acupuncture points and manipulations are contra-indicated during pregnancy)
- If the patient has a **psychotic illness**
- If the patient has recently taken drugs or alcohol.

Key factors when choosing a practitioner are:

- **Accreditation**, training and registration vary in different countries but certain criteria should be observed.
- Registered orthodox medical practitioners who offer acupuncture may not necessarily be trained in the art of Chinese Medicine. They may be trained to use acupuncture to treat minor problems but may not be trained to diagnose and treat in terms of the theories and principles of Chinese Medicine.
- Registered acupuncture practitioners have undertaken an agreed and recognised training programme. They have also achieved the standards in **anatomy and physiology**.
- Practitioners are required to adhere to a professional code of conduct and ethical standards.
- Check the registration of the practitioner with the appropriate professional body.

> **Discussion point**
>
> Why is it important to be cautious about choosing a therapist?

Needles used in acupuncture. Needles that are used by acupuncture practitioners are kept in totally sterile packs. **Sterilisation** standards are very strict and all practitioners must follow the rigorous guidelines. Disposable needles are the most common practice. These are manufactured and packed under sterile conditions. Any used needles should be stored safely in a 'sharps box' and incinerated to dispose of them.

The needles vary in size and thickness depending on the area of the body that is to be needled and the type of therapeutic effect that is desired.

The meridian system. In Chinese Medicine the meridian system consists of twelve main channels. Each channel has many specific **acupuncture points** which relate to specific organs. This system is not to be confused with the circulatory system of blood vessels, of arteries and veins. It is easier to consider the meridian system as an energetic distribution network allowing the flow of Qi (energy) in a similar way that a river follows its course varying from shallow to deep, quickly and slowly while always following a most 'natural' path.

Mary aged 59

Following an attack of **shingles** Mary was diagnosed with suffering from **neuralgia** in the back and chest. The symptoms included pain and itching and some remaining sores on her back and chest. Mary also complained of experiencing hot sweats, insomnia and feeling very low in energy. She also had bouts of depression and feelings of anxiety.

The Chinese diagnosis was 'blood stagnation' and heat, Kidney Yin energy is responsible for the appropriate cooling of the body. The body's ability to relax and rest was also deficient, hence the insomnia, anxiety and hot sweats.

The acupuncture treatment consisted of local needles being placed around the sores to 'move the stagnation' (interestingly the colour changed from dark purple to red while the needles were inserted, and continued to visibly lighten over the course of treatment). Needles were also used **systemically** to clear the heat caused by the **herpes zoster**. The Kidney Yin was tonified to allay the remaining symptoms.

After the first treatment the pain was gone and changed to itchiness and sometimes **numbness**. After six treatments the sores had practically gone leaving a slight numbness. The heat was 60% better, sleep and energy 75% better. Mary felt much better in herself and resumed her daily walk and started to see friends again.

Omar aged 38

Omar had been diagnosed with early osteoarthritis by his medical practitioner. His main symptoms were pain in his hands and feet, with a history going back five years but with the pain becoming more severe in the last year. Omar's description of the pain was like 'constant toothache'. He had been prescribed **anti-inflammatory** drugs but with little effect. Omar's job requires him to use a drill most of the day which **exacerbates** the pain in the hands. He was also experiencing a sense of weakness in his hands which greatly concerned him given his occupation. His emotional health appeared good considering the constant pain. However, Omar was experiencing uncharacteristic irritability, and at times felt low and lacking in energy and motivation, again not like his 'normal' self. On **palpation** the afflicted joints felt very cold and were white in colour, his lower back felt cold and he said he suffered with the cold quite badly.

Chinese diagnosis is **stagnation** of 'Qi' and 'blood' with invasion of cold in the channels particularly accumulating in the joints. In Chinese Medicine the Kidney Yang energy provides the fundamental power and warmth for the body, so an important part of the diagnosis was to 'warm and tonify' the Kidney Yang energy. If the channels of energy (meridians) could be likened to a central heating system, the cause of Omar's pain was due to blockage and cold trapped in the pipes and in addition the boiler itself was faulty and needed more capacity and a higher temperature if the same symptoms were not to recur.

The use of **moxibustion**, a warming herb ('mugwort') was essential in Omar's case, both on the affected joints, and on the system points, i.e. the kidney points in order to warm the underlying system. Acupuncture points were used on the local points to 'unblock' the energy on the painful joints and relieve the pain, and also on the kidney channel and other channels to strengthen the underlying energy.

After six weekly treatments Omar reported a 75% decrease in his painful symptoms. His irritability had disappeared, his energy increased, and there was a marked increase in his body temperature. After two further treatments Omar reported no pain at all over a three-week period. The treatments have been spaced at monthly intervals with the aim to space the treatments further apart. A patent herbal formula 'Meridian Circulation' has been prescribed which contains warming herbs to aid arthritis.

Along with the acupuncture, moxibustion and herbal treatment Omar was given advice on lifestyle and diet to aid treatment: take care to wrap up warm and keep dry, particularly hands and feet. Warming foods such as soups, stews, onions, garlic ginger, warming spices were recommended. Drinking warm water instead of cold, particularly in winter. Discussion of foods to avoid, particularly cold raw foods, citrus fruits and bananas which are energetically cold.

Case studies by kind permission of Jo Halliwell, Acupuncturist, Poole, Dorset

How complementary therapies can help with stress management

Depression and anxiety are the most common stress-related disorders that are presented to GPs. 20% of the working population are stress affected, resulting in high levels of absenteeism and poor productivity. The Health and Safety Executive (HSE) estimates that 13.4 million working days were lost in the UK in 2001–2002 due to stress.

The benefits of complementary therapies in stress management are:

- for the individual – improvements in self esteem, confidence and **coping strategies** aimed towards improving the quality of life
- for the organisation – decreased absenteeism and sickness rates, increased productivity, staff morale and **motivation**.

Time pressures, bullying, unrealistic deadlines, exhaustion can all lead to feelings of losing control if they persist over a long period of time

The Health and Safety Executive (HSE) document, 'Tackling Work-Related Stress', describes their recommendations for dealing with the problems of stress. They are developing a strategy for work-related stress which adopts the principles of 'Securing Health Together'.

This long-term strategy aims to achieve by the year 2010:

- 20% reduction in work-related stress
- 20% reduction in ill health to members of the public caused by work activity
- 30% reduction in number of working days lost due to work-related stress
- everyone currently not in employment due to ill health to be offered work where appropriate.

These strategies obviously have implications for people in the community and not in employment.

The HSE definition of stress:

> *The adverse reaction people have to excessive pressures or other types of demands placed on them.*
>
> (Health and Safety Executive, 2000)

The National Institute for Occupational Safety and Health (NIOSH) states that:

> *Work-related stress is caused when there is a mismatch between the job requirements and the individual's abilities, resources or needs.*

What is stress?

A certain amount of pressure is necessary to function well. It helps people reach their peak efficiency.

- When a person is under pressure the stress responses can act as a *spur*.
- The pressure to meet *deadlines* can increase our *energy* and *drive*.
- The stress faced in *competition* may enhance our *performance*.
- *Responsibility* for the safety and care of others improves our powers of *concentration*.

However, if these pressures become too intense, or are too prolonged, or we are 'working against the grain', then work suffers, as well as the individual – causing distress.

There is much that can be done to relieve stress. Good management, good support systems and the creation of a caring culture can prevent many of the undesirable effects.

If a person is in a threatening situation or fears and perceives that they are unable to cope well, a reflex action is triggered to prepare them for the emergency. This is called the 'fight or flight' or 'alarm reaction'.

The fight or flight response is the body's primary reaction to stress; the secondary responses vary with a person's emotional state.

Stress is a word that is often used loosely. Some people see it as fashionable to behave in a stressed way, shouting, becoming angry, blaming others, etc. Other people may prefer to either deny that stress exists and not to acknowledge its ill-effects, or to withdraw as a way of coping.

The stress response		
Causes of stress		**Coping with good coping strategies** Improved performance, more focused, increased energy and drive. Good balance in life
Work	Fight or flight ⇨	
Relationships		
Disagreements		**Stress-related problems** Changes in behaviour Lack of exercise, poor diet, **hypertension**, sleep problems, depression, anxiety attacks
Financial worries	Not coping ⇨	
New situations	⇩	
Bullying		**Breakdown**
Bereavement	**Burnout** and exhaustion ⇨	

Discussion point

What is the difference between pressure and stress?

This diagram helps to explain the two responses to stress more clearly. The 'alarm' response is the primary or first response to a challenge. The secondary response kicks in to help us meet those challenges over a longer period of time, e.g. while sitting an exam or running a race. The secondary response is also known loosely as the 'spice of life' response. If we never had any challenges, new experiences or responsibilities then life could be very dull and boring. The secondary stress response is the best antidepressant we can get. The production of noradrenalin gives us that feel good factor. Some people may even become addicted to risk taking activities to enhance this response. The essential message is to maintain a balance.

The stress responses

Alarm reaction
- **Adrenaline** increase
- Raised blood pressure
- Heart rate increases
- Increased alertness
- Reduced blood flow to inessential organs
- Tightening of **sphincters**
- Sweating

Secondary stress response

Resistance reaction
- Stimulates **adrenal cortex**
- Produces **cortisone** causing salt and fluid retention
- Raises blood pressure
- Reduces glycogen stores
- **Noradrenalin** production
- Dilates **peripheral blood vessels**
- Relaxes sphincters
- Retains **homeostasis**

> **Did you know?**
>
> 'Stress-related problems in the early stages are often curable, providing we do something about them.'

The following are some common SYMPTOMS of stress. Everyone may experience some of them occasionally, without the quality of their life being affected too much. Identifying physical symptoms and their frequency will help to decide on a plan of action that may be useful to reduce the ill-effects of stress in someone's life.

The following chart may help to indicate which PHYSICAL symptoms are experienced and how frequently.

Physical	Daily	Weekly	Specific situations
Grinding jaws			
Tension headaches			
Neck and shoulder pain			
Shallow breathing			
Diarrhoea			
Constipation			
Muscle tension			
'Butterflies'			
Back pain			
Ulcers			
Chest pains			
High blood pressure			
Itches and rashes			
Dizziness			
Blurred vision			

These are some common SYMPTOMS of stress. Everyone may experience some of them occasionally without the quality of their life being affected too much. Identifying emotional symptoms and their frequency will help to decide on a plan of action that may be useful to reduce the ill-effects of stress in someone's life.

The following chart may help to indicate which PSYCHOLOGICAL or EMOTIONAL symptoms are experienced and how frequently.

Psychological / Emotional	Daily	Weekly	Specific situations
Low confidence			
Self blame			
Depression			
Tension			
Worry			
Anxiety			
Memory lapses			
Feeling guilty			
Anger			
Poor concentration			
Moodiness			
Impatience			
Tearful			
Others			

Examples of complementary therapies that help to relieve stress are:

- acupuncture
- aromatherapy
- yoga
- art/drama therapy.

Assessment activity (AO4)

The Guide 4 — CASE STUDY

Within the Guide the readers will wish to have information that evaluates how well the service user's needs have been met. Within the evaluation:

1 Compare how well both complementary therapies and orthodox medicine have met the physical and emotional needs of the service user. You must evaluate in terms of:

- the impact of the service user's own approach to life
- how lifestyle contributes
- how belief contributes.

2 Compare the service user's experience to those of other people.

3 Draw valid and relevant conclusions making comparisons to theory or to the views of others about to what extent complementary therapies could work with or replace some orthodox treatments.

Remember to:

Make judgements within the evaluation, not straight statements.

Unit 9 Caring for Older People

Contents

About this unit

Within this unit you will investigate:

- the physical effects of aging on body systems
- the social, emotional and economic aspects of aging
- community care and support services for older people
- professional care workers
- legislation.

Making a positive contribution to society

Introducing this unit

Older people or older adults have a variety of needs. But, who are 'older adults'? Currently older adults are individuals who are receiving a state pension. For women this happens at the age of 60 years and for men the age for receiving a state pension is 65 years of age.

The government are discussing the possibility of changing these two different stages of providing state pensions but currently no decision has been made. Older people are living longer. This is the result of new technology, improved standards of living and greater awareness of what contributes to a healthy lifestyle.

Not all older people are infirm! Many are able to contribute in a very worthwhile way to the communities in which they live. For example, they could be members of committees, or help in charity organisations or participate in sports activities. Some will develop health problems, but it is the process of helping older people manage and cope with the problems that is really important.

For older adults who do develop health problems there is a wide range of services available to provide assistance. Each is designed to encourage as much independence as possible so that individuals feel in control of their lives. Those who work with older adults will tell you, if asked, how rewarding the work can be and how they learn a great deal from the experiences shared by those for whom they care.

9.2.1 Physical effects of aging on body systems

During the 20th century life expectancy changed from around 45 years to over 80 years for most people. The longest-living group is Japanese women, who are expected to live to over 83 years.

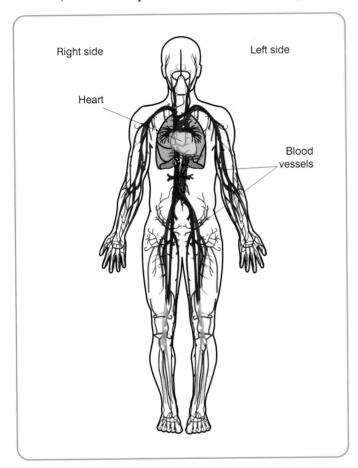

The circulatory system

Disorders of the circulatory system

Not all older people will experience disorders of the circulatory system but for those that do, conditions and diseases can be quite frightening and can affect their quality of life.

The circulatory system comprises:

- the heart – this lies from the middle to the left-hand side of the chest and pumps blood around the circulatory system. It is a little larger than a man's fist and is approximately 12 cm long, 9 cm wide and 6 cm thick.
- a closed system of tubes – arteries and veins that carry blood to and from body tissue.
- blood – which carries nutrients and waste.

Disorders of the circulatory system generally result in reduced flow of blood and reduced oxygen exchange to the tissues. Blood supply is also obstructed in such conditions as sclerosis of the arteries. The reduction of blood flow to the heart muscle can also result in dysfunction and damage to the heart. This is known as a heart attack or **myocardial infarction** which is caused by heart disease.

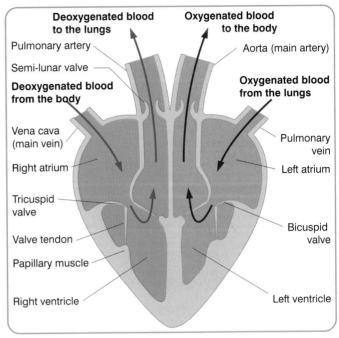

The structure of the heart

Heart attack

A heart attack is usually caused by a blockage in one of the coronary arteries that supply blood to the heart muscle. The blockage occurs when a blood clot lodges in an area already narrowed by **arteriosclerosis**. It can also be caused by the artery contracting and going into spasm. Viral infections of the heart, such as those experienced in influenza, can also give rise to a heart attack. Symptoms include a crushing pain in the centre of the chest. This radiates to either arm, more often the left arm. There can be pain in the jaw and the neck and the service user may also vomit or have a sudden bowel movement alongside the other symptoms. In some cases there are no symptoms at all and this is known as a silent heart attack. Death of heart muscle tissue and heart failure may result in congestive heart failure which weakens the heart's function. There can also be damage to other vital organs including the brain. This may occur if the heart is unable to pump necessary oxygen and blood to them.

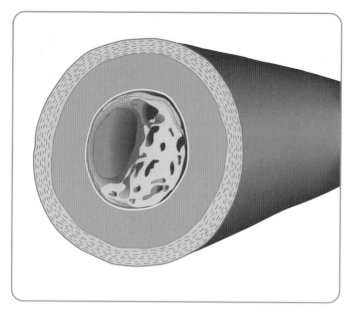

Clotted and deadly

Discussion point

Why do you think clotting is the biggest cause of heart disease?

Heart disease and heart dysfunction

Other common causes of heart disease in older adults are **degenerative** changes in the coronary blood vessels, and infectious diseases. Infectious diseases such as rheumatic fever, syphilis, and endocarditis, can also damage the valves of the heart. In addition, the heart muscle itself can be affected, for example **hypertensive** heart disease can cause it to enlarge, and it can become inflamed by rheumatic fever. **Arteriosclerotic** deposits in the coronary arteries result in the narrowing of these vessels, causing a reduction in blood flow and oxygen to the heart muscle. This condition is known as coronary artery disease. Radiating chest pain (angina pectoris) is the most **prominent** symptom of this condition. Hypertension and other forms of cardiovascular disease, either singly or in combination, can lead to a state in which the heart is unable to expel sufficient blood for the demands of the body. This is known as congestive heart failure.

Sclerosis

This is when thickening, hardening and loss of elasticity of the walls of the blood vessels occur. These changes are frequently accompanied by accumulations of cholesterol inside the vessel walls.

Lesions are formed on the arterial walls causing blistering and the accumulation of cholesterol which produces higher blood pressure in the system. This allows cholesterol and calcium to become embedded in the vessel walls forming hard plaques. As the vessel walls thicken, the passageways through the vessels narrow, decreasing the blood supply to the affected region. If the leg vessels are affected, there may be pain with walking and an onset of gangrene. When there is total clotting of a vessel (**thrombosis**) the result may be a heart attack (if it occurs in the coronary arteries) or **stroke** (if in cerebral arteries).

How can heart conditions and disease affect the quality of an older person's life?

Any form of heart disease can affect the quality of life experienced by an older person. For example they could:

- become dizzy or light headed
- have blurred vision
- suffer from lack of concentration
- have nausea or upset stomachs
- have headaches
- suffer from fatigue
- have rapid shallow breathing
- have chest pain.

Carol   Activity 1

Carol has been admitted to her local hospital with a suspected heart attack. Her doctor has given treatment and Carol has been instructed to rest as much as possible. She dislikes the idea of 'bed resting' as she is a very active person. This is affecting her socially. Carol wants to be more in command of the situation.

1 What could be the possible causes of the heart attack?

2 Why would the doctor tell Carol to rest?

3 How is the heart attack likely to affect Carol's quality of life?

Sensory impairment

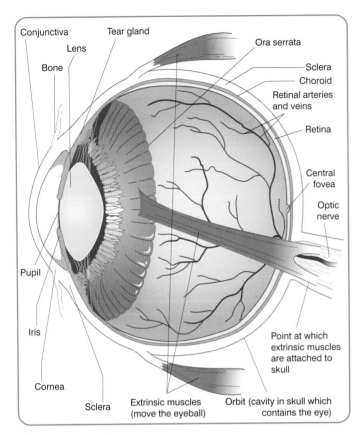

The structure of the eye

Sensory impairment involves the eyes and hearing. Both of these conditions can have an adverse effect on the health of older people. It is, however, much easier with today's medical knowledge to do something about most conditions that present themselves. One of the main points to remember is that conditions related to the eye and ear need to be diagnosed as early as possible.

Cataracts

Cataracts occur when the lens of the eye becomes opaque and impairs vision. This can cause blindness. In later life cataracts may be the result of degenerative changes brought on by aging or a systemic disease, an example of which is diabetes. Many individuals over the age of 60 exhibit some degree of lens **opacity**. Advanced cataracts are usually treated by surgical removal of the lens and implantation of an artificial lens. After cataract surgery, which is one of the most common surgical procedures in the UK, most service users do not require thick glasses or contact lenses. This is because an artificial fixed focus lens is implanted.

The results of successful cataract operations can enhance the life of many older adults as they no longer have to rely on others for help as they can see clearly and are able to carry out everyday tasks.

You can't be optimistic with a misty optic

Visual and hearing degeneration

As people age, their senses gradually become impaired. Sometimes this is only minor but at other times it can be a serious problem. The sensory systems include:

- sight
- hearing
- smell
- touch.

In this unit sight and hearing are the two main forms of impairment that are being considered.

Myopia (short-sightedness)

This is a defect of vision in which far objects appear blurred, but near objects are seen clearly. It happens because the eyeball is too long or the **refractive** power of the eye's lens is too strong. The image is focused in front of the retina rather than upon it. Corrective eyeglasses with **concave** lenses compensate for the refractive error and help to focus the image on the retina. Hard corneal contact lenses or soft hydrophilic contact lenses are another option. These usually offer better **acuity** and **peripheral** vision when compared to spectacles.

Contact lenses can be troublesome for older service users who tend to get eye infections or have hand tremors. Near-sightedness can also be corrected by using laser cornea surgery and a device called a **microkeratome** to flatten the eye. In some cases this is achieved by surgically implanting a corrective lens behind the iris.

Older people may have difficulty putting in contact lenses

Presbyopia or hyperopia (long-sightedness)

Long-sightedness is a condition in which far objects can be seen easily but there is difficulty in near vision. It is caused by a defect of refraction in which the image is focused behind the retina of the eye rather than upon it, either because the eyeball is too short or because the refractive power of the lens is too weak. Corrective spectacles with convex lenses compensate for the refractive errors. Some people who are already short-sighted will opt for bi-focal lenses. This is two lens prescriptions in one which stops them from having to keep changing their spectacles.

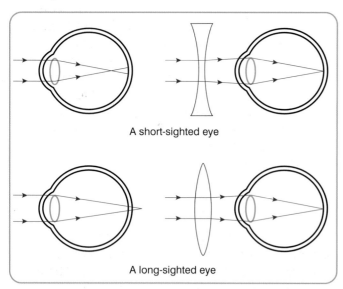

A short-sighted eye

A long-sighted eye

Visual defects are now easily corrected

Glaucoma

There are no symptoms in the early stages of glaucoma; the condition can be detected only by measurement of the **intraocular pressure**. As the disease progresses, often the only symptom is a gradual loss of peripheral vision. Chronic glaucoma can usually be controlled with eye drops or pills. Laser treatment is also effective in the early stages of the disease.

Discussion point

Why does glaucoma affect the quality of life of older adults?

Sarah   Activity 2

Sarah has been diagnosed with cataracts. She will need surgery to resolve this problem and the prognosis for a full recovery is good.

1   Draw a diagram of the eye and label it correctly.

2   Describe how cataracts affect vision.

3   Why is it important that Sarah's problem is corrected?

4   What will happen to Sarah's emotional and social well being if her condition is not corrected?

Hearing loss

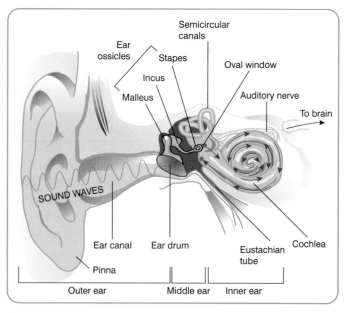

The structure of the ear

As people age they will often suffer from hearing loss. This will often be a gradual process where they begin to lose the ability to hear sound at certain frequencies. The loss may begin with the inability to hear sounds at the extreme ends of the range. These will be high or low and are exhibited by the person's inability to clearly hear voices of people who speak at these pitches.

Hearing loss can also be temporary and the most common cause is a build-up of wax. This is easily solved by dissolving or softening the wax and then syringing the ear. This should always be done by a professional as it is very easy to damage the ear drum.

Hearing problems are usually found in the following forms:

- Tinnitus, constant ringing in the ears which can become very depressing.
- Loss of hearing frequency at either the higher or lower range of sounds.
- Deafness due to excessive wax build-up in the ears, easily resolved by syringing.

How will older people be affected if they have sensory impairment?

Condtion	How quality of life is affected
Eye conditions and disorders	• unable to deal with daily living tasks • unable to read • unable to go out by themselves • social isolation.
Hearing impairment	• unable to communicate well • may become less acceptable to others because they shout or cannot hear • social exclusion.

Muscular-skeletal disorders

Many older people have disorders that affect the muscular and the skeletal systems. This can involve painful joints which can inhibit mobility or can be diseases and conditions of the bones that make moving very difficult or bones break easily.

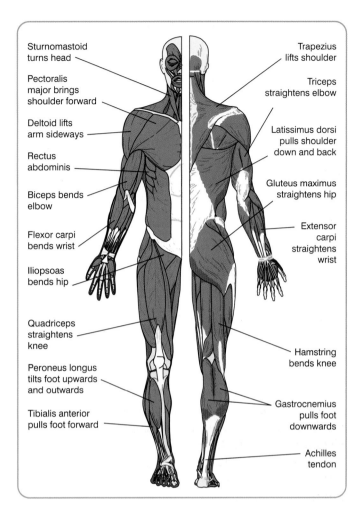

The muscular-skeletal system

Osteoporosis

Osteoporosis is often the result of the aging process as the ability to regenerate bone becomes less effective with age. The bones of older adults are likely to become 'thinner' and are, therefore, more likely to break. Women are more at risk of osteoporosis than men, because bone strength is affected by sexual hormones and men continue to produce testosterone throughout their life. The condition could be caused through 'hereditary' links, for example from family traits or through a lack of exercise, since exercise helps to strengthen bones.

Rheumatoid arthritis

Rheumatoid arthritis is a disease that presents painful inflammation of a joint or joints of the body, usually producing heat and redness. There are many kinds of arthritis. In its various forms, arthritis disables more people than any other chronic disorder. The condition can be brought about by:

- nerve impairment
- increased or decreased function of the endocrine glands
- degeneration due to age
- less frequently, it is caused by infection.

Rheumatoid arthritis, an **autoimmune disease** of unknown cause is the most crippling form of arthritis. Women are much more susceptible to it than men.

Rheumatism

This is the general term for a number of disorders that cause inflammation and pain in the muscles, bones, joints and nerves. In common usage the word rheumatism is often used to describe the effects of:

- arthritis
- bursitis
- neuritis
- gout.

These are all inflammatory diseases that affect mobility and the service user's emotional and social well being. For example, they can cause:

- an older person to become less mobile which can affect them socially as they can become socially isolated. Older adults who experience such conditions are encouraged to attend day care centres where they can meet with and talk to others of similar age.
- severe pain which may cause the person not to want to do anything in particular.
- lack of concentration.
- them to be unable to walk upstairs or for any long distance which could mean they have to depend on others.

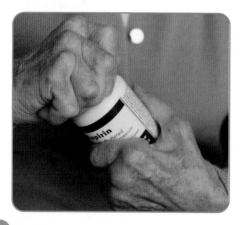

Keeping a grip on life is not always easy

Jane — CASE STUDY

Jane is suffering from rheumatoid arthritis. This is limiting her ability to get about. Her family supports her mobility but she has very few friends.

1. What are Jane's symptoms?
2. Why is it important that she tries to remain mobile?
3. What could be the causes of her arthritis?
4. Why would it not be good for Jane to become socially isolated?

Disorders of the nervous system

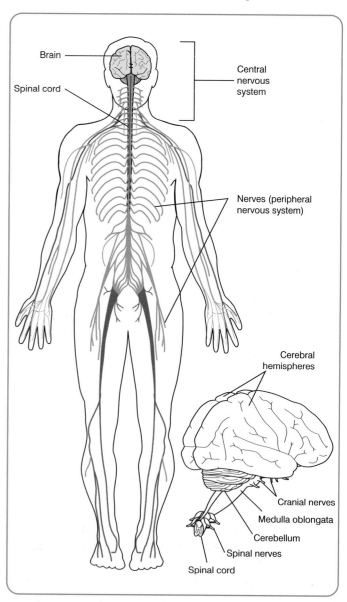

The nervous system

Damage caused by stroke

A stroke is caused by a block or interruption in the flow of blood to the brain. Quite often, if the flow of blood to the right-hand side of the brain is affected, the left-hand side of the body will be impaired and often there is sensory weakness.

The severity of the stroke will depend upon the areas of the brain that have been affected, as each part of the brain has a specific function. Many people recover from a minor stroke and gain full independence but others will be totally dependent on professional and informal carers.

Senile dementia/Alzheimer's disease

Senile dementia is generally caused by deterioration of brain tissue, though it can occasionally be traced to deterioration of the circulatory system. Major characteristics include short- and long-term memory loss and impaired judgment. Service users often exhibit a slovenly appearance and poor hygiene. Dementia disrupts personal relationships and the ability to function in a chosen occupation.

Alzheimer's disease can begin at a younger age, and deterioration of the brain tissue tends to happen much more quickly. Individuals who have experienced cerebro-vascular disease (particularly strokes) may develop similar brain tissue deterioration, with symptoms similar to Alzheimer's disease. Other types of dementia include Huntington's disease, Parkinson's disease, and Pick's disease. Some forms of familial Alzheimer's disease are caused by specific dominant gene mutations.

> **Discussion point**
>
> How can senile dementia affect the quality of life of an older person?

Multiple sclerosis (MS)

This is a chronic and slowly progressive autoimmune disease in which the body's immune system attacks the protective myelin sheaths that surround the nerve cells of the brain and spinal cord (a process called demyelination). This results in nerve damage and damaged areas that are unable to transmit nerve impulses. MS may cause visual difficulties, emotional disturbances, speech

disorders, convulsions, paralysis and numbness of various regions of the body. Bladder incontinence and muscular weakness are also common. The course of the disease varies greatly from person to person. In some service users, the symptoms **remit** and return. This can be at frequent intervals or sometimes after several years. In others, the disease progresses steadily.

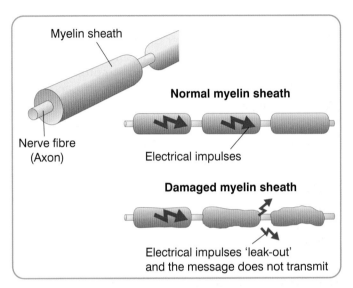

The damage to the covering is irreversible

> **MS** **Activity 3**
>
> MS is now a well recognised problem in our population. It is not an easy disease to diagnose and can be even more difficult to treat.
>
> **1** What systems of the body does MS affect and how can this be observed in the service user?
>
> **2** Describe what happens in the process of demyelination.
>
> **3** How can a service user's quality of life be affected by MS?

Disorders of the respiratory system

Lung cancer	• This is the uncontrolled growth of abnormal cells in the lung. Normal lung tissue is made up of cells that are programmed to recreate lung tissue. • Tumours form as a result of incorrect growth of cells. These clog up the lung and stop it functioning in the normal way. Because of the large size of the lungs, cancer may grow undetected for many years. • Lung cancer can spread outside the lungs without causing any symptoms. The most common symptom of lung cancer, a persistent cough, can often be mistaken for a cold or bronchitis.
Emphysema	• This disease enlarges the air sacs of the lungs. A major cause of emphysema is cigarette smoking. • Emphysema is a progressive disease that commonly occurs in conjunction with chronic bronchitis. • Symptoms are difficulty in breathing, cough with thick sticky sputum, and a bluish tinge of the skin. • If the disease progresses it can result in disability, heart or respiratory failure and, in severe cases, death.
COPD	Chronic obstructive pulmonary disease (COPD) is not a single disease but a collection of conditions that give rise to severe breathing difficulty. It covers many previously used clinical descriptions including chronic bronchitis, emphysema, chronic obstructive airways disease, chronic airflow obstruction and some cases of chronic asthma. All of these can result in irreversible lung damage and the following problems: • chronic bronchitis – with increased secretions and airway wall inflammation • airway disease – with increased mucus, airway wall thickening, scarring and narrowing • emphysema – with permanent destruction of the alveoli airspaces • on lung expansion – the pressure to drive expiration is lost • a drop in pressure – needed to maintain the airway during exhalation. COPD is a slow, progressive condition where service users suffer severe airway obstruction, which does not improve with time.

Roger   Activity 4

Roger is in hospital with COPD. He will need medication to resolve his problem but the prognosis for his recovery is good.

1. What do you think could have caused Roger's COPD?

2. Why is it important that Roger's problem is treated immediately?

3. What could happen if Roger's condition is not treated?

4. How could Roger's quality of life be affected by his medical problem?

How can respiratory diseases affect the quality of life for service users?

These diseases have many similar effects on the service user, the commonest are as follows:

- coughing up of blood can be very distressing and weakening
- general body weakness and the inability to remain mobile
- anaemia which makes the service user weak and short of breath
- generalised pain which stops the service user functioning normally.

Disorders of the digestive system

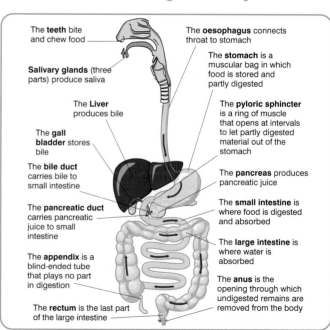

The **teeth** bite and chew food

Salivary glands (three parts) produce saliva

The **Liver** produces bile

The **gall bladder** stores bile

The **bile duct** carries bile to small intestine

The **pancreatic duct** carries pancreatic juice to small intestine

The **appendix** is a blind-ended tube that plays no part in digestion

The **rectum** is the last part of the large intestine

The **oesophagus** connects throat to stomach

The **stomach** is a muscular bag in which food is stored and partly digested

The **pyloric sphincter** is a ring of muscle that opens at intervals to let partly digested material out of the stomach

The **pancreas** produces pancreatic juice

The **small intestine** is where food is digested and absorbed

The **large intestine** is where water is absorbed

The **anus** is the opening through which undigested remains are removed from the body

The digestive system

The main parts of the digestive system comprise:

- the alimentary canal – oral cavity, pharynx, oesophagus and stomach
- the small intestine – duodenum, jejunum and ileum
- the large intestine – caecum, ascending colon, transverse colon, descending colon, sigmoid colon, rectum and anal canal.

The accessory organs are:

Teeth
Situated in the mouth and used to masticate food.

Tongue
Situated in the mouth and helps with swallowing.

Salivary glands
Secrete mixed water and mucous enzyme containing fluid into the mouth.

Sublingual
A pair of salivary glands, laying each side of the jaw.

Submandibular
A pair of salivary glands laying each side of the jaw.

Parotid
The largest of three pairs of salivary glands, laying each side of the jaw.

Liver
Wedge shaped, the upper right quadrant of the abdominal cavity that processes foods.

Gall bladder
Descends behind the first part of the duodenum, serves as a store chamber.

Bile ducts
Pressed near to the right lobe of the liver.

Pancreas
Is a gland in the retroperitoneum and consists of exocrine glands that secrete enzymes into the pancreatic duct tributaries and on into the duodenum. Responsible for a major part of chemical digestion.

Irritable bowel syndrome (IBS)

Irritable bowel syndrome, or IBS, is a problem that affects mainly the large intestine. The large intestine is the part of the digestive system that makes and stores stools. The word syndrome means a group of symptoms. IBS is a syndrome because it can cause several symptoms. For example, IBS causes:

- cramping
- bloating
- gas
- diarrhoea
- constipation.

IBS is not a disease. It's a functional disorder, which means that the bowel doesn't work as it should. With IBS, the nerves and muscles in the bowel are extra-sensitive. For example, the muscles may contract too much when a person eats. These contractions can cause cramping and diarrhoea during or shortly after a meal. Or the nerves can be overly sensitive to the stretching of the bowel (because of gas, for example). Cramping or pain can result. IBS can be painful. But it does not damage the bowel or cause any other diseases.

Emotional stress will not cause a person to develop IBS, but if a person already has IBS, stress can trigger symptoms. In fact, the bowel can overreact to things, including food, exercise and hormones.

Foods that tend to cause symptoms include milk products, chocolate, alcohol, caffeine, carbonated drinks and fatty foods. In some cases, simply eating a large meal will trigger symptoms.

Women with IBS often have more symptoms during their menstrual periods.

Discussion point

How is irritable bowel syndrome likely to affect a person's quality of life?

Ulcerative colitis

Ulcerative colitis is a chronic inflammation of the large intestine (colon). The colon is the last part of the digestive system. The rectum is the end of the colon, adjacent to the anus. In patients with ulcerative colitis, ulcers and inflammation of the inner lining of the colon can lead to symptoms of abdominal pain, diarrhoea and rectal bleeding.

Ulcerative colitis is closely related to another condition of inflammation of the intestines called Crohn's disease. Together, they are frequently referred to as inflammatory bowel disease (IBD). Men and women are affected equally by ulcerative colitis.

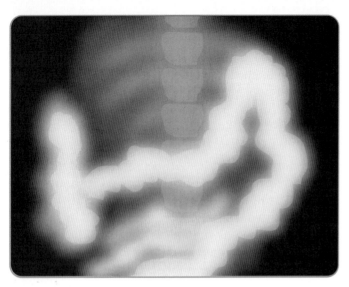

The digestive tract can easily be affected by colitis

Crohn's

Crohn's disease causes inflammation in the small intestine. Crohn's disease usually occurs in the lower part of the small intestine, called the ileum, but it can affect any part of the digestive tract, from the mouth to the anus. The inflammation severely affects the lining of the bowel. The inflammation produced can cause pain and often make the intestines empty frequently, resulting in diarrhoea.

Crohn's disease is an inflammatory bowel disease (IBD), the general name for diseases that cause inflammation in the intestines. Crohn's disease can be difficult to diagnose because its symptoms are similar to other intestinal disorders.

Molly	Activity 5

Molly spends a lot of time in her own home because she has Crohn's disease. Her doctor has given her medication to stop the bouts of diarrhoea. She has also been instructed to drink as much as possible. She is having some difficulty in getting to grips with the problem socially. Molly wants to be more in command of the situation.

1   What do you think Molly's biggest fears are?

2   Why would the doctor tell Molly to drink plenty of fluids?

3   What precautions do you think Molly should take before she goes out so that she can remain in control of her problem?

Chronic constipation

Chronic constipation is where service users have infrequent or difficult passage of faeces. Constipation may be caused by a lack of roughage or fluid in the diet. Also lack of exercise, certain drugs, or emotional disturbance can cause constipation. Sudden unexplained changes in bowel habit can be a symptom of a serious disorder and should receive medical attention. Most cases of constipation can be relieved by following a diet that includes adequate roughage and fluid and by establishing regular toilet habits to allow the evacuation of faeces.

How can digestive disorders affect the lives of older service users?

- severe pain
- embarrassment if there is no warning when needing to pass faeces
- loss of weight
- social isolation
- indigestion
- fever
- headaches.

The interrelationship of body systems

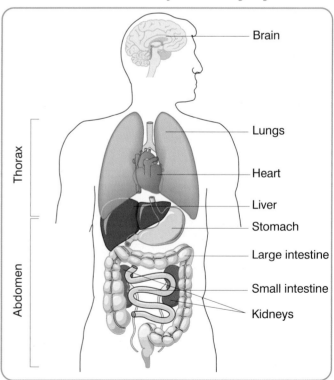

The interrelationship of human body systems

Caring for Older People
9.2.1 Physical effects of aging on body systems / Assessment activity 9.2.1 /
9.2.2 Social, emotional and economic aspects of aging

Human body systems must interact with one another in order to ensure effective metabolism. The heart and circulatory system work together with the respiratory system to circulate oxygenated blood around the body and to remove unwanted carbon dioxide, as the body will cease to function without a good supply of oxygen.

Each of the other organs have their own individual functions and have a nerve supply (nervous system), which speeds up or slows down reactions. They also have cells which are controlled by hormones. Each body system must relate to other body systems if the functions of the body are to work effectively.

Assessment activity 9.2.1

Physical effects of aging on body systems
CASE STUDY

Fawzia, who is 70 years old, has diarrhoea quite often. She finds that she can eat very little and has to avoid alcohol, spicy and fatty foods.

1. Draw a diagram of the digestive system and label the main parts.

2. Describe the main function of **five main** parts of the digestive system.

3. Identify one possible dysfunction of the digestive system that Fawzia may have. Describe **five** possible causes.

4. Explain the likely effect that this dysfunction could have on Fawzia's quality of life.

5. Explain some of the managing strategies Fawzia could use to help her cope.

Martin, who is 75 years of age, has impaired hearing.

6. What is the likely effect of this impairment on Martin's quality of life?

Marcus has had a heart attack.

7. Evaluate how having a heart attack could affect Marcus' quality of life.

8. Explain how the heart and the lungs interrelate within the human body.

9.2.2 Social, emotional and economic aspects of aging

Caring for the person as a whole, not just treating the individual parts

Poor physical and mental health can adversely affect social and emotional aspects of aging. In the previous section of this unit some of the physical effects have been discussed, but these do not occur in isolation as one is likely to influence the function of another aspect of development. The aim when providing care is:

- to alleviate the symptoms
- to allow an individual to enjoy the highest quality of life.

Caring involves:

- looking after the whole person
- the whole patient (holistic care)
- open and sensitive communication
- respect for the service user's choice
- focusing on enabling the service user to have the highest quality of life.

Increased isolation

Mobility problems, whether the result of muscular-skeletal problems or circulatory dysfunction, can result in increased **isolation** as a service user may be unable to go out for everyday activities, for example shopping or for social events. The impact is likely to be that the service user may not have the opportunity to talk to other people, to share views and opinions or to share ideas. This could mean that they rarely see others and become very inward looking. Their emotional health may, as a result, deteriorate and they may become withdrawn and lonely. Additionally, because they are not meeting other people, they will not be using their skills of communication and may talk to themselves or become very inward looking.

Such behaviour could lead to the service user not valuing themselves and having a poor self esteem. Loss of self esteem could mean that the service user starts to think that nothing is important. Intellectual stimulation is not available, socially they are not meeting others and consequently they become demotivated. Some older service users could just sit in a chair watching television all day, but even then they may not be actually registering what the programmes are about.

If only I hadn't allowed that to happen

This type of behaviour is to be avoided. Michael Argyle, a psychologist, puts forward as part of his theory that an individual's self concept and development of personal identity is to look at the reaction of others and that people judge themselves according to this. Argyle(1972) also indicates that people commonly regard their social role as part of who they are. Older people, therefore, if they are withdrawn and socially isolated, will not have any social role with which to compare themselves and consequently will feel that they have nothing to contribute.

Erikson (1979), when considering the eight stages of development, states that stage eight, for older people, is the most difficult stage of all the stages. This is because some older people become pre-occupied with their failures and the bad decisions they have made in life. If socially isolated, the older person who is influenced by such thoughts could, because they are alone and prone to be inward looking, become depressed, spiteful, paranoid and **hypochondrial**. They could also develop the patterns of senility with or without physical basis. Erikson called this maladaptive tendency '**presumption**', whereas the '**malignant**' tendency is known as '**disdain**', which is having contempt for life. An older person with this type of social exclusion can display behaviour that is hard to manage.

Cummings and Henry (1961), who are also theorists, defined the state of older people cutting themselves off from society as '**disengagement**'. They considered that this was 'an inevitable process in which many relationships between a person and other members of society are severed and those remaining are altered in quality'. This involves the reduction of life activities and ego in old age.

A person whose life is prone to isolation because of mobility problems is likely, therefore, to be encouraged to visit day care centres, luncheon clubs and to join in other recreational activities that are beneficial for older people, to avoid them spending too much time looking inward or backwards to events that have happened in previous life stages. The aim is to provide a purposeful role and interest and to help them become socially integrated.

Increased dependency on others

Some older people are prone to illness which can be short or long term. In such situations the service user can become dependent on others, whether 'others' are relatives or professional care workers. For example, the incidence of stroke cases is rising for people who are 65 years of age and older. Every year at least 120,000 people have a stroke, with 24,000 of these dying within a month. Those who survive often require continuing care.

Remind yourself of some of the illnesses that can be experienced by older adults by looking back at section 9.2.1.

Illnesses which can be fairly common to older adults, other than those previously mentioned in 9.2.1 are:

Illness	Effect on the individual
Stroke	Paralysis, lack of mobility, loss of speech, loss of vision
Incontinence	Lack of bladder and bowel control
Diabetes	Impaired glucose regulation
Dementia/Alzheimer's disease	Inability to remember in the short term

It is important for those who are ill to feel valued and to feel that an emotionally safe environment has been created. The practice of treating each person as an individual is recognised by the General Care Council as being very important. This means respecting the views, wishes and dignity of those who are ill. In order to achieve such aims, a supportive relationship is needed between the service user and the care worker. The care worker must ensure that they do not set themselves up as the target for other people's emotions. To do so could mean that the care worker may become angry, appear as a threat to the service user and may create an invitation to the service user to become aggressive.

Managing service users who are experiencing illness calls for a wide variety of skills. These include:

Effective communication
Speaking at an appropriate pace, using vocabulary that can be understood and actively listening

Allowing choice
Giving the service user options from which they can choose the way that is best for them

Assertive behaviour
Being confident and accepting other peoples' needs as well as your own

Giving support
This could be practical care or psychological, so that the service user can talk about issues that are causing them concern

Being respectful
Calling a service user by their preferred name, listening carefully and responding in a sensitive manner

Minimising risks
Prevent difficult situations arising and avoiding triggers for aggression

Creating trust
Staying calm and meeting the other person's self esteem needs

Promoting self confidence
Giving genuine praise when a service user has achieved a goal

Maintaining confidentiality
Not passing on information given to other service users or relatives and friends

How can I help?

Gerald Egan, a theorist, sets out a model which has three stages. In his model he discusses a systematic way of learning to work with another person to help them to cope effectively with life. The care worker's role is to help the service user to achieve this in order to maximise their quality of life and to increase their confidence. Egan's three stages are:

- **Stage 1: Exploration** – to explore issues through effective communication, listening and genuine acceptance.

- **Stage 2: Finding new perspectives** – looking at options open to the service user and considering the best and worst possibilities from the options.

- **Stage 3: Actions** – goals and strategy setting, problem solving and decision making.

Discussion point

How can Egan's theory help care workers when caring for those who are ill?

When service users are ill they will at times require the care worker to help them think about how best to manage the situation. By applying Egan's theory when caring, the care workers can encourage the service user to feel more confident about the decisions they are making as they will have:

- considered the situation
- received information and different views about how problems could be solved
- made decisions based on facts.

Inability to cope

The incidence of confusion and dementia is growing and is becoming one of the major health issues of the 21st century. The incidence of dementia increases with age. It affects:

- 1% of 65 year olds
- 40% of 85 year olds
- 50% of 90 year olds.

Dementia is not a disease; it is a syndrome or a group of **concurrent** syndromes caused by a number of illnesses. Older adults, rather than younger people, are more likely to develop confusional states. Older people are more likely to become confused when they are ill because as the body ages it has less **reserve capacity**. The physical causes of confusion include:

- infection
- metabolic causes
- electrolyte imbalance
- lack of oxygen
- physical trauma
- sensory problems.

Confusion can also be caused by emotional problems such as anxiety and grief. In 1961 Leiberman stated that confusion could be caused by 'Translocation shock', that is by moving a service user from one ward to another or from one type of home to another.

Dementia is difficult to diagnose. Often it is only through the elimination of treatable causes of dementia, and through brain scans and other investigations, combined with ongoing assessment, that an indication of the type of dementia that a service user is experiencing can be given.

Alzheimer's disease is a form of dementia. The brain of any older person will shrink with age. Memory impairment is a feature of extreme old age. Some doctors would argue that Alzheimer's disease is merely at the end of a continuum ranging from confusion at one end and Alzheimer's at the other. Research indicates that inflammation plays a major part in the development of dementia and Alzheimer's disease. The brain is covered with senile plaques which are accompanied by inflammatory changes. The changes lead to raised levels of protein (amyloid beta protein), which lead to degeneration of brain function.

Whether the service user is experiencing confusion, dementia or Alzheimer's disease, medication will be needed. Symptoms could include:

- hyperactivity
- agitation
- psychotic symptoms
- hallucinations
- depression.

However, medication will not be able to help with some other symptoms that may occur which could include:

- wandering
- repetitive questioning
- hiding or hoarding items.

In order to help relieve some of the impact of confusion, dementia or Alzheimer's disease a carer will need to establish a routine with a person who is confused or has some form of dementia. He/she will also need to keep the service user in surroundings and an environment that is familiar to them. A person who is confused or who has dementia will soon forget what to do if the carer is always 'doing things for them'. They will give up trying and will develop 'learned helplessness'. This is where the service user becomes totally dependent on the carer as a result of the carer's low expectation of them. Good practice is the carer encouraging the service user to do as much as possible for themselves. This can be achieved by encouragement and by empowering the service user.

Empowerment is an important aspect of helping a service user to cope. Even if a service user is confused, or has dementia or has a mental disorder, the person must be treated in a respectful way. If service users are not treated with respect they will lose their dignity. In turn this can lower self esteem and cause the older person to feel that they are not being valued. By empowering a service user, a care worker is providing them with the opportunity to make choices. A service user can only make choices if they are given sufficient information from which to make decisions. When considering how to empower service users it will be necessary to promote their sense of identity. This means recognising the values, beliefs and preferences the service user has.

Empowering a service user can result in their feeling valued

Mental health needs are an important aspect of caring for older service users. Mental ill health is known as a 'disorder' and this encompasses a wide variety of illnesses and conditions. Everyone's mental health is changeable and is often temporary. There is a large proportion of the population, however, who suffer from mental ill health, which is a psychiatric disorder that affects a person's thinking, feelings, mood and ability to relate to others around them. Symptoms can vary, for example according to *Rethink* those with severe mental ill health are likely to experience psychosis, which is a medical term identifying the symptoms where an individual lacks a sense of reality and loses the ability to respond appropriately in situations that are familiar. The duration of a mental disorder can be short or long term and may only become a serious problem when it interferes with a person's ability to cope with life on a day-to-day basis, or if the person's behaviour is a risk to themselves or others.

Mental disorders can include, for example:

- panic attacks
- schizophrenia
- dementia
- severe depression
- eating disorders
- drug addiction
- alcohol addiction.

It is common, as reported by research carried out by the *British Medical Journal*, for those who suffer from mental conditions to be rejected and avoided by others, as they are seen to be abnormal within society. People in society have an attitude of fear and discrimination towards those with mental health disorders, often resulting in service users feeling alienated from society.

A service user who feels rejected by society is likely to become withdrawn and socially isolated. Care workers need to have coping strategies for those for whom they care, if mental disorder has been diagnosed. These can be simple methods which help an individual to cope with the problems they have. Coping strategies must ensure that negative thinking is changed for positive approaches. For example, one way to help an older person would be to encourage them to write down their feelings. They could add photographs or pictures to personalise it. The writing would be personal to the individual and would remain confidential to them. This would help the person to feel in control and the sense of power should increase self esteem. Another way of coping would be to agree to having counselling sessions where they could share information with another. Again the individual would feel in control as they would determine what was shared.

Those service users who have mental disorders must learn to accept themselves for whom they are. They must learn to love and appreciate how they are, not what others want them to be. Communication is a major aspect in helping the service user to cope. Giving the service user full attention when speaking to them, listening actively and showing **congruency** is essential when interacting.

Tell me how you feel about that

Increased likelihood of potential danger to self and others

Mental health problems can affect people at different times in their lives and can do so in a variety of different ways. A person who has mental ill health can experience anxiety, depression,

schizophrenia and dementia. They may also self harm or be a risk to others in the community.

The Mental Health Act 1983 clearly sets out the circumstances in which a person who has a mental disorder can be treated without their consent. It also sets out the safeguards that the person with the disorder is entitled to. The Mental Health Act 1983 defines a mental disorder as:

- severe mental impairment
- mental impairment
- psychopathic disorder
- mental illness.

The Mental Health Act 1983 gives relatives and approved social workers and doctors the right to have a person detained under the Act for their own safety or to ensure the safety of others.

- When an application is put forward, a list of pre-set criteria is used to determine whether the person recommended for compulsory admission meets those requirements.
- An individual can be admitted for a period of 28 days. This cannot be renewed or extended.
- During the admission period the individual is assessed and decisions made as to whether treatment is required.
- Section 4 of the Mental Health Act 1983 deals with emergency admissions. A service user can only be admitted for 72 hours. To be held longer, the doctor in charge of the case must make recommendations.

Various people can, under the Mental Health Act 1983, ask for a person to be compulsorily admitted. These are:

- approved social workers
- the service user's relatives
- two approved doctors
- a qualified mental health or disabilities nurse
- police officers.

When a person is discharged, aftercare arrangements are made. This can include for example:

- counselling
- visits by community psychiatric nurses
- visits to or by clinical psychologists
- visits by occupational therapists.

Caroline   CASE STUDY

Caroline is 15 years old and attends a private all girl residential school. Her family are from a high socio-economic background, her father being a GP and her mother, although being at home, is involved with a lot of fundraising for charity.

At the school Caroline is bullied by her peers. She is often referred to as 'boffin' or 'geek' because she is quiet and does not join in activities with the others. They also tease her because of her weight.

Caroline decides that she will experiment with different diets to try and lose weight so that she looks similar to others of her age.

Eventually the dieting and losing a few pounds proves not to be enough for Caroline, so she starts missing meals altogether. By the end of the summer holidays it became obvious to Caroline's family that she had become obsessive with her weight and that losing weight was now ruling her life. Her family realised that her clothes no longer fitted and Caroline had become very withdrawn and could hardly concentrate on anything.

Caroline was visited by her GP who referred her to a psychiatrist. She was diagnosed as having anorexia nervosa, weighing just six stones.

She continued to lose even more weight and her family made a request for compulsory admission to hospital. She was fed by tube and given emotional support by specialists.

1. How are compulsory admissions made under the Mental Health Act 1983?

2. To whom was Caroline a risk? Why?

3. Write your own case study involving an older person who needs emergency admission.

4. Explain what happens when an emergency admission is made.

5. What help would be available for an older person when they are discharged?

Communication problems as a result of illness and disorders

In many situations, such as a service user who is confined to a nursing or residential home, the service user relies heavily on staff to aid communication. It is possible that for some service users their speech may have been affected as a result of dementia or a stroke. For example, if suffering from dementia, language ability breaks down and if the service user is not stimulated they will deteriorate very quickly. The inability to communicate can irritate a service user very quickly. It can also irritate the staff. Ways of encouraging an individual to communicate are given in the table below:

Ways of enabling service users	Why it is important
Make sure the environment is correctly organised.	Too much noise can inhibit communication. Incorrect seating and lack of personal space can also influence communication adversely.
Make sure what you are saying is very clear.	Service users who have senile dementia have difficulty processing what is being said.
Body language should be positive.	Sit at the same level and maintain eye contact. People who are ill or have senile dementia are extremely sensitive to body language.
Use short sentences.	Introduce one idea or piece of information at a time. Ideally about seven words in each sentence.
Listen.	Give the person full attention and try to pick up cues and prompts.
Check that you have been understood.	Learn to paraphrase and summarise in order to be sure that you have understood what has been said.
Make sure you remain calm.	Be prepared for an emotional display as many service users will want to communicate their feelings.
Do not appear to be too rushed.	The service user needs to know that you value them.
Give genuine praise.	It is important to let the service user know that you are aware of how much effort they have put into the communication.
Ensure any aids, such as hearing aids or spectacles, are being used.	Without these, communication will be inhibited.

It is important when communicating to give as much help as possible through signage and visual clues as the service user is more likely to respond. If the service user is familiar with their surroundings, for example familiar décor, their level of confusion and anxiety is likely to be lower. It is important to help the service user to feel valued and to treat them as you would hope others would treat you. This means applying the values of care in so far as remembering that service users have rights, to maintain confidentiality and to respect their individual opinions and beliefs.

Making sure the service user feels valued is an important aspect of communication

Roles of older people

Often the term 'old age' is used to describe someone's condition or behaviour rather than the number of years that they have lived. For example, sometimes when speaking we might say, 'Harold has aged a lot in the last five years, he's only 70 but he can't go for walks like he used to and he sleeps for most of the day'. This means that Harold has become more like the image that speaker has of 'an older person'.

Older adults as family members

Up until the age of 75 the majority of adults either continue to live in their own homes or to live with their families, as they are still able to look after themselves and contribute to the life of the family. After the age of 75 some older adults are likely to need the support of community care professionals or may need to go to nursing homes or residential homes as illness and confusion has meant that they need specialist care. Members of ethnic communities are still looked after by their families and few are found in residential homes.

Extended families are those who live in close contact with one another, through sharing either the same household or area in which they live. As a consequence they will be able to support one another, particularly those who are at the younger stage of older adulthood if they are not affected by illness.

For some families, giving practical support is quite difficult as the sons/daughters may not be living nearby; in fact they could live in another part of the country or even in another country! When relatives do not live near, social isolation could result for the older adult who lives alone.

> ### Discussion point
>
> What roles do you think older people can take within the family?
>
> Are all roles positive or can there be some negative outcomes?

Within the family older adults can often contribute by taking the following roles:

- having grandchildren for a holiday, giving the parents a well earned break and providing new experiences for grandchildren

- meeting the grandchildren from school, thus giving safety and security while parents are working

- baby-sitting – looking after the grandchildren when parents want to go out

- cooking for the family, providing a meal for when the family return from work

- being a 'listening ear', by just being there for the family

- helping to solve problems by considering issues from different perspectives

- stimulating and enriching the lives of the family, by sharing with them some of the family history and experiences

- providing love, affection and respect for family members.

Introducing new experiences can widen horizons

very useful and can give direction to a wide variety of voluntary organisations, for example:

Organisation	Examples of roles
Mencap	Drivers, assistants, clerical help
Oxfam	Shop assistants, sorting items, letter writing, filing
Help the Aged	Committee member, fundraising, shop assistant
WRVS	Delivering cooked meals
Save the Children	Raise money, committee member, visits
Faith groups	Visiting, helping with events, mentoring

Older adults can make very positive contributions to voluntary organisations. They give freely of their time, have a great deal of experience and are usually very enthusiastic about making a contribution.

Nina   CASE STUDY

Nina is 67 years old. She lives in the same community as her son, daughter-in-law and their two children, Amir who is seven years old and Usha who is five.

1. Give three ways that Nina can help support the family. Explain what she would do and how this would help.

2. Interview an older adult. Find out about their life history.

3. Share the information with others (changing the name for confidentiality reasons). Compare the similarities and differences between the older adults interviewed.

4. 'Older adults are not valued in today's society.' Discuss this statement with regard to their role in the family.

Older adults as voluntary workers

Older adults will often become involved with voluntary organisations, particularly in the younger part of old age. Their experiences and skills can be

Peter   CASE STUDY

Peter has recently retired from his role as a senior teacher in a large comprehensive school.

1. Provide advice for Peter to give him guidance about the type of voluntary role he could do.

2. Compare the differences between a voluntary informal worker and a professional care worker.

3. Explain how working in voluntary organisations helps the older adult.

Older service users make a positive contribution to society

Older adults as members of the community

All older adults are members of the **community** as they live in a particular area with others, sharing the same facilities. A community is made up of a variety of individuals from different life stages and from different backgrounds. Some will have similar interests, while others will view life from completely different perspectives.

A community will work in harmony. This is not to say tensions will not arise but by working in partnership many can be resolved. Such working together will be reflected in the care given to one another, in the standard of the available facilities and the esteem which members of the community have for their environment. As members of the community older adults will:

- be able to vote
- be able to express their opinions freely
- be able to make choices
- be able to contribute to voluntary organisations
- be able to use the facilities provided
- contribute to the views of that community whether these are political or general.

As members of the community, older adults will also make friends within their area and may also receive voluntary and health and social care support if they have specific needs.

Lifestyle changes that affect older people

Work patterns

Retiring will probably affect **work patterns** as most women cease working at the age of 60 while men retire at 65 years. However, not all men and women cease working at these ages. Some will continue in full-time employment for several more years while others may move to part-time work. In Western societies it is possible to be flexible according to the individual's preferences.

Those who continue in part-time work may do so for the same firm or may change their job completely and try something different. It is quite common for older adults, particularly at the younger end of this life stage, to continue working for a few years after they stop full-time work.

Retirement has a number of social consequences for older adults. These include:

- loss of social contacts, for example work colleagues
- change in status as 'work' provides status – for many they are proud of the job they have
- working means having a regular income whereas having a 'pension' can be limiting as far as the recreational activities that are available
- loss of friends because an older person may not be able to afford to visit or may not be able to visit due to ill health.

However, not all is gloomy when retiring. The vast majority of people enjoy the opportunity of not having to work, while others, for example over a quarter of those who reach retirement age, continue in employment beyond the age of retirement.

Time management by older adults

Discussion point

Why do some people want to continue working after the age of retirement?

For those who do not continue to work, time will need to be managed. The routine of getting up at a specific time, getting ready for the working day, participating in the work process and returning home at some point in the early evening is no longer present. Without good time management, the older adult could find that they 'drift' into doing nothing and no longer have a routine. It is not only individual days that need to be planned but also time over a period of a year, so that there is a change of task, some stimulation and challenge, and some recreational activity.

Before retiring, many older adults will attend preparation seminars to help them think about what they would like to do, when they would like to do it and how their proposed plans can be achieved. This is good practice, as at least some serious thought has been given to the way forward and some preparation made for managing the additional time that is available.

Leisure

Most older adults remain fit and active well into old age and having additional time can lead to increased opportunities for leisure activities. Leisure activities can contribute to:

- reducing stress
- relieving depression
- improving self esteem.

Older adults may need to have adapted leisure programmes that are within their physical abilities. Activities such as swimming or walking can help to maintain health, improve mobility, help older adults to meet new people and generally improve their quality of life.

Retirement is the ideal time to develop new leisure activities or to improve existing pursuits.

Many older adults enjoy travelling in the form of cruises which combine visiting new places, meeting new people and trying out new activities. Others will turn to mentally stimulating activities such as obtaining a degree or following language or computer courses in order to achieve something that was not possible for them to do in earlier life stages.

Leisure or recreational activities are important, whatever life stage a person is in, as they ensure that health and fitness are maintained. In older adulthood recreational activities are particularly important as they not only lead to physical fitness but also provide mental and social well being.

Different leisure activities contribute to physical, intellectual, emotional and social well being

Successful leisure activities can lead to 'positive self regard' which Carl Rogers, a theorist, considers to be a significant aspect of personal development, whatever life stage an individual is in. Having positive self regard leads to valuing self and experiencing feelings of 'worth'. This is very important for older adults as loss of status, from lack of work, could undermine their opinion of themselves and lead to low self esteem. Successful leisure activities can, however, boost morale, particularly if the activity is enjoyed and the participant feels that they have made progress and achieved the targets set.

Income will influence the type of leisure activities that can or cannot be undertaken by service users. Obviously some activities will cost more than others, but changes in economic patterns will be dealt with later in this unit.

Changes in health and care needs

As already discussed within this unit, older adults may experience changes in health needs, depending on the illnesses and conditions they experience. Such changes can produce the need for both **informal** and **formal** support.

Informal support

Informal support is the care given by those who are not paid to do so. In most cases such people may be unskilled and will also be available at times when professional care workers are not available. Informal care workers are most likely to be individuals who the service user knows and trusts. For example, these could include:

- immediate family members – husband, wife, sons, daughters. Such people are likely to be involved in the personal care of the service user, for example washing, changing, cooking and serving meals.

- extended family members – grandparents, aunts, uncles, nieces. Members of this group are likely to contribute by shopping or sitting with the service user for periods of time or helping to write letters or assisting with the laundry. The way in which they help is likely to be less personal.

- neighbours – those living near at hand. A neighbour can help by providing a snack, sitting and talking with a service user, making sure that medication is taken, if family members are not able to do so, or even by mowing the lawn, etc.

• friends – people who know the service user well and want to help. For example, they may take the service user for a walk or a car drive or they may take them for an appointment or just sit and share the gossip and news about what is happening in the world.

Other groups of people who are classified as informal carers could include:

• volunteer friends – untrained, or retired, or people who do not work who feel they can contribute to the service user's care, for example by driving or collecting books from the library.

• faith groups – individuals who belong to a faith group who probably know the service user, who wish to visit to keep the person company or to pray or to help in any other way that is useful.

• informal networks – this is a group of people who do not have any specialism in a topic but who may be experiencing the same problem. For example, a group of people who have previously had alcohol- or drug-related problems and who meet to talk through how they are feeling and the issues they have faced. By meeting and talking they provide support for one another which helps them to feel more confident about the future.

Theory into practice

Talk to a person who has been an informal carer. Find out what types of job they have done. Have there been any disadvantages?

Informal carers are invaluable as they can fill the gap left by professional care workers and can deal with all the daily routines which, if not done, could cause the service user to worry.

What can I do for you today Raj?

Formal support

The majority of older adults do not receive formal support. Formal support is given by individuals who have been formally trained and who are paid for the services that they offer. This could include, for example:

Types of formal support	Examples of those who give formal support
Health Service	Nurses, physiotherapist, dietician, radiologist, consultant, district nurse, health visitor
Social Services	Social workers, home care officer (home help), occupational therapist, counsellor, psychologist
Private organisations	Nurses, radiologists, physiotherapists chiropodists, health care assistants.

Examples of formal support

These examples are not exhaustive; there are many other job roles that would be classified as being involved in giving formal support, but too many to list here. Those carers who have such roles have been trained to the standards required by their occupational sector and will apply their skills in their day-to-day work. They do have set working patterns and are, therefore, only available according to the time they have and the number of service users they have to deal with. It is also possible that attendance on a service user may not be **consistent** as they may have to work in a different part of an area or follow a shift pattern of working.

Malik — Activity 6

Malik is in his thirties. He is recovering from a broken pelvis after a car accident. He is now at home and is managing with community care and support.

A neighbour of Malik is going to keep the garden tidy. A volunteer friend will collect the newspaper each day. The GP will call each week. The social worker has arranged for a physiotherapist to visit. Meals will be provided by an aunt. At the weekend a friend of Malik will stay at the house to look after him.

1 Identify four informal carers who are going to help Malik. Identify one task each would do.

2 Identify the formal support workers who will help Malik. Describe what each would do.

3 Compare the differences between informal and formal support.

Life expectancy and the effects of losing a partner

Death and the process of dying now occur mostly in those who are in the later stages of older adulthood as life expectancy is so much longer. Deaths generally occur in a hospital, a residential home, a nursing home or a hospice, with few older adults actually dying in their own homes. The effects of caring for the dying are quite emotional and those who experience the death of a partner, loved one or friend will need a great deal of support.

When an individual dies, relatives and friends often go through different stages of grieving. These can include:

- shock
- anger
- disorganisation
- emotional turmoil
- loss
- loneliness
- relief
- re-establishment.

Many older adults and families experience a sense of guilt about being able to cope. They could try to blame the staff at the hospital or at the hospice, for example. No one is ever prepared for death. Death and bereavement are things that happen to other people not to ourselves. Helping an individual to cope with such a situation is vital, therefore. How can a professional informal or formal support worker help a person to cope?

There are many ways that help can be offered to the person who has been bereaved. For example:

- spending time with the person to help them talk about their feelings

- making sure any relatives are informed (if there are any) and if the bereaved person wants someone contacted

- allowing the person to spend time with the person who is dying or has died

- providing tea, coffee or snacks for the individual as a way of showing concern

- contacting an organisation that specialises in dealing with bereavement, such as CRUISE

- making arrangements for the person who is bereaved to have their spiritual needs fulfilled

- making sure that the GP is aware of the death so that medication can be provided if needed.

It should be noted that sudden deaths must be referred to a **coroner** if:

- a GP or doctor has not seen the service user for the past two weeks
- if the service user has had an operation in the last 12 months
- if the GP/doctor does not know the cause of death
- if the death is sudden, as the result of an accident
- if there are any suspicious circumstances.

The effects of losing a partner, close relative or friend can last for months; the person may therefore need support for a long period of time. They may become isolated, not wanting to go out alone. They may worry as they do not know how they will manage financially or they could lack confidence having no one to talk with and to share joys and sadness.

Changes in economic situation

The income of older adults is generally made up of:

- state and/or private pensions
- occupational pensions
- any investments a person may have
- any earnings they may receive, e.g. if they have a part-time job
- any benefits to which they may be entitled.

Most older adults rely on a state or private pension and this could severely restrict their spending, causing them to experience poverty. The state pension is very low, so if this is the only source of income, many older adults are not likely to reach an acceptable standard of living.

Quite a number of older adults will not have paid into an occupational pension nor will they have invested any money while they were working, which would provide additional income during their retirement. This means that large bills such as maintenance and repair on homes or replacement cars would be very difficult to manage.

There are many additional costs associated with older adulthood. For example, older adults feel the cold more than they did when they were younger; consequently fuel bills are likely to be higher as they need to heat their home for longer periods. They may also find that they may now have to pay for public transport as they may not be able to afford to have their own transport. Using public transport may be expensive and this in turn could mean that the older adult may go out less.

There are some aspects of older adulthood which are advantages. These could include, for example:

- free prescriptions for medical conditions
- some insulation of homes is free depending on income
- fuel allowance at Christmas
- free security locks fitted by some crime prevention teams in conjunction with the police
- free bus passes in some areas.

Other benefits for which older adults could apply when living on a restricted income include:

Disability allowances

Tax credit

Council Tax benefit

Examples of benefits for those on low incomes

Income support

Housing benefit

Social relief/fund

For the older adult, retirement brings economic change in that they no longer have a regular working salary coming in at the end of each month. They will receive their state pension regularly but the amount will be considerably less than the amount received from working. As a result they are likely to spend less on:

- food
- clothes
- maintenance of home
- leisure activities
- wants.

There will be variations between older adults' spending means, but generally they will have less to spend and will have to work out very carefully how they spend their income. Recently, the government has tried to encourage employers to promote company pension or savings schemes to ensure that older adults do have sufficient income during retirement to be able to do some of the leisure activities that they were unable to do while at work.

Budgeting is a very important aspect of managing financial resources and older adults will need to do this to ensure that at the end of each month their outgoings do not exceed income. Older adults will also need to be encouraged to keep any money they have safe and not to 'keep it under the mattress!'

Now where can I put this so it is safe?

Assessment activity 9.2.2

Josh — CASE STUDY

Josh is 73 years old. He retired at 65 and has not worked since. He and his wife lived on their state pension and did not have any other source of income. Josh has mobility problems and is suffering from the early stages of dementia. Josh's wife, Margo, died a week ago and now Josh is living on his own. He is very worried about his future.

1. Explain how mobility problems and having dementia could have affected Josh's quality of life.

2. Analyse how the lives of Josh and Margo would have changed since they retired. Include information about:
   - roles of older people
   - increased likelihood of danger to self
   - communication as a result of illness
   - changes in lifestyle.

3. Compare the roles of informal and formal support workers, giving examples to illustrate the points made.

4. What are the financial effects of being retired on older people?

5. Losing a partner is proving to be very difficult for Josh. Identify **five** strategies that could be used to help a service user who has been bereaved, explaining how each would help.

6. Analyse the consequences of Josh becoming socially isolated.

9.2.3 Community care and support services for older people

The NHS and Community Care Act 1990 gave all people who needed support, the choice of whether they wanted to continue living in their own homes or whether they would prefer to be in some form of residential care. Obviously, for some older adults, making a choice is not possible, as their medical condition is such that some form of residential care is essential.

For other older adults, support can be provided within the community in which they live, so that they are able to continue living in their own homes. However, many may need some of the services that are offered in the community, such as hospitals, day care centres or domiciliary help.

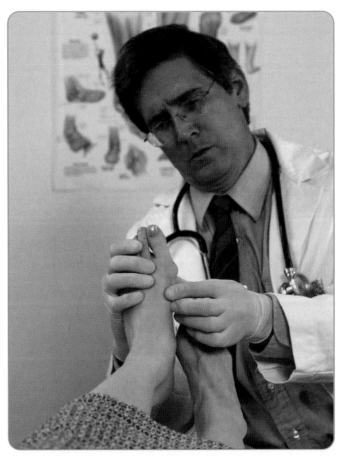

Different types of care for older people

Health care services

The National Health Service is organised by the Department of Health, which is directly responsible to the minister who oversees its work. The NHS will set policy goals for improving the nation's health. It also allocates funding and works with professional care workers and service users to develop standards of care.

The NHS Executive is a 'stepping stone' between the Department of Health and the Health Authorities, who decide on the types of care required in their area, depending on the nature of the population. The latter receives the policies and turns them into working practice, making sure that government policies are implemented.

The structure of the NHS is changing rapidly and may not be the same for any one area. One of the most recent developments is that of Trust Hospitals and GP surgeries joining together to plan and provide the care for their local area. These are known as PCTs (Primary Care Trusts).

The health care available for older people is the same as is available to all. Older people may use health services more than younger adults because of the aging process, as they often develop physical illness and conditions, particularly in the later stages of older adulthood.

The NHS provides a whole range of services. Examples of health services available to older people are:

Health services	Examples of services provided for older people
Hospital	• caring for people who are ill • operations • physiotherapy • outpatients clinics • dietary problems • radiography • geriatric care
GP (General Practitioner)	• monitors health • writes prescriptions • diagnoses illness • liaises with other agencies • may offer counselling services • may offer chiropody service
Community services	• nursing care • medical care • psychiatric monitoring and care • health advice

Different types of care for older people

Health services	Examples of services provided for older people
Dental practice	• checks teeth and gums • extracts and fills teeth • cleans teeth • takes impressions for and fits dentures
Chiropody	• cares for feet • removes corns and attends to bunions • trims nails
Optician	• eye tests • diagnoses disease related to the eyes • arranges for the correct lenses for glasses
Physiotherapy (community and hospital)	• designs exercise programmes provides exercise and massage to restore movement • provides advice
Walk in centres	• diagnosing basic conditions • providing advice

The services that older people use will depend upon their individual needs. Many will not use any services, others may, because of their condition, through the aging process, need to use several services.

Lucinda   CASE STUDY

Lucinda is 80 years old. She has recently had a stroke and has been in hospital. She is now ready to return to her own home. Her left arm is still slightly paralysed but she is able to use her right arm normally. She can move around very slowly but wants to be as independent as possible.

From the case study it is possible to see that while Lucinda has been in hospital she has received services from a variety of departments. For example:
- She has been nursed on the geriatric ward because she has been ill. Here she has received care and her health has been monitored.
- She has received physiotherapy to help her to move her limbs as normally as possible.
- She has had radiology services as MRI scans were required to find out exactly what damage had been done by the stroke and where.
- She has received help from the dietician as she was unable to swallow easily during the early days of the stroke so food had to be specially prepared to enable her to receive nourishment.

When Lucinda returns home she will return to the day care unit at the hospital to continue with some of the treatment she has already started.

NHS/Trust hospitals are **purchasers** and **providers** as they now work in joint arrangement with private organisations and social services. For example, the NHS hospital or Trust hospital may have undertaken a large number of hip replacement operations but other service users may also need this treatment. The hospital could approach a private hospital who will charge a stated fee for completing the additional operations. The NHS/Trust hospital will, therefore, meet the quota set by government targets and also reduce its waiting list.

Social care services

Social Services, which are part of the local authority, provide a range of services for older adults. The diagram below gives examples of the services provided:

Meals on wheels
Working with voluntary services to provide hot meals for service users who are unable to cook for themselves.

Day care centres
Centres where service users can spend time with others of similar age. Provides hot meals and personal care and support.

Assessment of need
Service users can have their needs assessed and care plans drawn up.

Domiciliary care
The provision of a home care officer (home help) to assist with daily living.

Respite care
Caring for those who are dying by providing medical and personal care and support.

Aids and equipment
Mobility and aids for moving/handling.

Sheltered accommodation
Warden assisted flats/bungalows. The warden visits twice daily to ensure care.

Counselling services
Available to those who are assessed as having a specific psychological need.

Social work provision
Social workers making assessments of needs, giving personal care and support.

Social Services are also both purchasers and providers. This is because they buy in some types of care and provide others from the resources they hold. Recently they have formed **integrated service provision** by working in joint teams which comprise the NHS and voluntary and private organisations. For example, when a service user returns home from hospital both NHS and Social Service staff plan the provision of care required.

Day care services

Hospital day care centre

Who attends and what do they do?

- service users recovering from a medical condition, e.g. stroke or who have a medical condition, e.g. rheumatoid arthritis, often attend
- service users can attend for a half-day session but some stay for a full day
- a meal is provided for those who stay for a full day
- group exercises are given to promote health and well being
- appointments are made for individual service users to see consultants, if this is required
- health monitoring is carried out, e.g. blood pressure, temperature
- advice and guidance is given about how to maintain health
- dietary advice is provided
- provides an opportunity for service users to meet and talk with others
- activities to stimulate intellect are provided
- liaising with other agencies can result when the care plan is reviewed and change is required.

Social Service/charitable day care centre

The main emphasis of the care provided for those service users who attend the hospital day care centre is on their medical conditions and monitoring their medical needs. Some socialisation is built into the programme, because health involves the 'whole' person, that is their physical, intellectual, emotional and social needs.

Service users who attend local authority or private or voluntary day care centres live in their own homes. Attending the day care centre is one way in which support can be provided.

Who attends and what do they do?

- service users who live in their own homes and who do not have major medical needs but they may be socially isolated
- service users usually attend for a full day
- the emphasis is on meeting and talking with others to help meet social and emotional needs
- a meal is provided at midday which ensures that those attending have a well balanced meal
- newspapers and journals are provided so that service users can have the opportunity to keep up-to-date with current events. Items of interest often make 'talking points'
- activities in small groups, such as cards, scrabble, dominoes are played by those who choose to do so
- whole group activities such as community singing, charades, quizzes are part of the programme
- social workers and care assistants help service users with any personal support required such as reading official letters and giving advice
- some service users will take the opportunity to have a bath as health care assistants will provide assistance with this task
- in some day care centres a chiropodist will be available.

Domiciliary services

Domiciliary services are those that are provided within the service user's own home. These could be any from those given below, depending on the needs of the service user:

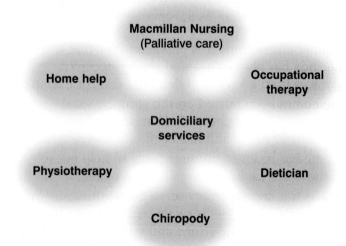

This list is not exhaustive but includes some of the services most commonly provided for people living in their own homes. Whether service users have to pay a contribution towards their costs or whether the service is entirely free depends very much on the income of the service user.

Nursing homes
Providing 24-hour medical care and personal care and support

Chiropodists, dentists, opticians
Providing goods and services for a charge

Residential homes
Providing 24-hour care and support

Day care centres

Private hospitals
Medical care and operations

Private and voluntary provision

Intermediate care
Recovery following hospital treatment

Faith groups
Providing a variety of services such as meals, company, driving to appointments

Help the Aged, etc.
National and local organisations providing advice and practical help

Luncheon clubs
Providing meals and company for older people

Private and voluntary services

Private and voluntary services have taken over some of the provision previously made by social services. Private organisations operate to make a profit while voluntary organisations generally give their services free. However, for some particular services they may make a small charge to cover the cost of resources used. Private and voluntary provision can include the services shown above.

How can services help service users to cope?

The ways in which services can help individuals to cope will mainly depend on the type of service provision provided. Generally, however, service users will be enabled to cope or to be empowered by:

- raising their confidence
- improving self esteem

- reducing pain
- improving mobility
- enabling socialisation
- improving everyday quality of life
- reducing personal danger
- giving the ability to cope
- reducing anxiety, stress or depression
- helping service users to feel valued
- increasing motivation.

Enabling service users means providing the means whereby they can make their own decisions, providing the opportunity to make choices and helping them to be in control of their lives and to contribute positively to their own lives and to the lives of others.

Miranda and Geoff — Activity 7

Miranda

Miranda is 79 and has recently had several accidents within her home which have resulted in broken bones and severe shock. After discussion between Miranda, her family and the GP, Miranda decides that she can no longer live in her own home and that she would benefit from 24-hour care and support.

Geoff

Geoff is 72 but has recently had a heart attack. He fell and broke his hips and now has difficulty in moving and with mobility. He is ready to leave hospital but is unable to look after himself. He will need 24-hour care and support.

1. Which type of residential provision will suit Miranda best? Give reasons to support your choice. How will this help Miranda cope?

2. Which type of residential provision will suit Geoff best? Give reasons to support your choice. How will this help Geoff to cope?

3. Explain how a luncheon club will meet the needs of those attending.

Kim has severe mobility problems and respiratory problems but wants to live in her own home.

4. Identify three different types of domiciliary help that could support Kim. Explain how each would help Kim to cope.

Assessment activity 9.2.3

CASE STUDY

Case Study 1: Bethany

Bethany is 78 years old. She is living in a residential home as she is suffering from a variety of minor illnesses and has to rely more on others for her care.

1   How can a residential home provide support for Bethany?

2   Explain how dependency on others will affect the quality of Bethany's life.

3   Explain how professional care workers could help Bethany to cope.

4   Explain how professional care workers could improve the confidence of the service users in their care.

Case Study 2: Bart

Bart is a service user who wishes to continue living in his own home. He has had a knee replacement which means his mobility is restricted. He also has asthma and is a little confused.

5   Identify three services that could assist Bart, explaining how each could help Bart to cope.

6   Six months later Bart decides that he would like formal support for 24 hours each day. Compare how a nursing home and a geriatric hospital could provide care for Bart.

7   Discuss the advantages and disadvantages of having domiciliary care in comparison to residential care.

9.2.4 Professional care workers

In health and social care organisations there are three main components of the care values. These are:

- promoting service users' rights and beliefs
- promoting equality and diversity
- maintaining confidentiality.

Each of the care values can be broken into components or parts:

Rights include:

- the right to be different, e.g. sexual orientation, beliefs
- freedom from discrimination, e.g. not to be singled out and treated differently
- confidentiality, e.g. to have all personal information kept private
- choice, e.g. to be able to make own decisions and to be consulted
- dignity, e.g. to be treated with respect
- effective communication, e.g. to have things explained and to be listened to
- safety and security, e.g. to be protected from harm
- privacy, e.g. having own space which is not invaded by others without consent.

How should the care values be applied in this situation?

Foster equality and diversity includes:

- understanding and not showing prejudice, stereotyping and labelling
- understanding and valuing the benefits of diversity
- understanding the bases of discrimination, such as gender, race, age, sexuality, disability or social class
- understanding of own beliefs and assumptions, and not being prejudiced.

Maintain confidentiality means:

- keeping personal information from unauthorised people
- not leaving files containing personal information where others can access them
- having passwords that must be used for accessing electronic records
- not gossiping about service users or speaking about them by name in front of others so that they can be identified.

The care values are a statement which underpins all practical caring.

How can professional care workers apply the care values?

Applying the care values means treating others as you would like to be treated yourself. For example:

Psychiatric nurse

A psychiatric nurse needs to find out how the service user is feeling, whether they have taken their medication regularly, and to change a dressing on the service user's leg. How can she do this and apply the care values? This could be achieved by:

- drawing the curtains around the service user when changing the dressing, to help maintain dignity.
- calling the service user by his/her correct name. This promotes respect between the service user and the care worker and promotes their rights.
- explaining to the service user that he/she needs to find out what medication has been taken. Using effective communication as they will ask open questions to encourage the service user to talk and closed questions to obtain specific answers. He/she will use the correct tone of voice, vocabulary that is not too difficult and allow the service user to ask questions, and also listen carefully.
- keeping his/her voice low in order to maintain confidentiality.
- making sure that any cultural requirements or beliefs are met, for example having a female nurse if the service user is a female and if it is traditional within the culture to have a same sex nurse in attendance.
- not talking about the service user to others in a way that they can be identified, in order to maintain confidentiality.

I need to change the dressing on your leg Mr Armstrong...

Correctly applying the care values

Other care workers will endeavour to apply the care values in a similar way. The table below gives examples of how each of the professional care workers listed could achieve this:

Professional care worker	How the care values would be applied
Health care assistant	• Explaining to the service user what they are going to do when taking temperature or a pulse (effective communication) • Asking the service user when they would like a bath (rights) • Talking quietly to a service user about their treatment (equality and confidentiality)
Occupational therapist	• Explaining how the aids could be used and adaptations of the home made (effective communication) • Talking about the service needs that are required and their availability (rights and equal opportunities) • Recognising that the service user has a different sexual orientation from their own and accepting the arrangements in the service user's home (accepting diversity)
GP	• Diagnosing illness and active listening (equal opportunity and effective communication) • Providing information about the range of services available (choice and rights)
Social worker	• Actively listening to the personal problems experienced by the service user (confidentiality and communication) • Making an assessment of need (rights and equal opportunities) • Talking with the service user about the range of services available (choices and effective communication)
Care assistant	• Arranging for a special place within the day care centre where the person can pray (promoting personal beliefs) • Asking the service user what they would like to do out of the activities being offered (choice) • Making sure that there is an option the service user can eat at lunch time (promoting individual rights and beliefs)

Activity 8

1 Working with another person try to find out about the day-to-day work of one of the professional care workers listed above.

2 When you have the information, describe how the care values would be applied in their day-to-day tasks.

3 Have a whole group discussion to compare how the care values could be applied.

Assessment activity 9.2.4

Ray and Robert — CASE STUDY

Ray and Robert are same sex partners. They have been together for fifteen years but Ray requires an assessment of need. A social worker has arranged to meet both Ray and Robert in order to do this.

1 Explain how the social worker can apply the care values when making an assessment of Ray's needs and when talking to both Ray and Robert about the situation.

The social worker agrees with Ray and Robert that they will require a care assistant to help out in the home and that both should visit the day care centre twice a week.

2 Explain how the care assistant who carries out the domiciliary help and the care assistant at the day care centre can apply all three components of the care values during their day-to-day work with Ray and Robert.

After a year of domiciliary help and visiting the day care centre, the social worker and Ray and Robert decide that the partners should move into residential care.

3 Analyse how the professional care workers at the residential home could apply the care values for Ray and Robert.

4 Evaluate how service users may feel if the care values are not applied.

5 Explain how a health care assistant could promote clients' rights and beliefs when bathing a service user.

Continued... — CASE STUDY

Andy visits a day care centre with a view to attending twice each week. On his preliminary visit he observes the following:

- a care assistant talking loudly and by name, about another service user, to one of the other people attending
- a service user being told they will have to wait to go to the toilet as the care assistant has to finish what she is reading
- a care assistant trying to hurry feeding a service user, who cannot feed themselves, because the care assistant wants to go to the shops.

6 Explain why the care values are not being applied and discuss the correct actions the care assistants should take.

9.2.5 Legislation

NHS and Community Care Act 1990

Legislation is important to everyone

The NHS and Community Care Act 1990 has introduced far-reaching changes to the way in which social services are provided in the community. It states that any adult who appears to be in need of services from the Local Authority (Social Services) is entitled to a needs assessment. Where services of the health or housing authorities may be needed, the local authority should notify those authorities and invite their assistance (section 47 of the Act). Once the needs assessment has been carried out, the Local Authority then decides whether services should be provided. Community Health Teams work to a set of criteria, which means that they give priority to people who have serious and persistent mental and other health problems.

The Act provides services and support for people in need in the community, particularly in the following groups:

- older people
- adults with sensory disabilities
- adults with learning disabilities
- adults with mental health needs
- children and families.

Included also are services and support for:

- people caring for others
- people with alcohol and drug-related problems
- people with HIV/AIDS
- black and other ethnic minority communities
- women at risk of domestic violence.

The Act sets out to help people live as independently as possible in their own homes, or in 'homely' settings in the community. The Act also aims to promote 'individual choice and independence' by:

- Promoting the development of domiciliary, day and respite services to enable people to live in their own homes wherever feasible and sensible.
- Ensuring practical support for carers as a high priority.
- Making proper assessment of needs and ensuring high quality 'packages of care' which should be designed in line with individual needs and preferences.
- Promoting wider user choice by making maximum use of private and voluntary providers as well as good quality public services and so increase the range of options available to individuals.
- Making agencies who provide care accountable for the services to the community by defining the responsibilities and the actual services to be provided.
- Introducing a new funding structure for social care.

Discussion point

How does the NHS and Community Health Act 1990 support the individual?

The Act aims to break the statutory agencies' monopoly on the provision of care by establishing a 'mixed economy of care'. This emphasises, firstly, the role of the family in providing care and secondly, the role of the independent sector, which means private, voluntary, and non-profit organisations, in providing services. Its purpose is to:

- Base services upon responding to individual need rather than attempting to fit people into existing provision.
- Ensure services adopt an equal opportunities approach, and should, in particular, be ethnically sensitive.
- Make sure services actively seek and act upon the advice of users and carers concerning the planning, implementation and monitoring of provision.
- Make sure services respond to local circumstances and requirements, and ensure that access to, and availability of, provisions are tailored to the needs of the local population.

Under the new arrangements, every applicant for care, who may be called a 'user', 'consumer' or 'customer', will have his/her needs assessed by a care manager, or by social work staff acting as care managers or care co-ordinators. This will result in an agreed plan, drawn up by the Social Services department to meet those needs where possible, in the best possible way.

New ways of providing service

As a result of the Act local authorities are to act more as enablers, purchasing care from others, known as 'providers'. Formal service contracts or service level agreements will be drawn up, specifying the care to be provided and its quantity and quality. It will include the monitoring arrangements and recognises the valuable contribution of volunteer carers.

Community care is not a new concept; it has been around for many years. But the community care changes are new. Community care generally means helping people, who need care and support, to live with dignity and independence in the community. This is very important to many people, for example those who have MS. It may mean being cared for in the home as well as, for some people, special needs housing or residential or nursing homes.

The government's aims are to:

- make the best use of public money
- encourage local authorities to set priorities
- ensure that local authorities check on the quality of care that is being provided
- encourage local authorities to use other organisations to provide services.

Molly
Activity 9

Molly spends a lot of time in her own home because she has arthritis. Her doctor has given her medication but she has to rely on the support of her family. She is having some difficulty coming to terms with the problem socially. Molly needs help.

1. How does the NHS and Community Care Act 1990 help people like Molly?

2. What might happen to Molly if this legislation was not in place?

3. What are the main purposes of the NHS and Community Care Act 1990?

The Care Standards Act 2000

One of the main purposes of The Care Standards Act 2000 is to standardise the level of care given to service users in any residential care setting. It sets out the minimum standards service users can expect, placing emphasis on the different individual needs of service users. It clearly states that residential homes and nursing homes must cater for the individual needs of each service user. As a result of The Care Standards Act 2000, the 'National Care Standards Commission', which is a non-governmental public body, was created. The purpose of this organisation is to regulate social and health care services previously not regulated by the local authority. It also includes the regulation of domiciliary care agencies, fostering agencies and residential family centres. The Care Standards Act 2000 states that service users in residential and nursing homes:

- must be consulted about their choice of home
- must be consulted about personal health care
- must have an acceptable daily life and social activities
- are entitled to have a complaints procedure in place and to be protected
- are entitled to have an environment that is acceptable
- should have sufficient staffing to meet their needs
- should have the required standard of management and administration.

These standards are measurable and the regulators of residential homes look for evidence of them.

Discussion point

What effect do you think this Act will have on residential care settings?

What does this mean for care settings?

Service users have very little choice about the residential or nursing home they choose because places are very hard to find. So, while they have the right to choose, this does not often happen. Also nursing homes are very expensive so most people have to have an 'assessment of need' before Social Services agree to pay the costs. Some service users are private payers. Most nursing and residential homes will have a mixture of people who are paying privately and those who are being fully or partly paid for by Social Services.

The service users in nursing and residential homes are given a choice of GP. It is probable that the home will have an identified GP, but some individuals choose to remain with the GP they had previously.

Most residential and nursing homes will have a complaints procedure in place and also a 'Mission Statement'. These are placed in a folder in each service user's room so that they, and their relatives, can read what the complaints procedures are and about the purpose of the home and what it is trying to achieve.

All staff who work in residential and nursing homes are either trained or are being trained. Anyone who starts as a care assistant or a health care assistant has to achieve the Foundation Standards, set by the Care Standards Act 2000, within six weeks of starting at the home. Health care assistants usually follow NVQ courses.

Shamil
Activity 10

Shamil is a resident of the Sunny Days Elderly Care Home. He has no close family and at present shares a large room with another resident. He would much prefer to have his own room.

1. Under the Care Standards Act what is Shamil entitled to?

2. Does Shamil have the right to complain and, if so, how?

3. What standard of qualification should Shamil's carers be accredited with?

Carers (Recognition and Services) Act 1995

The Act is aimed to protect or at least recognise the vital importance of informal carers in the community. This Act allows the needs of informal carers to be assessed separately from the individual for whom they are caring. Although it does not demand that services are provided, it is a step forward in recognising that the informal carer has needs which are distinct and not always the same as the person that they are caring for. Before this legislation, local authorities, for the most part, did provide services in order to assist the informal carer to maintain their caring role, even though not legally obliged to do so.

Assessments have to be requested by the informal carer but sometimes they will be offered. If they are specifically requested, the Social Services department has a LEGAL obligation to provide them, but the obligation isn't there if they are not requested.

Informal carers have rights under the Carers (Recognition and Services) Act 1995. Social workers have to listen to informal carers and assess their 'ability to care'. They must make an assessment and take it into account when they decide what services to provide for the person being cared for.

Discussion point

Why might informal carers be reluctant to apply for assessment?

To qualify for an assessment, the informal carer must provide or intend to provide a substantial amount of care on a regular basis. The care provided will help the person cared for to continue to live at home in safety. It is only possible to have an assessment under the Carers (Recognition and Services) Act 1995 if the person cared for is being assessed for community care services or if their needs are being re-assessed because their circumstances have changed. If the person cared for refuses to have an assessment, it is possible to qualify for an assessment under the Carers and Disabled Children Act 2000.

During the assessment a professional from the Social Services department will visit to talk about the type of help needed. They may ask about the tasks carried out by the informal carer at present, whether they are willing and/or able to continue with the tasks and what assistance they would like to help with care in the future.

Following the assessment a decision is taken about what services the person cared for should have. These could be:

- changes to the house, and special equipment
- help with personal care for the person for whom they are caring
- help with shopping, cooking, cleaning, etc.
- a meal delivered to the home
- a place at a day centre for the person for whom they are caring
- respite care, if appropriate, for the service user for whom they are providing care.

Monty   Activity 11

Monty spends a lot of time in his own home because he has Parkinson's disease. His doctor monitors his progress twice a week. Monty requires constant care from his wife and a neighbour. His disease is progressive and he requires 24-hour care.

1. What legal obligation do Social Services have to Monty?

2. How might Monty's carers benefit from the Carers (Recognition and Services) Act 1995?

3. Why do you think the Carers (Recognition and Services) Act 1995 is often referred to as the 'nothing Act'?

Mental Health Act 1983

The majority of people with mental health problems are admitted to hospital or treated in the community on a voluntary basis and have the same rights as everybody else. These people are sometimes referred to as 'informal' patients. However, a small number of people are detained under a section of the Mental Health Act 1983. People who are compulsorily detained are sometimes referred to as 'formal' or 'sectioned' patients. Formal patients do not enjoy the same rights as informal patients and are not free to leave the hospital without permission.

The Mental Health Act 1983 is very complicated and covers legislation governing all aspects of compulsory admission to hospital, as well as the treatment, welfare and aftercare of patients. It provides for mentally disordered people who need to be detained in hospital in the interests of their own health, their own safety or the safety of others.

Different sections of the Act refer to varying lengths of time that a person may be detained, their rights including how they can appeal, if appropriate.

A person admitted under a section of the Act should know which section they are being detained under so that they can be aware of their rights, including their right to appeal, if appropriate. Under Section 132 of the Act, hospital managers have a legal duty to give a detained patient and their relatives this information.

In most cases, people are placed on a section of the Mental Health Act 1983 because two doctors have made medical recommendations, and an approved social worker has made an application. This agrees that the person needs to be in hospital for assessment and/or treatment, and that their health, or safety, or the safety of others would be at risk if they did not receive care in hospital.

Applications for compulsory admission to hospital can be made either by an approved social worker (ASW) or by a nearest relative. Where the ASW intends to complete an application, the nearest relative must be consulted, although their decisions are not binding. If consultation with the nearest relative is not practicable, then they must be informed as soon as possible afterwards.

Admission under the Mental Health Act requires much consideration

Nearest relative

The Mental Health Act 1983 defines what is meant by a nearest relative. This is because the nearest relative can be involved in the admission process. The nearest relative can be:

- husband or wife
- son or daughter
- father or mother
- brother or sister
- grandparent
- grandchild
- uncle or aunt
- nephew or niece.

The three most common ways of being admitted under the Mental Health Act 1983 are:

Admission for Assessment – Section 2

This Section should normally be used when people are in need of compulsory detention in hospital. This Section lasts for up to 28 days and is for assessment. Medical recommendations would usually be made by a consultant psychiatrist. The person's GP and the ASW or nearest relative make the application. Patients have the right to appeal to the Mental Health Review Tribunal (MHRT) within 14 days of admission.

Admission for Treatment – Section 3

Section 3 is for treatment and can last for up to six months, although in practice most patients detained under this Section will be discharged well within this period, but if necessary it can be renewed. The application can be made by an ASW or nearest relative, with two medical recommendations (as with Section 2). An ASW making the application must consult with the nearest relative and if this person objects to the application, then the ASW cannot proceed, unless they obtain a court order under the provisions of Section 29 of the Act. Patients can appeal to the Mental Health Review Tribunal (MHRT) within six months of admission. If patients fail to exercise this right there will be an automatic referral to the MHRT after six months.

Emergency Assessment – Section 4

People can be detained for emergency assessment for up to 72 hours if considered urgently necessary. Admission has to be recommended by one doctor and the application made by either the ASW or nearest relative. As soon as possible during this time the person should be given information about the procedures that will follow.

Discussion point

Does the Mental Health Act 1983 give doctors and social workers too much power over an individual's rights?

Information the service user should receive

When a service user is admitted, they have a right to the following information:

- a clear explanation of the reason for the detention. This should be given both verbally and in writing
- a clear explanation of the Section they have been placed on and the effects of that Section
- an interpreter, if necessary, to communicate their rights to them
- information about the care and treatment including the purpose of any treatment
- a clear explanation of their right to appeal against their detention (for which they have the right to free legal representation)
- information about social security benefits
- information on how to complain and who to complain to
- information about the plans for discharge.

Information the nearest relative should receive

The service user's nearest relative has the right to the following information:

- to be informed and involved in decisions about their admission to hospital
- information about the Section they are on
- information about their rights under the Act
- the ability to authorise in writing another person to act as the nearest relative. Both parties must agree this in writing and this authorisation can be revoked at any time
- information about treatment plans (but only if they want them to have this information)
- information about the proposed discharge plans and dates
- ability to request the discharge where they are on Section 2 or Section 3 (as explained above)
- appeal to the Mental Health Review Tribunal (MHRT) for a review of the detention where the consultant has barred a discharge request
- appeal to the MHRT where they are detained under Sections 37, 47, or 48 of the Act. The nearest relative can only appeal after six months have elapsed from the date the order began, and then once during each subsequent 12-month period
- the nearest relative's right to appeal to the MHRT does not in any way affect the service user's own rights of appeal.

Gerard	Activity 12

Gerard is a paranoid schizophrenic who is refusing to take his medication. His violent tendencies now make him a danger to himself and to others. His relatives have become very worried and have contacted his social worker.

1 How might Gerard's admission to hospital be made under the Mental Health Act 1983?

2 Who could be classed as Gerard's nearest relative?

3 What information would Gerard be entitled to about his admission and treatment?

4 What information would Gerard's nearest relative be entitled to about his admission and treatment?

Health Act 1999

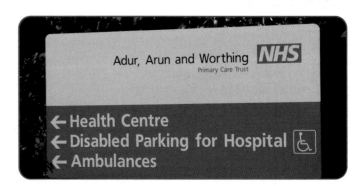

Under the new system there is less red tape

The distinction between health and social care is often unclear to service users, who complain of being pushed from pillar to post in sorting out different parts of their care packages. The Health Act 1999 introduced 'flexibilities' to remove perceived obstacles. These included allowing health bodies and local authorities to set up pooled budgets; delegate functions, by nominating a lead commissioner or integrating provision; and to transfer funds between bodies. This would be done in the form of Primary Care Trusts.

The Department of Health originally intended that 16 trusts would be launched across England in April 2002 but only four went ahead. There are now seven care trusts. However, only two of these, Northumberland and Witham, Braintree and Halstead, which both provide and commission older people's services, are based on the PCT model. The other five are what was described separately in the NHS Plan as 'mental health and social care trusts'. These five are: Sandwell in the West

Midlands, and Sheffield, which were launched recently; Manchester, Bradford, Camden and Islington in North London, which went live in April 2002.

The new powers to enabled health and local authority partners to work together more effectively came into force on 1 April 2000. These were outlined in Section 31 of the Health Act 1999.

These partnership arrangements for health bodies include:

- Strategic Health Authorities
- Primary Care Trusts

together with any health-related local authority services such as:

- Social Services
- housing
- transport
- leisure and library services
- community and many acute services.

The new powers

- *Pooled funds* – this is the ability for partners each to contribute agreed funds to a single pot, to be spent on agreed projects for designated services.
- *Lead commissioning* – where the partners can agree to delegate commissioning of a service to one lead organisation.
- *Integrated provision* – the partners can join together their staff and resources so that the management structures can integrate. This can then give a seamless service using all of the qualities of all of the joined organisations.

Discussion point

How successful do you think this Act will be and why?

How should this help improve services?

The aim is to enable partners to join together to design and deliver services around the needs of users rather than worrying about the boundaries of their organisations. These arrangements should help eliminate unnecessary gaps and duplication between services. The general idea was to free the local care providers from many levels of bureaucracy. However, the uptake of this opportunity has been slow but should show dividends in the future.

Barchester General Hospital — Activity 13

Services at Barchester General Hospital have been seen to be in decline in recent months. The hospital has a massive overspend of £3 million and some of its services are being duplicated and run poorly. The management have stated that they are constrained by government rules and regulations.

1   Using resources that are available to you and the guidance of your tutor, research and outline the best course of action that the hospital could take.

2   What will be the advantages of your suggested action?

Assessment activity 9.2.5

Legislation — CASE STUDY

Dawn is an informal carer for her husband Reg. Reg has multiple sclerosis and requires quite a lot of care. Dawn is feeling worn out and does not know how long she will be able to continue caring for Reg.

1   Which Act could possibly help Dawn? Explain how it could assist her.

The social worker for Reg and Dawn decides, that some domiciliary and day care may help to reduce Dawn's caring role.

2   Evaluate how the NHS and Community Care Act 1990 could enable this to happen.

3   Explain **three** different types of domiciliary help that Dawn and Reg could receive. How would this help Dawn to cope?

At a later date it is decided that Reg needs residential care in a nursing home.

4   Analyse how the Care Standards Act 2000 would contribute to the quality of care Reg receives at the nursing home.

5   Evaluate how the Mental Health Act 1983 could be used to assist a family where the father has become extremely violent due to his illness.

6   Evaluate the impact of the Health Act 1999 on service provision.

Unit 1: Promoting Quality Care

AS Level for OCR Health and Social Care Moonie N (Series editor) (2005), Heinemann

BTEC National Care Walsh M, Stretch B, Moonie N, Herne D, Miller E, Webb D (2003), Heinemann

BTEC Nationals Health Studies Stretch B (2002), Heinemann

Care S/NVQ Level 3 Nolan Y (2001), Heinemann

Every Child Matters Report Lord Laming, Department of Education and Skills. Presented as a Green Paper CM5850 8 Sept 2003

Nursing in Care Homes (2nd edition) Nazarko L (2002), Heinemann

Social Work Themes and Issues and Critical Debates Adams R, Dominelli L, Payne M (1998), Macmillan Press

Social Care Level 4 Frances F, Scourfield P (2004), Heinemann

Sociology a Modular Approach Gleeson D (general editor) (1990), Oxford University Press

Websites

Commission for Racial Equality, What is the CRE? (Online). Available from: http://www.cre.gov.uk/

Directgov.uk (2005) Changes to the Disability Discrimination Act in October 2004 (online). Available from: http://www.direct.gov.uk/

BBC News, Every Child Matters. Available from: http://news.bbc.co.uk1/hi/uk.3085044.stem

Student resources, Where do prejudices come from? (Online). Available from http://www.studentresources.mrpete.net/

The General Social Care Council (2005) Codes of Practice and FAQS (Online). Available from: http://www.gscc.org.uk/

Unit 2: Communication in Care Settings

Acquiring Interpersonal Skills (2nd edition) Burnard P (1996), Chapman and Hall

AS Level for OCR Health and Social Care Moonie N (series editor) (2005), Heinemann

Care S/NVQ Level 3 Nolan Y (2001), Heinemann

Communicate Burnard P (1992), Arnold

Communication and Language: A Handbook of Theory and Practice Thompson N (2003), Macmillian

Counselling Skills for Nurses Tschudin V (1982), Baillere and Tindall

Development and Sequences in Small Groups Tuckerman B W (1965), *Psychological Bulletin* 63, No. 6

Learning to Council Sutton J, Stewart W (2002), How to Books

Motivation and Personality (2nd edition) Maslow A H (1970), Harper and Row

OCR Nationals in Health and Social Care L2 Fisher A et al (2005), Heinemann

People Skills Thompson N (1996), Macmillan

Personality and Interpersonal Behaviour Bales R F (1970), Holt, Rinhart and Winston

The Science of Mind and Behaviour (4th edition), Gross R (2001), Hodder & Stoughton

The Skilled Helper Egan G (2002), Brooks/Coles

The Social Psychology of Interpersonal Behaviour (5th edition) Argyle M (1972), Penguin

Websites

Braille:
www.brailleeplus.net

Statistics and Definitions: IRR News;
http://www.irr.org.uk/statistics

The General Social Care Council (2005) Codes of Practice and FAQS (Online).
Available from:
http://www.gscc.org.uk/

Makaton Information for Parents and Carers, Walker M (1996),
Makaton website;
http://www.makaton.org/docs/imformationforparentsand Carers-A5green.pdf

What is the care value base? (2004). Available from:
http://216.239.59.104/search?q=cache:Hr6yDZ9aMJ:ecs.lewisham.gov.uk

Unit 3: Promoting Good Health

AS Level for OCR Health and Social Care Moonie N (Series Editor) (2005), Heinemann

BTEC Nationals Health Studies Stretch B (2002), Heinemann

BTEC National Care Walsh M, Stretch B, Moonie N, Herne D, Miller E, Webb D (2003), Heinemann

Care S/NVQ Level 3 Nolan Y (2001), Heinemann

Nursing in Care Homes (2nd Edition) Nazarko L (2002), Heinemann

Promoting Health: A Practical Guide, Ewles L and Simnett I (1992), Scutari Press

Social Policy and Welfare Walsh M et al (2000), Stanley Thorne

Care in Practice for Higher Still Miller J (Editor) (2000), Hodder & Stoughton

The Psychology of Happiness Argyle M (1987), Methuen

Knowledge & Control in Health Promotion: a test case for social policy and social theory Beattie A in Gabe J et al (1991) Sociology of Health Service. Routledge

Websites

Trends in UK stats. Since 1900:
http://www.parliament.uk/

Health inequalities:
http://www.hda.nhs.uk/Documents/health_inequalities_concepts.pdf

Celebrating our Cultures: Guidelines for Mental Health Promotion with the South East Asian Community:
http://www.nimhe.org.uk/downloads/SEAsion.pdf#

Independent Inquiry into Inequalities in Health – Black Report:
http://www.archive.official-documents.co.uk/document/doh/ih/tab1.htm

Immunisation:
http://www.immunisation.nhs.uk/

Proposals for NHS Plan 2000:
http://www.nhsia.nhs.uk or http://www.dh.gov.uk

Healthy Schools Award:
http://www.wiredforhealth.gov.uk

Antenatal Tests:
http://www.babycenre.co.uk

Self Examination for Testicular and Breast Cancer:
http://www.cancerresearch.uk.org
http://www.cancerbacup.org.uk

Unit 4: Health and Safety in Care Settings

AS Level for OCR Health and Social Care Moonie N (Series Editor) (2005), Heinemann

BTEC National Care Walsh M, Stretch B, Moonie N, Herne D, Miller E, Webb D (2003), Heinemann

Care S/NVQ Level 3 Nolan Y (2001), Heinemann

Health and Safety Executive (2001) Health and Safety in Care Homes London: HSE

Health and Safety Executive (2001) Handling Home Care London: HSE

Nursing in Care Homes (2nd Edition) Nazarko L (2002), Heinemann

Safety Signs and Signals: The Health and Safety (Safety Signs and Signals) Regulations 1996 (2002) London: HSE

Websites

The Department of Trade and Industry Safety Site:
www.doh.gov.uk

The Control of Substances Hazardous to Health Regulations 1988:
www.hse.gov.uk/coshh

The Reporting of Injuries, Diseases and Dangerous Occurrences Regulations 1985:
www.riddor.gov.uk

Health and Safety Executive website:
www.hse.gov.uk

Information on cctv
www.cctv-information.co.uk

information on fire extinguishers
www.firesafe.org.uk

www.hse.gov.uk

Unit 5: Caring for People with Additional Needs

A Practical Guide for Disabled People or Carers: where to find Information, Services and Equipment (2003), Department of Health

Care S/NVQ Level 3 Nolan Y (2001), Heinemann

Caring About Carers: A National Strategy for Carers (1999), Department of Health

Fair Access to Care Services: Guidance on Eligibility Criteria for Adult Social Care (2002), Department of Health

Framework for Assessment for Children in Need and their Families (2000), Department of Health

Good Practice in Caring for Young Children with Special Needs Dare A, O'Donovan M (2002), Nelson Thornes

Health and Social Care (Advanced) Moonie N et al (1994), Heinemann

Human Biology for AS Jones M, Jones G (2004), Cambridge University Press

Human Health and Disease Fullick A (1998), Heinemann

Inside the Caring Services Tossell D, Webb R (1994), Edward Arnold

The Principle of Normalisation in Human Services Wolfenberger W (1972), NIMR

Valuing People: A New Strategy for Learning Disability for the 21st Century: Planning with People; Towards a Person-Centred Approach; Guidance for Implementing Groups (2002/1), Department of Health

Websites

Advice and support for parents of children with a disability. Available from:
www.parentscentre.gov.uk

British Council of Disabled People, information on social inclusion and civil rights. Available from:
www.bcodp.org.uk

Community care. Available from:
www.communitycare.co.uk

Department of health. Available from:
www.dh.gov.uk

Government website on the needs of carers: Available from:
www.carers.gov.uk

Information on Makaton. Available from:
www.makaton.org.uk

National Portage Association. Available from:
www.portage.org.uk

The General Social Care Council (2005) Codes of Practice and FAQS (Online).
Available from:
http://www.gscc.org.uk/>

The Disabled Living Foundation. Available from:
http://www.dlf.org.uk/

Unit 6: Working in Early Years Care and Education

A Practical Guide to Activities for Young Children Hobart C, Frankel J (1995), Stanley Thornes

A Textbook of Nursery Nursing: The Essentials Gilbert P (1997), Stanley Thornes

AS Level for OCR Health & Social Care Moonie N et al (2005), Heinemann

Babies and Young Children Beaver M, Brewster J, Jones P, Neaum S, Tallack J (2002), Nelson Thornes

Certificate Child Care and Education Tassoni P (2000), Heinemann

Child Care and Development Minett P (2004), John Murray

Child Development Brennand H, Fairclough J, Hall V, Nicholson E, Rees E (2001), Hodder & Stoughton

Child Development: An Illustrated Guide Meggitt C, Sunderland G (2000), Heinemann

Childcare and Education Bruce T, Meggitt C (2002), Hodder Arnold

Children's Care, Learning and Development NVQ Level 3 Tassoni P, Bulman K, Beith K, Robinson M (2005), Heinemann

Diploma Child Care and Education Tassoni P, Beith K, Eldridge H, Gough A (2000), Heinemann

OCR Nationals Level 2 Fisher A, Seamons S, Blackmore C, Snaith M (2005), Heinemann

Social Learning Theory Bandura Al (1976), Prentice Hall

Websites

BBC Web site:
www.bbc.co.uk/parenting/childcare

CACHE:
www.cache.org.uk

Child Care Registrations:
www.childcarelink.gov.uk

Connexions Careers Service:
www.connexions-direct.com

Department for Education and Skills:
www.dfes.gov.uk

Ofsted:
www.ofsted.gov.uk

Play Therapy:
www.playtherapy.org.uk

Pre-school Learning Alliance:
www.pre-school.org.uk

Qualifications Curriculum Authority:
www.qca.org.uk

Starting a Day Care Centre Rasmussen V (2004):
www.startingadaycarecenter.com

SureStart:
www.surestart.gov.uk

Under Fives:
www.underfives.co.uk

Unit 7: Health as a Lifestyle Choice

Anatomic Etherington K (2000), Global Book Publishing Ltd

AVCE Sports Science Fullick A (1998), Heinemann

PE Essentials Neate D (1996), Bath Press

Principles of Anatomy and Physiology Tortora G, Grabowski S (2000), Wiley

The Exercise Health Connection Neiman D (1998), Human Kinetics

Vitamins and Minerals Handbook Ursell A (2001), Dorling & Kindersley

Websites

Saving Our Lives, Our Healthier Nation
www.ohn.gov.uk

The British Nutrition Foundation
www.nutrition.org.uk

The Department of Health
www.doh.gov.uk

The Food Standards Agency
www.foodstandards.gov.uk

General health and physiology:
www.bbc.co.uk/health
www.bupa.co.uk/health
www.howstuffworks.com
www.sportengland.org
www.ymca.org.uk

You will also find many more local organisations through your local NHS and
government websites.

Unit 8: Complementary Therapies

Chinese Medicine Williams T, Element

House of Lords – Science and Technology – sixth report 6.33, Department of
Health, 2001

National Guidelines for the Use of Complementary Therapies in Supportive and Palliative Care, Marianne Tavares, The Prince of Wales's Foundation for Integrated Health, The National Council for Hospice and Specialist Palliative Care Services

New Choices in Natural Healing Dollemore D, Giuliucci M, Haigh J, Kirchheimer S, Callahan J, Rodale Press Inc.

Personnel Today Management Resources One Stop Guide to Managing Stress Jordan J, Cooper C, Reed Business Information

Relaxation Techniques – A Practical Handbook for the Health Care Professional Payne R A, Churchill Livingstone – Medical Division of Longman Group Ltd

Social Readjustment Rating Scale Holmes T, Rahe R, first published in the *Journal of Psychosomatic Research* 1967, vol.11, p. 214.

The Alternative Health Guide Inglis B, West R, Michael Joseph Ltd

The Complete Book of Relaxation Techniques Sutcliffe J, Quarto Publishing plc and Headline Book Publishing plc

The Essential Guide to Holistic and Complementary Therapy, Beckmann H, Le Quesne S, Thomson Learning

The Which? Guide to Complementary Therapies Barnett H, Which? Books

Websites

ABC of complementary medicine – Complementary medicine and the patient
Catherine Zollman and Andrew Vickers:
http://bmj.bmjjournals.com/cgi/content/full/319/7223/1486
BMA – complementary & alternative medicine – submission to public petitions committee
The British Medical Association:
http://www.bma.org.uk/ap.nsf/Content/publicpetitioncam

Complementary and Alternative Medicine
The United Kingdom Parliament Select Committee appointed to consider Science and Technology:
http://www.parliament.the-stationery office.co.uk/pa/1d199900/1dselect/1dsctech/123/...

Complementary medicine – before you start:
http://www.parliament.the-stationery-office.co.uk/pa/1d199900/1dselect/1dsctech/123/...

Complementary Therapies – Overview of different forms of Complementary Therapies
ACAS (Asian Community AIDS Services):
http://www.acas.org/treatment

Issues in Complementary Therapies: How We Got to Where We Are
Mariah Snyder and Ruth Lindquist:
http://www.nursingworld.org/ojin/topic15/tpc15_1.htm

Warning on complementary therapy
BBC News:
http://www.alternativehealth.co.nz/cancer/warning.htm

4Health from Channel 4:
http://www.channel14.com/health/microsites/C/comp_medicine/features1.html

Unit 9: Caring for Older People

A Way of Being Rogers C R (1980), Houghton Mifflin

Care S/NVQ Level 3 Nolan Y (2001), Heinemann

Concepts in Education Lieberman M (1961), Rank McNally

Department of Health, Fair Access to Care Services (Guidance of Eligibility Criteria For Adult Social Care) (2002), Department of Health

Growing Old: The process of disengagement, Cummings F, Henry W (1961), Basic Books

Identity and the life Cycle Erikson E H (1979), Norton

Nursing in Care Homes (2nd Edition) Nazarko L (2002), Heinemann

On Becoming a Person Rogers C R (1961), Houghton Mifflin

Principals of Anatomy and Physiology Tortora G, Grabowski S (2000), Wiley

Social Care Level 4 Frances F, Scourfield P (2004), Heinemann

Social Work Themes and Issues and Critical Debates Adams R, Dominelli L, Payne M (1998), Macmillan Press

The Life Cycle Completed Erikson E H (1982), Norton

The Skilled Helper Egan G (2002), Brooks/Coles, USA

The Social Psychology of Interpersonal Behaviour (5th edition), Argyle M (1972), Penguin

Websites

Age Concern. Available from:
www.ageconcern.org.uk

Better Government for Older people network. Available from:
www.bgop.org.uk

Community Care. Available from:
www.communitycare.co.uk

Community Service Volunteers: Available from:
www.csv.org.uk

Department of Health (Jobs within social care). Available from:
www.socialcarecareers.uk

National Health Service. Available from:
www.nhsdirect.nhs.uk

NHS website about jobs. Available from:
www.nhscareers.co.uk

Nursing Journal. Available from:
www.nursingolderpeople.co.uk

The General Social Care Council (2005) Codes of Practice and FAQS (Online). Available from:
http://www.gscc.org.uk/>

Abdominal muscles	muscles of the abdomen (six pack)
Access	to be able to reach
Accreditation	a qualification in accordance with the requirements of the accrediting or awarding body
Achievements	skills which have been mastered/learnt
Acronym	letters to represent whole words, e.g. SOLER
Acuity	sharpness of thought or vision
Acupuncture points	certain points on the body, known to acupuncturists, where appropriate treatment is applied
Acus	needle
Acute and chronic	severe and persistent
Adjuvant	a substance used in a vaccine to increase the body's immune response
Adrenal cortex	the outer surface of the adrenal glands found on the top of each kidney
Adrenaline	a hormone that stimulates the body to be alert
Advocate	a person who will speak on behalf of another
Aerobic	the use of air in respiration
Agar	a jelly-like substance in which some vaccine components are grown – 'tissue culture'
Agoraphobia	an abnormal fear of open spaces or public places
Aims	the intentions or outcome of an activity – a broad goal to be met
Alimentary canal	the digestive system from the oesophagus to the rectum
Allergen	substance that causes an allergic reaction
Amino acids	the chemical building blocks of protein
An equality clause	making sure there are no differences between men or women who are doing exactly the same work
Anaemia	lack of iron in our body system that leads to the reduction in the formation of red blood cells
Anaerobic	respiration without the use of air and using other chemicals
Analgesic	relieving pain or a pain relieving drug
Analyse	to consider in detail
Anaphylactic shock	where all of the body systems crash and fail to work

Anatomy and physiology	a study of the structure and workings of the body
Ancillary	providing essential support
Anecdotal	a story that is not entirely supported by fact
Antidepressant	a substance or technique to reduce or eliminate the feelings of depression
Anti-discrimination policies	documents within a care setting that help to prevent discrimination being demonstrated both to service users and care workers
Anti-discrimination	promoting individual value or self worth; making sure discrimination does not occur
Anti-inflammatory	a treatment or medication to reduce inflammation
Arteriosclerosis	the formation of plaques on the inner lumen of the artery creating a narrowing
Arteriosclerotic	hardening of the arteries
Asbestos	any fibrous minerals that are incombustible and resistant to chemicals. It was widely used in the form of fabric or board as a heat-resistant structural material
Asphyxia	lack of oxygen in the blood due to restricted respiration; suffocation
Assumptions	personal thoughts about a situation which are not based on facts
Attachments	bonds/feelings developed with parents and primary carers
Attenuated	weakened – pathogens (organisms that produce disease, e.g. a virus) are attenuated to make them safe when used in a vaccine
Attenuating	weakening or reducing in strength
Auditory	something which can be heard
Autoimmune disease	a disease that affects the functioning of the immune system, e.g. AIDS
Barrier	something that prevents access
Beliefs	personal feelings which are important to the individual
Benefit–risk ratio	a comparison between the potential benefits compared to the possible risks of a course of action
Beri-beri	a vitamin B1 deficiency that leads to a nervous disorder
Bias	a leaning to a particular view or way
Biceps	muscles in the anterior upper arm

Birth to Three Matters	a framework which is intended to provide support, guidance and challenges for providers of care and education of babies and children up to the age of three years
Body language	using facial expressions, gestures, body movement to add meaning to the communication
Bogus practices	practices that are unproven to achieve the stated objective and do not conform to accepted good practice
Bond	the feelings of love between parents and their baby
Boundaries	a framework in which to work
BTEC	Business and Technology Education Council (Edexcel)
Burnout	a person's inability to cope with everyday activities
CACHE	Council for Awards in Children's Care and Education
Cannula	a small tube for insertion into a body cavity, as for draining off fluid, or introducing medication
Carcinogenic	something that is cancer forming
Cardiovascular	referring to the heart, arteries and veins
Characteristics	unique components that help make a person or objects individually identifiable
Characters	individual personality, particular traits a child demonstrates, for example kind, caring, lively, inquisitive, etc.
Chemically	using chemistry, i.e. by utilising the techniques of elements, the compounds they form and the reactions they undergo
Child protection register	a list of children who are at risk
Childminder	a person who looks after children in their own home for payment
Cholesterol	a fatty chemical produced as a product of fat digestion that in the correct proportions is beneficial to the body
Chromosomes	paired strands of genetic material that contain our genes
Circulation	the transportation of the blood around the body
Clinical opinion	the view of a medical professional(s)
Closed societies	not sharing ideas, keeping things to themselves

Code of ethics	guidelines or rules of conduct for working in accordance with best practice
Code of practice	a framework showing the policy that is required or the way a task should be carried out
Codes of conduct	a framework showing how to carry out one's tasks, e.g. a code of conduct for nurses, midwives and health visitors
Cognitive development	to do with thinking and understanding
Community	where we live; the area immediately around us
Competitive	challenges where there is a winner
Complex	involved; taking from different sources and making as one
Component	a part of the whole
Compromise	to meet part way
Concave	to curve inwards as in a lens
Concepts	ways of organising knowledge and information so it can be understood
Concurrent	more than one running at the same time, e.g. several illnesses
Congruent/ Congruency	being genuine
Conscience	moral feelings; the difference between right and wrong
Consistent	constantly related to the same event each time
Constipation	blockage or compaction of the large bowel
Construction	building and joining together to create an item
Constructive criticism	criticism that is meant to be helpful or to improve the subject of the criticism
Consumables	items which are bought and used up
Consumers Association	a financially independent organisation, dedicated to testing products and services available to the public and reporting its findings in order to achieve better standards
Context	putting what is said into background information; giving the words meaning by placing in a specific situation, e.g. a care setting or to a specific service user
Continuing professional development	a requirement by many professional bodies for their members to continue to learn after qualification and to keep up to date with new teachings

Continuity	without any break
Contra-indications	signs or symptoms that indicate against the use of a particular substance or treatment
Contributor	a person who provides information, money or help
Controlled trials	tests of medicines or medical treatments that have in-built safeguards to ensure that the results are accurate
Convey	to show; to demonstrate
Co-operate	to work together with others for a common aim
Co-operative play	play that involves children joining in with other children
Coping strategies	any techniques or practices that enable a person to manage better
Coroner	a qualified doctor/legal professional who decides on the cause of death in suspicious circumstances
Corrosive	capable of destroying or eating away solid materials
Cortisone	a hormone produced in the body to fight off infection
Cross infection	infection which spreads from one item/person to another
Crucial	very important or essential
Culture	the society in which we live, its rules, traditions and organisation
Curriculum	set pattern of learning which is followed throughout education
Cyclical	in a circle
Daily routine	actions which occur regularly on a daily basis
Decodes	unravels the message; to make sense of the words
Degenerative	the breakdown of tissue or a structure due to a disease or dysfunction
Deprived	disadvantaged, having to go without
Dermatitis	inflammation of the skin
Determination	strength of mind and willpower to achieve success
Development	learning new skills and abilities as a child gets older
Diagnostic systems	identifying the problem by the use of recognised procedures
Differentiation	making work or activities different to meet the needs of all children
Dignity	pride and self respect
Dilates	make wider

Dilemma	something that may have no right or wrong answer; having to balance one side against another
Direct	openly
Discipline	ensuring children behave in an acceptable manner
Disclosed	to tell to others information which was secret
Discrimination	considering or treating someone as being of less value or less worth than ourselves
Disdain	not to think highly of self or others
Disengagement	not attached; to be apart
Diversity	recognising that each person is different and may have different views and opinions
Domiciliary	providing services in the service user's own home
Duties	tasks which have to be completed as part of the job
Early intervention	treatment or changes that are introduced early
Early Learning Goals	levels of achievement children are expected to have achieved by the end of the Foundation Stage
Early years curriculum	teaching and learning which is designed to nurture and develop knowledge and skills at an appropriate level during the foundation stage – birth to six years
Economic factors	the amount of money available, income and expenditure
Educare	provision of care and education within one organisation
Educational	something which promotes the learning of children
Effective anaesthesia	the absence of sensation, to either a local area of the body (local anaesthesia) or to the entire body (general anaesthesia), usually effected by the administration of gases or drugs to enable surgical procedures to be administered
Egocentric	self centred
Eligible	qualifying for/entitled to
Empowered	to be in control and make choices for yourself
Empowerment	feeling in control
Encodes	interpreting a message

Endurance — the ability to exercise for a longer period of time without tiring

Engaging — encouraging another to respond or become involved

Enhance — to improve or to make better

Entrenched — firmly established

Environmental — our surroundings

Episodic — happens at identifiable times and then stops, e.g. one episode

Ethically sensitive — being aware

Evacuation — to leave a building in an orderly manner in an emergency

Exacerbates — makes worse

Excreted — to be pushed out of or removed from

Excruciating — extremely and agonisingly painful

Expenditure — the amount of money which is spent

Experiential learning — developing understanding and skills through doing things

Extended (family) — not immediate family but other relatives, e.g. aunts, uncles, nephews, nieces

External agencies — providers of support outside the organisation

External factors — circumstances, facts or influences that are outside or unaffected by normal controls

Facilitate — help to make something happen

Facilities — places to go including health, recreation, work

Fad — something that becomes popular and fashionable

Fast-twitch fibres — muscle fibres that activate quickly and tire quickly

Fine motor skills — skills involving fine movement of the hands and fingers including writing, drawing, using a knife and fork

Fluctuating energy levels — variations in the feelings of strength and stamina

Food intolerance — the inability for a person to eat certain foods without that food causing unpleasant symptoms

Formal qualifications — recognised accreditation from examination boards achieved through completion of courses and examinations

Formalin — a strong antiseptic and preservative

Fortified — to make stronger or to add to improve

Foster families — families who look after children on a temporary basis

Foundation Stage Curriculum — phase of education for children from 3 to 5 years

Fundamental — essential parts; the basics

Gender socialisation — learning male/female roles for the future

Genes — units of genetic information passed from the parent to the offspring, that give rise to our make up

Genetic — biological; inherited

Gestures — hand movements to help understand oral speech

Global market — worldwide availability

Glycogen — stored sugar, found in the liver

Gregarious — being able to mix easily with others

Gross motor skills — skills involving the use of large muscles in the body including walking, running, climbing

Growth — increase in height and weight

Haemophiliac — a blood disorder which prevents or restricts the ability of blood to clot and results in the sufferer bleeding profusely from even small wounds

Hamstrings — muscles running down the back of the leg

Hazards — dangers

Herd immunity — the phenomenon by which members of a community who are not immune to a disease are still protected from it provided sufficient numbers of people in that community are immune.

Herpes zoster — the virus that causes shingles

Higher socio-economic — a term used in sociology to describe those members of society who are above average in intellect, earnings or achievement

Holistic — aimed at the whole person – body and mind

Homeostasis — the maintenance of equilibrium or balance in the body

Hypertension/ Hypertensive — high blood pressure

Hyperventilation — a type of over-breathing that can cause some unpleasant symptoms

Hypochondrial — a psychological symptom that leads people to suppose that they are suffering from a disease they don't have

Immunity	to be resistant to disease		**Isolation**	alone; not with anyone else
Impact	the changes which happen as a result of certain actions		**Job roles**	different jobs carried out by individuals
Implement	put into effect		**Joining-in play**	when children join in the same games and activities
Income	the amount of money which is earned/comes into a family		**Judgements**	to express one's own views and thoughts or those of theorists; to make informed, reasoned decisions
Incompatible	will not match up or is not right for an object, person or situation		**Key worker**	a care worker responsible for ensuring needs are met
Incontinence	the inability to control movements of the bladder or bowel		**Lack credible evidence**	an absence or lack of sufficient facts to make an argument or proposition believable
Indemnity insurance	insurance that provides protection against legal action by others in specified circumstances, e.g. professional negligence		**Language skills**	the ability to speak and communicate
Indirect	not obvious		**Learning activities**	games and actions with the aim of developing knowledge, understanding or skills
Inessential	not necessary			
Inferior	of lower standard		**Learning goals**	levels of achievement which children should reach by a certain age
Informal	in a relaxed manner			
Ingestion	to take food or liquid into the body		**Learning styles**	the different ways children learn, some have preferred learning styles others learn using a combination
Inhaled or ingested	breathed in or swallowed			
Inhibited	stopped from achieving; prevented		**Legislation**	the process of making laws
Inquisitive	having an enquiring mind and wanting to gather information		**Literacy**	reading and understanding the written and verbal word
Insomnia	the inability to sleep properly		**Logical**	in an orderly manner
Instinctive	actions which people carry out without thinking about them – they happen naturally		**Looking-on play**	play involving one child alongside another when they demonstrate awareness of each other but do not actually interact
Insurance	indemnity should there be an accident, the insurance will pay any money required to replace broken objects or compensation in the event of a child being hurt if the care workers were negligent		**Loss of libido**	loss of sexual urges
			Making a connection	linking; joining one thing with another in a meaningful way
			Malignant	aggressive – applied to cancer cells that are fast growing and invasive
Integrated service provision	working together to give a service		**Malpractice**	improper or negligent professional treatment
Intellectual development	learning and remembering knowledge and understanding		**Management committee**	a group of people responsible for planning and making decisions about the running of an organisation
Interaction	communication between individuals		**Manifested**	showed signs and symptoms
Interacts adversely	acts each on the other in a hurtful, contrary or injurious way		**Manipulation**	the manual examination and/or treatment of a part of the body
Intervertebral	in between the vertebra or segments of the backbone		**Manipulative (play)**	play that involves using the hands to achieve a goal
Intestine	small bowel		**Manual handling**	handling goods or the lifting and moving of goods by the use of hands only
Intraocular pressure	pressure that builds up within the eye			

Medications prescribed or unprescribed pharmaceutical products

Mentoring system a person who helps another to understand what is happening, why it's happening and how to cope with a situation

Message information

Microbiological cells or structures that are only visible with a microscope

Microkeratome a piece of equipment that allows the precise cutting of corneal disc or other tissue to a precise thickness

Mimic to copy and carry out the actions themselves

Monosyllabic single syllables

Motivation the inspiration or stimulus to act in a particular way, providing the incentive and enthusiasm to succeed

Motor giving rise to, sending or imparting activity or motion

Moxibustion the use of a warming herb called mugwort

MRSA Methicillin resistant Staphylococcus Aureus – a bacterium which is resistant to antibiotics.

Multi-cultural society a variety of people from different origins

Multi-disciplinary approach members from different sectors working together

Multi-disciplinary team professionals from different disciplines working together for the needs of one service user

Muscular-skeletal reference to the muscles and bones of the skeleton

Mutant changed in shape, structure or form for whatever reason

Myocardial infarction the reduction of blood flow to the heart muscle caused by an arterial blockage and leading to a heart attack

National Curriculum ten subjects which children have to follow throughout their education from Year 1

National Standards minimum standards which providers must not fall below – they aim to provide a baseline which will encourage continuous improvement and development

Natural talent ability which is not taught or learnt but occurs to a high level of achievement

Naturopathic principles the treatment of disease without drugs

Nausea the feeling of sickness

Needs requirements of individuals

Networks different members who work independently joining together to share ideas as a group

Neuralgia intense intermittent pain along a nerve

Nitrosamines a chemical that affects function in the body

Non-inflammatory not tending to cause inflammation, i.e. localised swelling, redness and/or pain

Non-specific not clearly defined, vague

Non-verbal not using words/language; using body language

Noradrenalin a secondary stress hormone that helps us to cope over a longer period of time

Norms the expectations that people have of others within a group – what people regard as normal

Notifiable denoting certain infectious diseases such as smallpox, outbreaks of which must be reported to the public health authorities

Nuclear family mother, father and children living together

Numbness loss of feeling

Objectives specific goals to be achieved in delivering the intended aims or outcomes

Obscure to cover or reduce the vision of a person

Ofsted regulatory body for childcare provision

Opacity an unclear area of an object that is usually clear, or an object that stands out and is more visible

Open societies sharing new ideas

Orthodox medicine the medical procedures normally practised in the UK, USA and most Western or developed countries, utilising drug therapy and/or surgery to cure disease

Osteoarthritis a disease of the joints of the body

Outdoor play playing outside in the fresh air using various equipment

Outreach team care workers who go out from the setting into people's homes within the community

Over the counter   any purchase that can be made in a shop without prescription

Overt   obvious and out in the open

Paediatrician   doctor who specialises in children and their diseases

Palpation   to feel with the fingers and hands

Parallel play   when children play alongside each other without interacting

Paramouncy principle   of the most importance, e.g. a child

Paramount   the most important, vital

Partnership approach   working together to achieve the same aims and objectives

Pathogen   the organism that produces disease; a virus, for example

Peer group norms   doing the same as people who are of the same age

Peripheral   on the edge of

Peripheral blood vessels   those blood vessels that are near the surface of the skin and at the far ends of the hands and feet

Personal needs   requirements individuals have to enable them to survive

Pharmaceutical industry   the industry involved in the development of drugs and medicinal products

Phenylketonuria   a genetic disease where there is a high abnormal presence of the protein phenylalanine. Tested in babies by using the Guthrie test

Philosophy   the use of reason and argument in seeking truth and knowledge

Phobias   unnatural fears of objects, animals or places

Physiological changes   the changes that occur within the body's normal systems

Placenta   the organ that joins the blood supplies of mother and baby, occasionally referred to as afterbirth

Play   activities which are carried out for pleasure

Polyunsaturated fats   lighter fats that prove more beneficial to the body

Positive positioning   being in a place which shows interest to others and demonstrates that they are valued

Potential   the level of achievement a child is capable of reaching

Powerful mechanism of voluntary self regulation   a strong structure for regulating procedures or practices, that is done on a voluntary basis and not required legally

Preferential treatment   receiving attention before others

Prejudiced   being against another person because of the way they look or speak without really knowing them

Prejudices   personal feelings which could discriminate against others

Pre-schools   groups attended by children before they start school formally

Presumption   to assume

Primary health care   the first tier of health care, usually consisting of professionals with day-to-day responsibility for the health of patients; i.e. general practitioner, health visitor, midwife, etc.

Primary medical care   the same team as above, but with reference to the provision of initial diagnosis and medical treatment

Primary socialisation   the people who first influence a child

Principles   basic standards which have to be maintained by care workers

Prioritised   selecting in order of importance

Private services   those which are run as a business to make a profit

Product liability cover   insurance that provides protection against legal action by others, with specific reference to the use of proprietary products

Professional bodies   organisations set up to represent a profession, usually developing a set of rules to ensure that its members are regulated and practise in accordance with the requirements of the rules

Professional referral   to be passed to a specialist by another

Profile   information about an individual which gives an image of their ability and achievements

Progressive degeneration   gradual physical or chemical changes that reduce efficiency

Projectiles   an object thrown forward; capable of being or designed to be hurled forwards

Prominent   main; major, first

Prospective   people who may be interested

Provider	giving services; having the ability to carry out the service required
Proximity	closeness; distance between one person and another
Psychiatric hospitals	hospitals where mental illness is treated
Psycho-therapeutic	the treatment of mental disorders by psychological means
Psychotic illness	an illness of the mind causing disturbing thoughts and behaviour
Public sector organisations	state funded organisations that provide community services, e.g. NHS, police, fire and rescue, Social Services and education
Puncture	prick
Purchaser	buying services from others
Quadriceps	muscles in the upper leg
Qualifications	recognised achievements which could include GCSEs, A levels, GNVQ, NVQ, BTEC/OCR certificates and diplomas
Qualities	personal characteristics
Rancid	something that is rotten and inedible
Randomly selected	chosen without any method, preconceived objectives or reason
Rapport	developing an understanding and relationship with others
Reactive depression	a type of depression experienced after a loss or major life-changing event
Receiver	the person listening to the response
Reception class	the first class a child attends when they start school
Records	information which is kept about a child or service user which could include personal information and achievements
Redress	compensation
Reflecting	thinking about
Refractive	the changes that are observed when light travels through another medium
Regimes	a system or collective way of doing something
Registered practitioners	a professional whose name is on the register of practitioners who are approved by, or who have satisfied the tests prescribed by, or who are licensed by the regulating body
Registration	joining a group and having details kept by a central organisation

Reinforcement	providing rewards for achievement
Relaxant	a substance or procedure that induces or brings about the feelings of relaxation
Relevant	to the point; relating to a particular matter
Remit	a responsibility given to a person
Repetitive	happens again and again
Reserve capacity	extra strength to draw on for protection
Residential care	providing 24-hour care
Respiratory	relating to respiration and the lungs
Respiratory infection	infection in airways to lungs, causing breathing problems
Respite	temporary rest from caring for someone
Responsibilities	recognised actions which have to be carried out
Restrictive	limiting
Rickets	a vitamin deficiency that causes children's bones to weaken and bend (bow legs)
Rigidity	stiffness
Risk assessments	checks which are made in a setting to ensure there are no hazards, and risks are kept to a minimum
Role models	people who others like to copy or aspire to become like
Routine	regular activities which are carried out in a certain timescale
Rural	areas in the country which are often isolated
Saturated fats	fats that have a large molecular structure that can cause artery blockages
Scientifically proven	has undergone trials and tests that have followed set procedures to ensure that the results are conclusive
Scope	the range that something covers, e.g. a range of services
Screening	tests/checks which are carried out to find out unseen/hidden features
Secondary socialisation	the things that affect us as we grow and develop
Self advocacy	teaching how to represent self
Self awareness	knowing ourselves
Self esteem	the opinion we have of ourselves
Self image	the picture we have of ourselves

Self referral	to take oneself for a professional consultation
Self regulating	the regulation of a profession or other body by the members of that organisation
Sender	the person passing on a message
Sensory nerve endings	the terminations of the nerves that transmit the feelings of touch
Shared-care families	when parents have separated and children spend equal time with each of them, parents share responsibilities for the child
Sheltered accommodation	a form of housing accommodation (usually flats), that have various levels of support services available to the occupants, e.g. on-site warden, communal lounges, emergency alarms, etc.
Shingles	a painful inflammation of the nerves caused by the herpes zoster virus
Siblings	brothers or sisters
Skills	ability to carry out certain actions
Slow-twitch fibres	muscle fibres that activate slowly and tire slowly
Social co-ordination	the ability to put things together in an acceptable way to show interest and effective use of skills when communicating
Social evolution approach	tools to help shared thinking
Social exclusion	not being accepted by others; being prevented from joining, e.g. a group
Social skills	ability to interact with others, acceptable behaviour when in the company of others including manners, conversation
Society	the wider group of people with whom we live
Solitary play	when a child plays alone without taking any notice of others who may be near
Spats	a cloth, leather or plastic covering which covers the leg
Special needs	particular requirements because of additional needs/difficulties
Sphincters	openings or valves to the bladder and to the bowel
Spontaneous	to happen suddenly and often without identifiable cause
Spontaneously	without being told to do something

Stages of development	achievement of particular skills and ability by a certain age
Stagnation	a state of inactivity
Stamina	feeling of strength
Standardised and accredited	specific standards for a qualification and accreditation (by an awarding body) means that the awarding body confirms that these standards have been achieved
Statistics	a science concerned with the collection, classification and interpretation of data
Statutorily regulated	regulated and monitored services in accordance with legal requirements
Statutory obligation	a legal requirement
Statutory provision	services which have to be provided by law
Statutory registered health professionals	practitioners who are required by law to have achieved an appropriate standard of competence to practise, and who are on the register of their professional body as such, i.e. doctors, nurses, midwives, etc.
Statutory self regulation	the regulation of a profession or other body by the members of that organisation as required by law
Step-families	when parents have separated and then remarried – the new partner is a step-parent and any children step-brothers/sisters
Stereotyping	having preconceived ideas about a person or group of people, expecting members of the same group to behave in the same manner
Sterilisation	the act of purification, cleansing or disinfection to ensure freedom from living micro-organisms
Stigma	a weakness; a blemish
Stimulation	inspiring and motivating children to carry out actions which will help their learning
Stoma bags	a bag attached to the surgically created orifice in the abdomen (stoma) which acts as the anus – the bag collects all the waste products (faeces)
Strata/ Stratification	dividing people into layers
Strategies	actions taken to overcome a problem

Stroke — where a vessel in the brain either becomes blocked or bleeds and causes localised damage to the brain tissue due to oxygen starvation

Subsidised — partially paid for by the government or others

Supplementation — to add to something that is already there, as in a supplement

Systemically — concerning the whole body

Tai Chi — a form of oriental exercise based on an old martial art

Temperament — the nature or characteristics of a person

Tensions — two sides that must be considered when a request is made which could impact on one another – there is no right or wrong answer

Therapeutic — contributing to the cure of disease or general or mental well being

Therapeutic intervention — the introduction of a procedure that is intended to cure or improve a condition

Third party referral — to let a professional know about a concern when you are not related in any way

Thrombosis — a clot that forms in a blood vessel

Toxic overload — the poisonous effects of certain substances called 'toxins'

Trace — a small amount of

Tranquillisers — drugs that make a person calm or sedate

Transferred — moved from one to the other

Triceps — muscles in the posterior upper arm

Trihalomethanes — hydrocarbon chemicals that are toxic to the body

Unconditional positive regard — accepting a person as they are, not trying to change them into something different

Uncritical acceptance — acceptance without question

Unprocessed — a food product that has had nothing done to it

Urban — in towns or cities

Values — views that are central to the beliefs and ways of the culture; standards which a person sets for themselves or others within their family

Vetted — checking for any illegal actions/ convictions which could make them an unsuitable person to care for children

Victimisation — treating someone less favourably than others

Vigilant — on your guard, wary or cautious

Virus — an organism that needs to live inside a cell to grow and reproduce – viruses cause many types of disease, including the common cold

Vocabulary — words which can be spoken with understanding

Voluntary organisation — run on a 'not-for-profit' basis, often linked to charitable organisations

Vulnerable — at risk, unable to fend for themselves

Wider society — those beyond the family or extended family

Withdrawal syndrome — a series of symptoms experienced by some people when trying to reduce dependency on drugs or alcohol

Work patterns — the time we work, e.g. full-time, shift work, part-time, etc.

Notes

Notes